ANALYTICAL DESIGN
of LINEAR FEEDBACK CONTROLS

ANALYTICAL DESIGN

George C. Newton, Jr.

Associate Professor of Electrical Engineering
Associate Director, Servomechanisms Laboratory

Leonard A. Gould

Assistant Professor of Electrical Engineering

James F. Kaiser

Instructor in Electrical Engineering

All of the Massachusetts Institute of Technology

# of LINEAR FEEDBACK CONTROLS

NEW YORK · JOHN WILEY & SONS, INC.

London

SECOND PRINTING, FEBRUARY, 1961

Library of Congress Catalog Card Number: 57-10811

Printed in the United States of America

PREFACE

Analytical design of linear feedback controls. What does the phrase *analytical design* mean? We mean by this phrase the design of control systems by application of the methods of mathematical analysis to idealized models which represent physical equipment. In the analytical design procedure described in this book the starting point is the system specifications. These include descriptions of the input, the disturbances, and the desired response. Also included is a statement of the basis on which the system performance will be judged; this statement is in the form of a performance index. The design objective is to minimize (or maximize) the chosen performance index. Analytical design theory is a presentation of ways and means for accomplishing this objective.

In this book the reader will find a comprehensive discussion of the analytical design procedure for two performance indices. For systems subject to transient input signals, the integral-square error is used as a performance index. For stochastic input signals, on the other hand, we use the mean-square error. All the analytical procedures presented use a linear, time-invariant, mathematical model for the physical system.

The analytical design theory of this book is in distinct contrast to the design methods described in the majority of introductory textbooks on the subject of feedback control. After presenting ways of analyzing system behavior for transient and sinusoidal excitations, these textbooks discuss a number of ways of modifying the parameters that are under the designer's control so as to improve the system response. Included in these ways of improving system behavior are cascade forms of compensation such as lead networks, lag networks, and lead-lag networks. Other methods include the use of auxiliary feedback loops as when a positional servomechanism is stabilized by tachometric feedback. Taken altogether these methods amount to a trial-and-error design procedure. The approach is to guess at a likely form of system compensation, to analyze it to see if it performs satisfactorily, and, if it does not, to try a new form of compensation. By repeating this process a designer who has sufficient insight, experience, and skill is often able to arrive at a satisfactory design for a control system. Unfortunately, the trial-and-error design procedure provides no criterion for terminating the sequence of trials when difficulty is encountered in meeting the specifications. There is no way of knowing if the performance demanded in the specifications can be obtained or not. This difficulty is overcome by the analytical design method.

According to analytical design theory, the best compensation for a feedback control system is implicitly determined by the specifications. When the designer applies the analytical design method he proceeds directly from the problem specifications to the compensation that minimizes or maximizes the specified performance index. By this method the design is accomplished once and for all without recourse to a series of trial-and-error designs. If the performance obtained with compensation determined by the analytical procedure is not satisfactory, the designer is certain that no compensation can be found that will meet the specifications and that either the performance specification must be relaxed or some of the other specifications must be altered. This ability to detect inconsistent specifications is a great advantage for the analytical design method. Unfortunately, computational effort is often greater with this method than with the trial-and-error design procedure. Thus we frequently find the most effective approach to be a combination of the two techniques.

The purpose we have in mind in writing this book is twofold. First of all, we wish to present the results of our research on the analytical design method and to indicate the factors that fundamentally limit the performance of linear systems. The reader of this textbook should gain considerable insight into how such factors as input noise, disturbances, non-minimum-phase fixed elements, and saturation tendencies in the fixed elements place definite bounds on the performance that can be achieved in linear systems. Such an insight cannot be had through the study of the trial-and-error design procedure. Our second objective in writing this book is to consolidate the literature in the field of analytical design theory so as to make it more readily available to engineers and scientists. We hope we have done this in such a way as to point out the practical utility of what may seem to many practical engineers to be abstruse theory without application to the real world.

The book is organized as follows: A brief history of the control art together with information on the basic block diagrams and notation used in the design of control systems is given in Chapter 1. Chapter 2 discusses minimization of integral-square error through parameter adjustment. After an introduction to stochastic signals given in Chapter 3, the adjustment of parameters to minimize the mean-square error is discussed in Chapter 4. Chapter 5 introduces a variational approach to the problem of minimizing the mean-square error for systems possessing no fixed elements. This approach is extended in Chapter 6 for both mean-square and integral-square error to systems having fixed elements that are beyond the control of the designer. Chapters 7 and 8 discuss the use of constraints in control system design. How to avoid saturations within the fixed elements is the subject of Chapter 7. Chapter 8 discusses the design of control systems for minimum bandwidth when the value of a performance index is specified. Much of the analytical design theory presented in the foregoing chapters is put to practical application in Chapter 9, which presents a detailed discussion of one aspect of the design for a servomechanism to drive a large radio telescope. By means of Chapter 9 we have endeavored to give the reader an understanding of how analytical design theory is used in conjunction with trial-and-error design techniques to solve practical problems.

This book is written at what might be called a semi-advanced level. It is intended for engineers and scientists who have had some graduate training or who are willing to do collateral reading. It is also intended for graduate students taking advanced work in the theory of feedback control. Although originally planned as a monograph on analytical design theory, we have included, in order to make it more useful in a graduate course on control theory, four appendices which review Fourier and Laplace transforms, the application of the theory of functions to the problem of stability determination, the gain-phase plane methods of trial-and-error design, as well as other trial-and-error design techniques. A table of special integrals needed in applying analytical design theory to practical problems and a discussion of the

gain-phase relationship for minimum-phase transfer functions constitute two other appendices.   Also, we have included some problems to
illustrate most of the principles discussed in the text.   With these
additions, the book should be satisfactory for a one-semester graduate
course on advanced linear feedback control theory, especially if it is
supplemented by outside reading or additional material presented by
the instructor on the trial-and-error design procedure.

This book is the outgrowth of four years of experimentation in presenting analytical design theory to graduate students in the electrical
engineering department at the Massachusetts Institute of Technology.
We are indebted to our students for the contributions which they have
made through their criticism and constructive suggestions concerning
the course notes.   We are also indebted to the writers of the original
papers in the field of analytical design theory.   Among these we should
especially mention Professor Norbert Wiener and Professor Y. W. Lee,
both at the Massachusetts Institute of Technology.   We also wish to
express our thanks to Mrs. Ida E. Williams for her fine work in typing
the manuscript and to Messrs. Robert Kramer and John L. Preston
for valuable assistance in proofreading.

G. C. NEWTON

L. A. GOULD

J. F. KAISER

Cambridge, Massachusetts
June, 1957

CONTENTS

Contents

1

REVIEW OF
THE CONTROL ART

1.1 FEEDBACK CONTROL

DEFINITION OF FEEDBACK CONTROL. A simple example of a feedback control system is a man steering a ship. The helmsman's duty is to maintain the heading of the vessel in accordance with the commands issued to him by the officer in charge. He does this by first observing the error in the ship's heading. This error is found by comparing the actual ship's heading, as determined by reading some form of compass, with the ordered heading. In accordance with the observed error, the helmsman turns his wheel and thereby deflects the ship's rudder. In response to the rudder deflection the ship acquires a turning rate which in time will alter the ship's heading in a direction to reduce the error. By continually observing the error the helmsman is able to manipulate his wheel so that the ship's heading approximates the ordered heading. When the sea is calm and there is little breeze, the helmsman's task is easy and he is able to hold the desired heading within a very small error. With a rough sea or a strong wind, the helmsman's task will be more difficult, and he will be unable to maintain the heading as accurately.

Keeping in mind the foregoing example, let us state a possible definition of a feedback control system. A feedback control system is a combination of elements which cooperate to maintain a physical quantity, termed the output, approximately equal to an ideal output that is related to other physical quantities, termed inputs.   In addition, a feedback control system has the following characteristics: (1), the action of the system on the output is determined, in part, by the value of the output; and (2), the energy necessary to alter the output is supplied primarily from sources other than the inputs.   In the above example the ideal output is the desired heading of the ship which, as far as the helmsman is concerned, is identical with the ordered heading or input received from the commanding officer.   The output is fed back upon itself in this example since it is a component of the error used by the helmsman in determining how he should turn his wheel.   The energy to turn the ship is supplied primarily by the propulsion machinery which causes the ship to move through the water and thereby gives rise to a turning moment as a result of the rudder deflection.   The action of the waves of the sea on the hull and of the wind on the superstructure are additional inputs to the system which are commonly called disturbances because the ideal output ordinarily is not related to them.

The term *feedback control system* has a rather broad meaning.   It includes all devices that involve feedback and power amplification whether they be electronic, mechanical, pneumatic, or hydraulic in nature.   The more specialized term *servomechanism* refers to any feedback control system whose output is the mechanical position of one object relative to another.   The terms *servomechanism* and *positional control system* are synonymous.   On the other hand, the term *regulator* refers to any feedback control system in which the ideal output is either constant or slowly changing and the primary task is to maintain the actual output at its proper value in the presence of disturbances.

WHY IS FEEDBACK CONTROL USED?   To answer this question, let us consider the alternate method of control, which is control without feedback, often termed *open-loop control*.   With open-loop control the actuator supplying the output must have sufficient stability so that the output stays within tolerance irrespective of how environmental conditions vary with time.   In addition, with open-loop control, because the signal driving the actuator may not correspond closely with the output itself, complicated and difficult-to-realize compensation may have to be interposed between the input signals and the output.   For example, in a servomechanism the servomotor may act like an integrator.   Assuming the ideal output to be identical with the input, this means that the input signal must be differentiated in order to form the signal for the actuator.   Accurate differentiation is always a difficult process. Furthermore, any physical servomotor will not integrate exactly in the presence of load torques; therefore, special compensating means would have to be provided to reduce the errors that would otherwise be caused by load-torque disturbances. The three major reasons for employing feedback control are: (1) The process or actuator which supplies the output may have signal transmission characteristics that make accurate open-loop operation very difficult. (2) With feedback the precision of control can be made to depend largely upon the equipment used to measure the output and to compare it with its ideal value. This fact may enable accurate control to be achieved in spite of inaccuracies and variable characteristics in the actuator or process. (3) The effect of disturbances on the output may be suppressed by employing feedback, thereby obviating the need for the elaborate disturbance compensators that would be needed with open-loop control.

IMPORTANCE OF FEEDBACK CONTROL. The great importance of feedback control in modern life is easily ascertained by counting the control systems that each person uses. In the home we find temperature controls for the heating plant or air-conditioning system, for the oven of the kitchen stove, for the refrigerator, for the hot water heater, and possibly for other appliances. Electronic voltage regulators and automatic gain controls are ordinarily present in the radio and television equipment. If the refrigerator is electrically powered, the pressure in the evaporator is automatically controlled. Float controls for water level are used in the water closet tanks and possibly in the automatic washing machine. In the automobile there is the voltage regulator, the thermostat controlling the engine coolant temperature, and the oil pressure regulator to mention just three important controls. As he drives the operator of the automobile represents an elaborate multiple feedback system controlling the position of the car on the road, governing the speed, and regulating the distance to other vehicles. The industry in a city could not be carried on without feedback controls. The instrumentation and control equipment for an oil refinery represents a very significant part of the capital investment and makes possible the very large output per worker employed. The general trend in other industries which are not so highly "automated" as the oil industry is generally in the direction of more automatic controls. Man's acquisition of knowledge through research is being expedited by feedback control through the new experiments that are made possible by better apparatus employing automatic controls. Last, but not least, is the military defense of our way of life made possible by automatic controls. As just one example, we have the modern high-speed jet aircraft with its numerous control systems without which the pilot could not fly. From this brief résumé of the applications of feedback controls in our daily lives we can only conclude that they are a vital part of our civilization.

DEVELOPMENT OF FEEDBACK CONTROL SYSTEMS. As mentioned in the next article, the art of feedback control has been developing for at least 4,000 years in order to reach its present state. Of course, most of this development has taken place since the Industrial Revolution. Most of the control systems mentioned above have been developed by a process known as "gadgeteering." This process comprises invention, construction, test, and much modification and retesting. Many of the systems successfully developed by this procedure have not yet been successfully analyzed. Although gadgeteering has sufficed for the development of many controls that are in daily use, the current trend is towards more work on paper and less on hardware in the development stages. World War II was a major impetus to the mathematical analysis of feedback control systems. This impetus arose from the military need for a large variety of accurate servomechanisms in connection with fire-control and other applications. As the result of these wartime developments we now have a fairly well-organized design procedure for control systems which can be represented by linear mathematical models. This design procedure we shall term the *trial-and-error design method* since it begins with an educated guess as to the form of the system and, by analysis, sets one or a few parameters to arrive at the first tentative design. This tentative design is then checked by analysis to see that its performance meets the specifications. If the computed performance is unsatisfactory, the design is modified in a direction indicated by a combination of experience and analytical insight. Then a new performance check is made. By repeating this process a satisfactory design often may be obtained. This analytical trial-and-error design method frequently is called *synthesis*, but in reality it is merely gadgeteering on paper rather than with hardware. We should not deprecate this method, however, because it is a tremendous advance over hardware gadgeteering and, in the hands of even relatively inexperienced engineers, it can lead to quite satisfactory designs.

During World War II and more recently, control engineers have been exploring areas of performance analysis and design beyond the trial-and-error design of linear systems. Distinguished primarily by the feature of increased complexity is the area of *systems engineering* which deals with aggregates of feedback control systems such as are found in modern weapon systems. Combinations of feedback control systems requiring systems engineering undoubtedly will have a future in the information-processing and control systems necessary to put automation into effect in industry. Another area receiving considerable attention is *human engineering*, particularly the aspect that deals with the human operator as an element in a control system. A third area that is receiving considerable current attention is the field of *non-linear systems*. As is to be expected, progress is not rapid in this field although interesting applications of non-linearities are being made to control systems in order to improve certain performance characteristics. A fourth area that is being looked into by control engineers is the field of *analytical design techniques* for linear systems. Analytical design techniques are in sharp contrast to trial-and-error design methods since they proceed directly from the problem specifications to the design without the need for human intuition. It is this fourth area of analytical design techniques that is the subject of this book.

SUMMARY. The current state of the art of feedback control appears to be as follows: The trial-and-error design method has been highly developed and forms the theoretical base on which all control engineers build their individual pyramids of knowledge. Exploratory work is being done in the fields of systems engineering, human engineering, non-linear systems, and analytical design techniques to supplement trial-and-error methods for the design of linear systems. The majority of the control systems in current daily use have been developed by a process of hardware gadgeteering; frequently this design technique is the most expeditious for low-performance systems or for complicated, highly non-linear systems. When the performance requirements are high and the system can be represented by a linear model, it is almost always profitable to precede the hardware phase in the development of a control system with a paper study employing either the trial-and-error design methods which are the stock-in-trade of practically all control engineers, or alternatively, the analytical design techniques which are described in this book. Finally, the rapid development of improved components for control systems should be pointed out. The creation of new or better transducers, error-sensing means, semiconductor amplifying devices, magnetic amplifiers, electric, hydraulic, and pneumatic motors has given the designer increased freedom in transforming his plans on paper into actual hardware.

1.2 EARLY HISTORY

The art of feedback control is very old. All living organisms, including man, are complexes of feedback control systems reacting to their environment.   On this basis, feedback control originated with life itself.   However, we ordinarily think of the art of feedback control as beginning with its first conscious employment by man.   By conscious employment we mean human activity, at a conscious rather than a subconscious level, that would come within the compass of what we now call feedback control; we do not mean the assigning of a name to this type of activity since this has obviously occurred only recently.

The first recorded evidence of human activity in the field of feedback control comes from Babylonia and is about 4,000 years old.   In an era about 2,000 years before the birth of Christ, Babylonia had the most advanced civilization on the face of the earth.   By means of a highly developed irrigation system using waters from the Tigris and Euphrates rivers, the Babylonians achieved an agricultural productivity that enabled them to support the highest population density known up to that date.   Their yields per acre were not exceeded until modern times.   Modern engineering has its roots in the irrigation systems built and operated in ancient Babylonia.   In irrigating his land the Babylonian practiced feedback control since he consciously regulated the moisture content of the soil by opening and closing ditches.   The recorded evidence for this is contained in the set of laws codified and inscribed on stone by order of King Hammurabi approximately 2,100 years before Christ (G.1).*   The code of Hammurabi comprising 282 laws is the oldest known law code in the world.   A number of these laws relate to irrigation, and a typical one is translated as follows: "If anyone open his ditches to water his crop, but is careless, and the water flood the field of his neighbor, then he shall pay his neighbor corn for his loss."   Archaeologists believe that Hammurabi promulgated very few new laws in establishing his code, but merely wrote down what had long been the law and custom of the land.   How far in advance of his code irrigation had been practiced is not definitely known.   We can only conclude that the laws of King Hammurabi contain the first known evidence of legal penalties for the malfunction of a human operator in a feedback control system.

Having established the approximate date and location of an ancient feedback control system employing human operators, we now should like to know when the first automatic feedback control system was devised.   Usher (U.7) in his book on the history of mechanical inventions refers to a clepsydra or water clock which employs a float control to regulate the water level in the chamber containing the metering

* Symbols in parenthesis when used in the text identify references in the Bibliography.

orifice. Figure 1.2–1 depicts the principle of operation of such a water clock. Usher states that the method of regulating water level by means of a float-operated valve was used by the Arabs in connection with water clocks possibly as early as the beginning of the Christian era, but unfortunately he cites no exact reference. In passing, we should note that clepsydrae were recognized as the most accurate time keepers, and were preferred to mechanical clocks, well into the seventeenth century. After the seventeenth century the mechanical clock displaced the water clock.

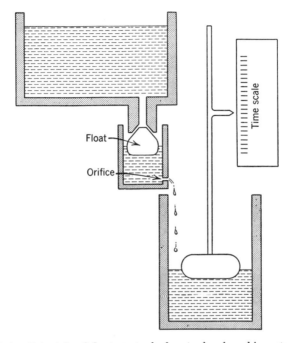

Fig. 1.2–1. Principle of float control of water level used in water clocks.

Although not strictly a feedback control system, Sir Isaac Newton's method of successive approximations for solving equations, devised about 1675, definitely embodies the idea of feedback. In this method the error in satisfying an equation generated by an estimated value for the root is fed back through a mathematical operation to form a new estimate for the root. By repeating the process a sufficient number of times, the root is found to the desired accuracy (provided the process is stable).

The first definite evidence of an automatic feedback control system carries the date 1750. Wolf (W.5) credits Meikle with the invention in that year of an automatic turning gear for windmills.   Before 1750 windmills had been developed by the Germans, the Dutch, and the English and had reached rather large physical sizes.   The Dutch turret windmills in particular had grown to sizes so large that manual steering of the turret to bring the sails into the wind required considerable effort.   Generally, a sloping boom attached to the turret was hauled around by means of a rope wound around a capstan.   Andrew Meikle's invention eliminated the need for manual adjustment of the turrets. A sketch showing the principle of his so-called "fantail" gear for turning windmills into the wind is shown in Fig. 1.2–2.   By means of an

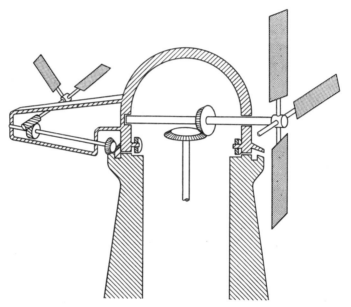

Fig. 1.2–2.   Meikle's "fantail" gear for turning windmills into the wind (1750).

auxiliary windmill at right angles to the main sails, an error in the heading of the turret is converted into mechanical motion.   This mechanical motion is transmitted by means of gearing to the turret, thereby causing it to rotate until the axis of the auxiliary windmill is at right angles to the wind direction.   The art of mechanical power transmission had so advanced by this time that Meikle was able to employ gear ratios of the order of 3,000 to 1 between the auxiliary windmill and the turret.

Thirty-eight years after Meikle's invention James Watt came forward with his fly-ball governor for the steam engine.   Wolf states that Watt probably adapted his governor from fly-ball regulating devices used in windmills to control the clearance between the grinding stones. Unfortunately he gives no details about these earlier regulating devices.

During the late 1700's and early 1800's developments were taking place in the science of mathematics that were destined, after the lapse of a century or more, to have a profound influence on the analysis of feedback control systems. In particular, in the year 1779 Laplace began the development of the transformation that bears his name today (G.2). Laplace's work antedates that of Fourier. The closely related Laplace and Fourier transformations are foundation stones in the modern analysis of feedback control systems. About one generation after the Laplace transformation was born, Cauchy, almost single-handedly, began bringing forth that beautiful mathematical structure known as the theory of functions of complex variables. Without the transformation theory of Laplace and Fourier and without the complex variable theory of Cauchy the tremendous strides that we have witnessed since World War II in the analysis of feedback control systems and, for that matter, in the analysis of electrical problems in general, would have been impossible.

During the latter part of the nineteenth century servomechanisms began to appear in the form of steering apparatus for ships. With the advent of steam power, and the increase in the size and speed of vessels thereby made possible, increasing difficulty was encountered with direct mechanical control of rudders. The solution of this problem came in the form of steam power drives or servomechanisms interposed between the helmsman and the rudder. Typical of such early rudder servomechanisms is Higginson's steering gear shown in U.S. Patent 248,464. Crude as this kind of equipment was, it served its purpose well, and it is only fairly recently that steam steering gear has been supplanted by electric and hydraulic equipment. Also, during this period of rapid industrial development we find a parallel mathematical development which a half-century later is used considerably in the analysis of control systems. This development was Routh's stability criterion set forth in 1877.

The analysis of feedback control systems began in 1868 with Maxwell's paper, "On Governors" (M.2). After a considerable lapse this was followed by three classical papers—Minorsky's (M.3) "Directional Stability of Automatically Steered Bodies" in 1922, Nyquist's (N.9) "Regeneration Theory" in 1932, and Hazen's (H.2) "Theory of Servomechanisms" in 1934. A number of other papers were published during the early 1900's in the fields of process control and governing. The most comprehensive bibliography, which includes 2,083 references up to the year 1952, was published by the AIEE (A.6). A summary of the important early references pertaining to feedback control is given in Table 1.2–1.   These references cover a time span of the order of 4,000 years, although there are many long gaps.   Nevertheless, one cannot fail to be impressed by the long history behind this art which today is called feedback control.

Table 1.2–1.   Important Early References Pertaining to Feedback Control

DATE	ITEM
2100 B.C. (approx.)	Laws of the Code of Hammurabi which relate to irrigation of land in Babylonia
0–1700 A.D.	Float-operated valves for water clocks
1675 (approx.)	Newton's successive approximation method for finding real roots of equations
1750	Meikle's turning gear for windmills
1779	Laplace started developing his transformation
1788	Watt's application of the fly-ball governor to the steam engine
1789–1857	Cauchy's theory of functions of a complex variable
1868	Maxwell's paper, "On Governors"
1877	Routh's stability criterion
1881	Higginson's steering gear (U.S. Patent 248,464)
1922	Minorsky's paper, "Directional Stability of Automatically Steered Bodies"
1932	Nyquist's paper, "Regeneration Theory"
1934	Hazen's paper, "Theory of Servomechanisms"

1.3   MATHEMATICAL MODELS; PRINCIPLE OF LINEAR SUPERPOSITION

The modern scientific approach to engineering in large measure consists of the formulation of problems so that methods of mathematical analysis may be applied.   In the era of World War I, engineers could use relatively crude approaches to their problems and depend upon the protection afforded by relatively large factors of safety to keep them out of trouble.   Gradually the pressure for decreased costs and increased performance has narrowed the factors of safety that can be used and have thereby necessitated more exact designs.   Feedback control systems are no exception to this general trend.   Indeed, the success which engineers have experienced through designing them on a scientific basis has helped to inspire the increased use of scientific methods in other branches of engineering.

The exact behavior of physical devices when examined in sufficient detail is generally so complex as to preclude a precise description. Even moderately accurate descriptions of the individual components that make up a control system ordinarily would lead to such an involved over-all representation that analysis would be blocked.

The analytical log jam that would result from a more or less exact description of a control system is avoided by simplified descriptions for the physical devices making up the system. These simplified descriptions are called *mathematical models*. It is in his choice of mathematical models to represent the hardware making up a control system that the designer has the greatest opportunity to display his skill, and simultaneously has the greatest chance to err.

As an example of the variety of mathematical models which can represent the same physical device, consider the iron-core reactor. The simplest model is the linear flux versus magnetomotive force relationship. The next simplest is the same linear relationship with sharp saturation. Then come approximations for the actual saturation which display various degrees of sharpness. For power applications different approximations to the hysteresis loop may be used. For magnetic amplifier purposes the core material may be described by a rectangular hysteresis loop even though it actually has rounded corners. At sufficiently high frequencies the iron-core reactor may be represented by a capacitance. The electrical engineer has devised numerous mathematical models to represent the iron-core reactor under special operating conditions. He has not yet devised a universal description which will encompass its behavior for all modes of operation.

Feedback control systems are conveniently classified in terms of the mathematical models that are employed in their analysis. Broadly speaking, there are two major classifications: linear systems and non-linear systems. It will be recalled that a linear system is one in which the response is proportional to the stimulus. In particular, the response to two stimuli A and B acting together is the sum of the responses obtained for stimulus A and stimulus B each acting alone. The term *superposition* has been assigned to this property of linear systems. Any mathematical model for which the principle of superposition does not hold is called a non-linear system.

Linear systems can be subclassified into the following types: time-invariant, time-varying, and sampling. For the time-invariant type of linear system, the response to a stimulus is independent of the time at which the stimulus is applied. This is not so for the time-varying type. A sampling linear system is a special case of the time-varying type in which one or more parameters vary in a periodic fashion.

Non-linear systems have not been broken down into classes in quite the same way as linear systems have. For control purposes we may classify non-linear systems by the features most obviously giving rise to non-linearity. As one example, we have relay systems in which the non-linear response of the relay to the control signal is the major non-linearity.   Somewhat related to relay systems are quantized data systems, which are becoming more numerous as the trend toward digital transmission of data grows.   Another important form of non-linear system is represented by one with a non-linear override, i.e., one that would be linear except for relay or other type of non-linear operation which comes into play for certain signal values.   Non-linear overrides on otherwise substantially linear controls have been and will continue to be an important form of non-linearity.   Finally, we should mention the area of programmed controllers for sharply saturating devices which in their unsaturated range are substantially linear.   Indications of improved transient performance have stimulated considerable interest in this area during the late 1940's and early 1950's.   However, there has been practically no reduction to practice of these ideas.

As pointed out above, it is in the field of linear systems that the greatest advances in analysis have taken place.   In comparison, non-linear system analysis seems to have advanced but little.   However, in spite of the advanced state of linear system analysis, there appears to be room for further developments.   The material of this book is concerned with one of these.   It is concerned exclusively with the analysis of linear models.   Non-linearity is considered only to the extent that saturation is recognized and a design procedure is devised which tends to keep signal levels within bounds.

Let us now examine a little more closely this property of linearity which seems to be so fundamental to analytical progress.   The key to its meaning is contained in the word *superposition*.   Through superposition the output of a linear system resulting from a complex input signal can be found as follows: The input signal is first resolved into a set of simpler time functions of identical form.   Next, the response of the system to one of the simple time functions is found.   Then, by adding up the responses to the individual members of the set of simple time functions making up the input signal, the output corresponding to the total input signal is found.   There are a large number of forms of simple time functions to choose from in selecting one for this procedure.   In this book we shall use the *unit impulse* as our simple time function.

The unit impulse can be defined in a number of ways.   Here we can think of it as the limit of a rectangular pulse obtained when the amplitude is increased toward infinity and the width is decreased toward zero while the area is maintained equal to one unit of time.   Figure 1.3–1 Curve *A* illustrates a rectangular pulse.   The unit impulse as a function of time will be indicated by the symbol $\delta(t)$.   The integral of the unit impulse from minus infinity to the time t is the unit step function which we will denote by the symbol $\delta_{-1}(t)$. Since the unit step function is more easily visualized than the unit impulse the latter should probably be defined in terms of the former. Equation 1.3–1 is

$$\delta(t) \triangleq \lim_{T \to 0} \frac{1 \text{ unit of time}}{T} [\delta_{-1}(t) - \delta_{-1}(t - T)] \qquad (1.3\text{–}1)$$

such a definition. Because it is impossible to draw a picture of the unit impulse, the graphical symbol shown in Fig. 1.3–1 Curve B is an

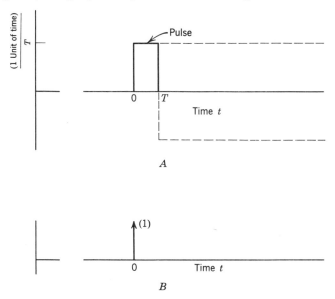

Fig. 1.3–1. (A) Pulse as difference of two step functions. (B) Symbol of unit impulse.

arbitrary sign commonly used to represent the unit impulse. The number in parenthesis represents the strength of the impulse as measured by the area beneath it.

The response of a linear system to an impulse input signal has a shape that is characteristic of the system. The ordinates of the impulse response are proportional to the strength of the input impulse. The strength of the impulse is measured by the area beneath it. By dividing the impulse response by the strength of the input impulse a normalized impulse response is obtained. This normalized impulse response is called the *system weighting function*. The dimensions of the system weighting function are always output units over input units times reciprocal units of time. The system weighting function for a linear system is independent of the strength of the exciting impulse and

therefore uniquely characterizes it.   Figure 1.3–2 Curve A shows a
typical system weighting function.   The weighting functions for
models of actual physical systems are always zero for negative time
since it is physically impossible for an effect to precede its cause in
time.   We thus conclude that a physically realizable weighting function must be zero for negative time.   By the term *physically realizable
weighting function* we mean a normalized impulse response corresponding to a linear system which has the possibility of being physically
realized in the sense that hardware could be constructed which is

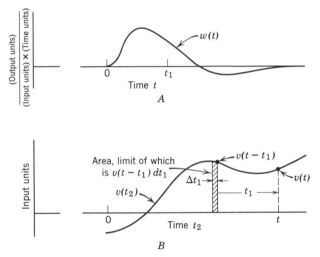

Fig. 1.3–2. (A) System weighting function.   (B) Resolution of input into sequence
of infinitesimal impulses.

analogous to the model.   Practical considerations may prevent actual
realization of many theoretically realizable system weighting functions.
     As a practical matter, no physical system could be tested to deter-
mine its impulse response by subjecting it to a truly impulsive input
signal.   Such an input would destroy the system because of the large
voltages, currents, or forces that would be involved.   To measure the
impulse response of a physical system it could be subjected to a step or
ramp input and the impulse response deduced by differentiating the
measured response an appropriate number of times.   Alternatively,
rectangular pulses of short duration compared to the response time of
the system could be used as approximate impulses.
     Having defined the impulse and the system weighting function, we
are now in a position to discuss quantitatively the concept of superposition.   Figure 1.3–2 Curve B shows a typical input signal labeled

$v(t_2)$. We seek the value of the output at any arbitrary time t. Consider the contribution to the output attributable to the input at time t_1 in the past relative to the present time t, i.e., at time $t - t_1$. We can imagine an infinitesimal impulse corresponding to the infinitesimal time dt_1 multiplied by the input amplitude $v(t - t_1)$. The infinitesimal output $dq(t)$ resulting at time t from the infinitesimal impulse is simply the weighting function evaluated at time t_1 multiplied by the impulse strength. In symbols this result is expressed as

$$dq(t) = w(t_1)v(t - t_1) \, dt_1 \qquad (1.3\text{--}2)$$

By the principle of superposition we can find the total output at time t by adding up the contribution of all the infinitesimal impulses. Since we are dealing with infinitesimals, the addition process corresponds to integration. The variable of integration is t_1, the age variable of the system weighting function. We thus have for the total output at time t

$$q(t) = \int_{-\infty}^{\infty} dt_1 \, w(t_1)v(t - t_1) \qquad (1.3\text{--}3)$$

The right side of this equation is known as the *convolution integral*. It represents one possible mathematical formulation of the principle of superposition. For realizable weighting functions $w(t_1)$ is zero for t_1 negative, and there is no contribution to the output over the interval from minus infinity to zero. Consequently for realizable weighting functions the lower limit of the integral of Eq. 1.3–3 may be replaced by zero.

In the frequency domain there exists an alternate way of formulating the relation of a linear system to its input. This formulation is entirely analogous to the time domain relationship given by Eq. 1.3–3. In fact, the frequency domain relationship can be obtained from Eq. 1.3–3 by making a Fourier transformation of both sides. In this book the complex frequency variable is noted by the letter s for both the Fourier and the Laplace transformations. A brief background discussion of these transformations is given in Appendix A. Transforming both sides of Eq. 1.3–3, we have

$$\int_{-\infty}^{\infty} dt \, e^{-st}q(t) = \int_{-\infty}^{\infty} dt \, e^{-st} \int_{-\infty}^{\infty} dt_1 \, w(t_1)v(t - t_1) \qquad (1.3\text{--}4)$$

The left integral is the Fourier transform of the output which we will denote by $q(s)$. By interchanging the order of integration on the right side we obtain

$$q(s) = \int_{-\infty}^{\infty} dt_1 w(t_1) \int_{-\infty}^{\infty} dt \, e^{-st}v(t - t_1) \qquad (1.3\text{--}5)$$

Changing the variable of integration in the first integral (the one on the right) from t to $t - t_1$ yields

$$q(s) = \int_{-\infty}^{\infty} dt_1\, e^{-st_1} w(t_1) \int_{-\infty}^{\infty} d(t - t_1) e^{-s(t-t_1)} v(t - t_1) \quad (1.3\text{--}6)$$

where the exponential factor e^{-st_1} has been factored out of the first integral and associated with the second. Regarding $t - t_1$ as a new variable, the first integral may be evaluated independently of the second. The first integral is the transform of the input signal $v(s)$. The second integral is the transform of the weighting function, which we will denote by the symbol $W(s)$; this transform is called the *system function*. Abbreviating Eq. 1.3–6 by use of the symbols for the system function and the input signal transform permits us to write

$$q(s) = W(s)v(s) \qquad (1.3\text{--}7)$$

as the frequency domain equivalent of the convolution integral of Eq. 1.3–3.

1.4 BLOCK DIAGRAMS AND NOTATION

Control engineers have found it convenient to employ graphical symbols in the form *block diagrams* to represent signal relationships in linear systems. Figure 1.4–1 (*A*) is an elementary block diagram representing the time domain relationship of Eq. 1.3–3. The block stands for the system, and the weighting function describing the system may be inserted in the block. The output q of the block is obtained by convolving the input with the weighting function. Figure 1.4–1 (*B*) is a block diagram in the frequency domain. Here the system function may be written inside the block and the output transform $q(s)$ is obtained as the product of the input transform $v(s)$ and the system function $W(s)$. Block diagrams are especially useful in representing the interrelationships of internal signals within a feedback control system. By the introduction of a symbol for the operation of addition or subtraction of two signals and by employing blocks to represent input-output signal relations for the individual elements of a control system, a detailed signal-flow diagram for the over-all system can be developed. Such a block diagram is much more meaningful to the control engineer than the equivalent set of simultaneous equations that it replaces since it bears to some degree a schematic resemblance to the physical system on which the linear model is based whereas a list of equations on a piece of paper appears much more abstract.

Since World War II, committees in the various professional societies have been working toward a common nomenclature on block diagrams and symbols for feedback control systems. As of this writing no standard has been approved by the American Standards Association. The Feedback Control Systems Committee of the AIEE has approved an AIEE Proposed Standard of Terminology for Feedback Control Systems; this proposed standard was circulated in April 1954 and is substantially unchanged from the 1951 report of the AIEE Subcommittee on Terminology and Nomenclature of the Feedback Control Systems Committee and the Working Group of the American Standards Association Committee for Letter Symbols for Feedback Control Systems. This report was published in *Electrical Engineering* in 1951

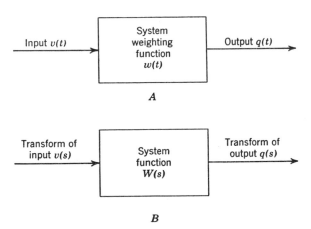

Fig. 1.4–1. Elementary block diagrams. (*A*) Time domain representation. (*B*) Frequency domain representation.

(A.5). Figure 1.4–2 is Fig. 2 of this report entitled, "Block diagram of feedback control system containing all basic elements." In this book certain departures from this block diagram will be necessary from time to time but in a general way an attempt is made to adhere to the AIEE scheme of notation and symbols. This scheme is to use the letter g to represent elements feeding signals toward the output end of the control system and the letter h to represent elements feeding signals back from the output toward the input end of the control system. The letter v is used to represent the input signal and the letter q to represent the output; these symbols are arbitrary and represent a compromise. Since the emphasis in this book is on the over-all performance of feedback control systems, the distinction made between the reference input r and the command v in the AIEE nomenclature will not be needed. Likewise, the distinction between the controlled

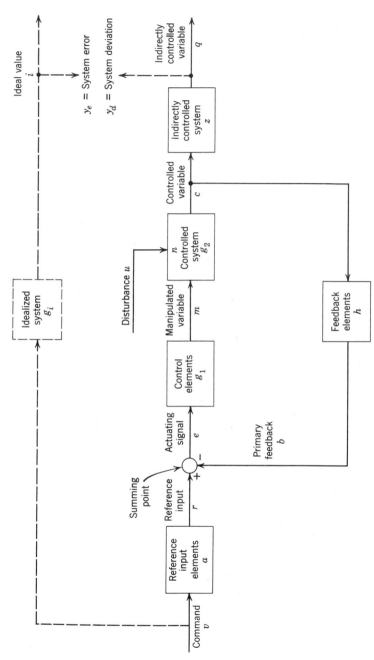

Fig. 1.4-2.   Basic block diagram and symbols approved by the AIEE Feedback Control Systems Committee.   Reproduction of "Fig. 2.   Block diagram of feedback control system containing all basic elements" of AIEE Committee Report, *Electrical Engineering*, *70*, 905–909 (1951).

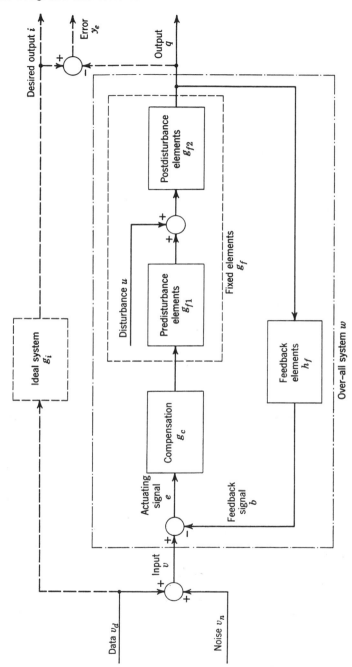

Fig. 1.4-3. Block diagram and symbols used in this book.

variable c and the indirectly controlled variable q will not be made. The phrase *indirectly controlled variable* is too lengthy, and we shall replace it with the word *output*. It then seems logical to use the word *input* in place of *command* since this corresponds to *output*.

Another important point of difference between the AIEE nomenclature and that of this book is the implied nature of the input v. From Fig. 1.4–2, the fact that the *ideal value* or *ideal output* is obtained by a linear operation on the input v implies that the input signal is free of all noise or corruption. One of the important considerations of this book is the use of a feedback control system as a filter to remove noise from the input signal. Therefore the input signal is considered to be composed of two components, the *noise* v_n and the *data* v_d. The ideal output is presumed to be related to the data component of the input only. Figure 1.4–3 shows the modified block diagram and nomenclature that will be used in this book. The *fixed elements* of the control system are designated by the symbol g_f. A *disturbance* u entering the fixed elements is accounted for by adding it in at the proper point between the input and the output of the fixed elements. The weighting function of the portion of the fixed elements preceding the entrance of the disturbance is indicated by the symbol g_{f1}; the weighting function of the parts following, by the symbol g_{f2}. The control elements or *compensating elements* for the control system are indicated by their weighting function symbol g_c. The weighting function symbol h_f is used to represent the *feedback elements*. The *error* between the ideal output i and the actual output q is designated by the symbol y_e in agreement with the AIEE nomenclature. The term *ideal system* (rather than idealized system) is used to represent the weighting function g_i relating the data component of the input signal to the ideal output. The over-all relation of the output q to the input v is represented by the weighting function w corresponding to the normalized impulse response of the combination of elements enclosed in the large dotted block. In the frequency domain capital letters will be used for the transfer functions corresponding to transforms of weighting functions. However, for signals small letters will be used for both the transforms and the time functions themselves; explicit indication of the argument t or s will be used where necessary to resolve doubt. A list of the more important symbols used in this book along with their meanings is given in the glossary.

1.5 THE CONTROL PROBLEM

Historically, feedback control systems were built and used long before they were analyzed and designed. In control systems that employ human operators, the success achieved may be attributed to the versatility of the human being which permits him to adjust over very wide ranges the character and degree of his response to one or more stimuli. With the advent of all-mechanical control systems, such as turning gear for windmills and centrifugal governors for steam engines introduced during the eighteenth century, feedback control phenomena began to be observed which the early inventors and engineers must have found very frustrating indeed. As they increased the sensitivity of their systems in an effort to diminish the operating errors, instances of sustained hunting must have been observed. However, it was not until after the Civil War in the United States that James Clerk Maxwell wrote his paper, "On Governors" and thereby secured to himself the honor of initiating the analysis of feedback control systems. Even though Maxwell's analysis followed Watt's application of the governor to the steam engine by 80 years, more than 50 additional years elapsed before the analysis of feedback control systems became fashionable in the engineering world. In the meantime, large numbers of more or less successful feedback control systems were built and used.

What is the feedback control problem? Why does the analysis and design of feedback control systems require such special treatment that numerous textbooks have been written on this subject and yet more are being added each year? This article attempts to answer these questions which must be in the mind of every newcomer to this field.

In the classical view, a feedback control problem could be identified almost always as a stability problem. To the early workers in the field, the problem of assuring stability was nearly always the foremost consideration. Of course, the stability problem grew out of the desire for improved performance as measured by decreased errors. By increasing the gain or sensitivity of his control system the engineer soon learned that he could reduce its error. However, a point was soon reached beyond which further increase in gain caused the system to exhibit sustained oscillations of the output even though the input was quiescent. This phenomenon, often called hunting, so plagued the control engineer that even to the present time it has all but dwarfed the many other aspects of the feedback control problem. In linear mathematical models, the stability problem was first treated in terms of differential equations. By means of Routh's stability criterion, developed in 1877, the coefficients of the characteristic equation could be tested to see if the system was stable or unstable (see Appendix B). Unfortunately, Routh's criterion gave relatively little information as to the degree of stability. Consequently, it was frequently necessary to solve for the roots of the characteristic equation in order to be sure that all the transient modes were sufficiently well damped.   Another disadvantage of this early approach to the stability problem arises from the involved way in which important system parameters may enter into the coefficients of the characteristic equation.   Even with fairly simple systems, a compensating network time constant or the system gain may appear in several coefficients, thereby complicating the prediction, by means of Routh's criterion, of the effect on stability of changes in these parameters.

During the early 1940's a considerable advance in feedback control analysis took place when Nyquist's stability criterion began to be applied to feedback control systems (see Appendix B).   Nyquist enunciated his criterion in 1932 in connection with the problem of feedback amplifier design.   By employing Cauchy's residue theorem in his proof, Nyquist helped bring function theory to the attention of the designers of communication networks and feedback control systems. As a result, since 1940, function theory has been increasingly applied in the design of filters and control systems.   These applications follow Cauchy's original development of the theory of functions of complex variables by approximately 100 years.

Closely following the introduction of Nyquist's stability criterion, control engineers began to employ the frequency response method for setting the gain of feedback control systems in accord with specifications on the degree of stability (H.1).   The frequency response approach gave increased insight into the selection of compensating networks.   Gradually a fairly standardized procedure for the trial-and-error design of feedback control systems has evolved.   This procedure is well described in numerous textbooks.   A brief résumé of certain aspects of this design procedure is given in Appendices C and D.

In addition to the stability aspects of the control problem, several other factors must be considered.   Fundamentally, a feedback control system can be viewed as an information processing system, in much the same way as a filter or network in communications is viewed.   Eventually the signal transmission aspects of the feedback control problem may be handled in terms of information theory.   At the present time, however, this part of the problem is generally treated by consideration of the system's response to periodic, transient or stochastic input signals.

Feedback control systems are distinguished from filters in several important respects.   First of all, they may employ components over which the designer has no control.   These elements are referred to as the fixed elements of the system.   Such fixed elements occur in the form of servomotors, plants or processes which are to be controlled and which are designed primarily on the basis of factors other than their controllability.   In connection with positional servomechanisms, the servomotor frequently represents a fixed element in the sense that the designer has relatively few choices open to him.   Particularly at high power levels servomotor choice is quite limited.   The designer must accept the dynamic characteristics of the fixed elements that are available to do the job and limit himself to the design of the best possible compensation means to be incorporated with these elements.   Thus the fixed-element aspect of the control problem introduces a complexity normally not present in the filter problem.

A second distinguishing aspect of the feedback control problem is the frequent presence of disturbing signals introduced at other points than in the input.   Usually these disturbing signals are introduced into the fixed elements.   Ordinarily the objective is to minimize or at least limit the effect of these signals on the output of the control system.   Examples of disturbing signals are load torques in positional servomechanisms, pressure, temperature, speed or other parameter variations in process controls, and prime-mover load in governors.   Usually the filter problem is free of disturbing signals except for noise disturbance of the input data.

A third respect in which feedback control systems and filters differ is in the nature of the components employed.   Filters almost uniformly employ electrical elements which can be constructed accurately and which are stable over long periods of time.   Control systems on the other hand often employ mechanical, hydraulic, or pneumatic elements which have less reproducible behavior than high-quality electric circuit elements.   This practical problem often causes the control designer to stop short of an optimum design because he knows full well that the parameters of the physical system may deviate considerably from the data on which he bases his design.

Finally, the signal transmission requirement may be another feature that distinguishes the feedback control problem from the filter problem.   Ordinarily control systems process relatively low frequency signals but this is only a matter of time scale.   A more significant distinction exists.   In many control applications it is essential that the desired output be obtained instantaneously in time.   Error is assessed in such cases as the instantaneous difference between the desired output and the actual output.   This is in distinct contrast to the usual filter problem where the object is to reproduce a desired signal shape or wave form and where it is unimportant whether the output signal is produced instantaneously or after a reasonable delay.   In filter theory,

signal wave form is considered satisfactory if the amplitude of the
frequency response is constant and the phase shift is linear over a
sufficient band of frequencies.   Considerable attention is devoted to
minimizing amplitude and phase distortion from these desired characteristics.   In a control problem, a linear phase shift may be the
cause of excessive error when the desired output must be obtained
instantaneously.

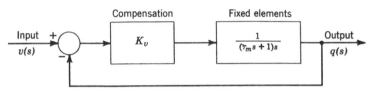

Fig. 1.5–1.   Simple control system.

In order to show how stringent a requirement for instantaneous
reproduction of a signal can be, let us consider an example.   Figure
1.5–1 shows a block diagram of a simple second-order control system.
The input to this control system is the triangular wave shown in the
solid line of Fig. 1.5–2.   Let us assess the performance of this control
system from two viewpoints.   As one view, let us assume the ideal
output is instantaneously equal to the input signal; as the other, let
the ideal output be identical to the input signal in wave form but
lagging by a small amount of time τ_d as shown in the dotted curve of
Fig. 1.5–2.   Physically, our simple control system could represent a

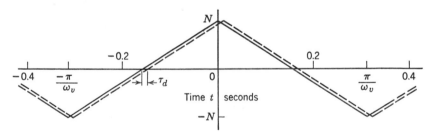

Fig. 1.5–2.   Input signal and ideal output.

positional servomechanism with the fixed elements corresponding to
an electric servomotor driving a pure inertia load.   Assuming the
motor has a decaying exponential response of output acceleration to a
step input voltage, the transfer function of the motor will be as indicated in the block diagram.   The time constant τ_m is simply the ratio
of the combined moment of inertia of the motor and load divided by
the electrical damping.   The compensation used with this servomotor

is a pure gain corresponding physically to a motor voltage that is instantaneously proportional to the actuating signal. In the block diagram the gain of the servomotor and the compensation are lumped together in a single constant K_v. Physically this constant represents the ratio of the steady-state output rate to the actuating signal when the latter is held constant. This ratio is frequently called the *velocity constant*. In order to obtain numerical answers in this example, values for all the parameter values must be assigned. A typical value for the motor time constant τ_m for an instrument servomechanism is 0.01 second. A typical value for the velocity constant K_v is 100 second^{-1}. Let us take the frequency of the input triangular wave to be 10 radians per second. In addition, we shall measure the performance quantitatively by the root-mean-square (rms) error. Specifically we shall use the ratio of the rms error to the rms input as the performance measure.

In view of the periodic nature of the input signal, one way of computing the rms error is by means of a Fourier series representation for the error. The input can be expanded into a Fourier series, and the output can be computed by evaluating the steady-state system response to each term of the input series. By linear superposition, the output can be constructed by adding together the response for each term of the input computed as if there were no other terms present. In the complex Fourier series representation the input signal can be represented as

$$v(t) = \sum_{n=-\infty}^{\infty} v_n e^{jn\omega_v t} \tag{1.5-1}$$

where ω_v is the fundamental frequency of the input signal and v_n is the Fourier coefficient of the nth term in the series. By the standard technique for evaluating these coefficients, v_n is found to be

$$v_n = \frac{4N}{\pi^2 n^2} \quad \text{for } n \text{ odd}$$

$$v_n = 0 \quad \text{for } n \text{ even} \tag{1.5-2}$$

for the triangular wave shown in Fig. 1.5–2. The error response for the specified input signal can be represented also by a Fourier series which we shall write as

$$y_e(t) = \sum_{n=-\infty}^{\infty} y_n e^{jn\omega_v t} \tag{1.5-3}$$

By squaring, integrating, and averaging the error it is a simple matter to show that the rms error can be expressed in terms of the Fourier coefficients as

$$\left(\overline{y_e^2(t)}\right)^{\frac{1}{2}} = \left(\sum_{n=-\infty}^{\infty} y_{-n}y_n\right)^{\frac{1}{2}} \tag{1.5-4}$$

By definition the error is the difference between the desired output and the actual output. Thus

$$y_e(t) = i(t) - q(t) \tag{1.5-5}$$

But the desired output and the actual output can both be expresssed as Fourier series as follows:

$$i(t) = \sum_{n=-\infty}^{\infty} i_n e^{jn\omega_v t} \tag{1.5-6}$$

and

$$q(t) = \sum_{n=-\infty}^{\infty} q_n e^{jn\omega_v t} \tag{1.5-7}$$

Thus the Fourier coefficients for the error are given by

$$y_n = i_n - q_n \tag{1.5-8}$$

By Eq. 1.3–7 we express the output in terms of the input and the system function $W(s)$ as

$$q(s) = W(s)v(s) \tag{1.3-7}$$

Here the system function for the chosen values of the velocity constant K_v and the motor time constant τ_m is given by

$$W(s) = \frac{1}{1 \times 10^{-4}s^2 + 1 \times 10^{-2}s + 1} \tag{1.5-9}$$

From steady-state frequency response theory we know that the nth Fourier coefficient of the output signal is given by

$$q_n = W(jn\omega_v)v_n \tag{1.5-10}$$

Where the desired output is instantaneously equal to the input signal, we have

$$i_n = v_n \tag{1.5-11}$$

When the desired output is the input signal lagged by a time τ_d the Fourier coefficients for the desired output are given by

$$i_n = v_n e^{-jn\tau_d\omega_v} \tag{1.5-12}$$

Substituting these values for the Fourier coefficients of the desired output and the actual output into Eq. 1.5–8 yields

$$y_n = [1 - W(jn\omega_v)]v_n \qquad (1.5\text{–}13)$$

as the Fourier coefficient for the error when the desired output is instantaneously equal to the input. Similarly, when the desired output is the input signal delayed by a time τ_d, we have

$$y_n = [e^{-jn\tau_d\omega_v} - W(jn\omega_v)]v_n \qquad (1.5\text{–}14)$$

By means of these two equations and the expression for v_n given by Eq. 1.5–2 together with Eq. 1.5–9 for the system function $W(s)$, numerical values for the Fourier coefficients of the error response are computed. These values are substituted into Eq. 1.5–4 in order to determine the rms error. The rms value of the input signal, which is needed as the base for normalizing the rms error, can be computed by a formula similar to Eq. 1.5–4 or by direct integration and averaging of the input signal squared.

The computation of the rms error for this example has been carried out in accordance with the procedure outlined in the preceding paragraph. The result is a normalized rms error of 11.3 percent when the desired output is considered to be instantaneously equal to the input signal. When the desired output is taken to be the input signal delayed by 0.01 second, the normalized rms error drops to 1.5 percent. Additional insight into the meaning of these error values is given by Fig. 1.5–3, which shows the error response wave forms for the two cases. For this example, a requirement for instantaneous reproduction of the input signal causes a sevenfold increase in the rms error above the value obtained when a small delay is permitted. This demonstrates very markedly the severity of a requirement for instantaneous reproduction of an input signal.

In summary, the control problem differs from and requires separate treatment from the filter problem because of the four major features which distinguish it. These are:

1. The desired output signal is frequently instantaneously equal to the input signal. This requirement, as we have seen above, imposes a much more severe specification on the design of a control system than is normally imposed on the design of a filter, where some delay in the reproduction of the desired wave shape is permitted.

2. Major parts of the system may be fixed and beyond the designer's control. The only design freedom available is in the compensation to be used with these fixed elements. This is in distinct contrast to the

filter problem, where the specifications seldom include fixed elements within the filter.

3. Disturbing signals may enter into the control system at points other than the input. The suppression of the effect of these disturbing signals on the output of the control system may be a major requirement. In filter design, the problem of disturbing signals is either nonexistent or considerably less severe.

4. The control designer must frequently work with components whose parameters are not accurately specified and which may vary considerably with time. This is partly because mechanical, hydraulic, or

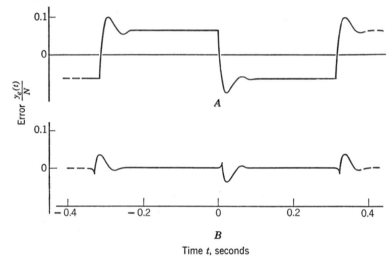

Fig. 1.5–3. Error response of second-order system to triangular-wave input. (A) Ideal output identical to input. (B) Ideal output equal to input delayed by 0.01 second.

pneumatic components may be used, particularly in the output side of a control system where appreciable power is required. This situation is very different from that facing the filter designer, who has available highly accurate and highly stable electric circuit elements.

In spite of the differences between the feedback control problem and the filter problem, they include much common ground. Both concern information processing systems, and both may have stability considerations since active filters are becoming more common.

1.6 TRIAL-AND-ERROR VERSUS ANALYTICAL DESIGN METHODS

The preceding article has attempted to define what the control problem is about. In this article we briefly discuss methods for solving the control problem.   The view of this book is that there are broadly two design procedures for linear control systems.   The first procedure we shall call the *trial-and-error design method*.   It has developed rapidly since the late 1930's and is the one normally discussed in first-course treatments of feedback control theory.   It is assumed that the reader is more or less familiar with at least one of the numerous books on this subject such as References A.3, B.6, B.7, C.3, M.1, and T.3 listed ·in the Bibliography.   The second design procedure we shall call the *analytical design method*.   This approach to the design of feedback control systems was apparently started by Wiener in the early 1940's. Because it has developed more slowly than the trial-and-error method, there are relatively fewer references.   Typical books treating the analytical design method to some degree are References H.1, J.1, S.6, T.7, T.8, W.2, and W.3.   Among the papers on the subject are References B.5, L.1, N.1, N.2, W.1, and Z.1.   In the paragraphs below, we attempt to give a bird's-eye view of these two design procedures in order to orient the reader before starting the detailed treatment of the analytical method.

The trial-and-error design method begins with a statement of the specifications for the control system that is to be designed.   Included in these specifications are statements concerning the input and disturbances acting on the control system together with a statement of the objective or output desired from the control system.   Next, some statement must be made as to the error that is allowed in realizing an approximation to the desired output.   If there are fixed elements in the control system, and there usually are, their performance characteristics must be defined.   Finally, a specification of the degree of stability expected of the control system must be made.   The specifications form the starting point of the trial-and-error design procedure.   If they are not given to the designer at the outset, and they often are not, he must seek them out before he can logically begin the actual design.

With the specifications established, the design may begin.   The trial-and-error design procedure is carried out primarily in the frequency domain.   The first step is to select tentatively a form of compensation.   Initially, a relatively simple form of compensation is usually chosen on the basis of the past experience of the designer.   The parameters for the compensation, other than the system gain, are established by a combination of the designer's experience and consideration of the phase and magnitude characteristics of the fixed elements of the system.   The second step is to set the system gain in accord with the stability requirements laid down in the specifications. Such a stability requirement may be in the form of a gain margin, a

phase margin, or a peak magnification value. The next step is to
determine if the system error is satisfactory. This is a problem of
analysis and is carried out either in the frequency or time domains,
depending on the nature of the input, desired output, and disturbance
specifications. Normally, the trial-and-error design procedure is discussed in textbooks on the basis that these signals are either transient,
sinusoidal, or periodic. However, there are no fundamental reasons
why stochastic signals cannot be treated. The last step in the design
procedure is carried out if the error is out of bounds and consists of
repeating the three preceding steps with a more elaborate form of compensation. This process is continued until the specifications are met.
The trial-and-error design method is summarized in Table 1.6–1.

Table 1.6–1.   Outline of the Trial-and-Error Design Procedure
A. Specifications:
   1. Input signal
   2. Desired output
   3. Disturbances
   4. Allowable error
   5. Fixed elements
   6. Degree of stability
B. Design procedure:
   1. Tentatively select a form of compensation (on the basis of past expe-
      rience). Establish the parameters for the compensation exclusive of
      the system gain.
   2. Set the system gain in accord with the stability requirement.
   3. By analysis, check to see if the error is satisfactory.
   4. If error is out of bounds, repeat procedure, using more elaborate com-
      pensation. Continue this process until specifications are met.

   At first blush, the trial-and-error design procedure outlined above
may appear to be rather crude. However, after a moderate amount of
experience almost any person with a sound engineering background can
employ this method successfully to design a rather large variety of
control systems. Because of its two prime advantages, viz., simplicity
and the use of mathematics that is familiar to most engineers, anyone
with a serious interest in feedback control should become familiar with
the trial-and-error design method. Although it is not the purpose of
this book to treat the trial-and-error design method, some of the analytical techniques used in carrying out its several steps are given in
Appendices C and D.
   Unfortunately, the trial-and-error design method is beset with certain fundamental difficulties, which must be clearly understood and
appreciated in order to employ it properly. From both a practical

and a theoretical viewpoint its principal disadvantage is that it cannot recognize an inconsistent set of specifications. By inconsistent specifications we mean a set that calls for a design that is theoretically not attainable. The trial-and-error design method provides no test to determine if the problem is solvable at the outset. Theoretically, an unsuspecting designer faced with an inconsistent set of specifications might continue the trial-and-error design procedure through an infinite number of cycles. Practically, a designer who possesses limited patience would obviously stop the process after a limited number of trials. Unfortunately he has no sure way of convincing those who set the specifications that the fault lies with them and not with him. Another disadvantage of the trial-and-error design method is that the designer may end with a control system that has more bandwidth than is necessary to meet the specifications. Ordinarily it is desirable to keep the bandwidth of a control system as small as possible in order to ease the practical problem of realizing in physical form a reasonable approximation to the linear model upon which the design is based. Finally, the trial-and-error method of design has been developed primarily for situations in which the desired output is identical to the input. Relatively little consideration has been given to the more sophisticated situations in which the desired output is functionally related to the data component of the input signal. It is because of these disadvantages of the trial-and-error technique for designing control systems that this book on the analytical approach to feedback control has been written.

The specifications that form the starting point of the analytical design procedure differ in two respects from those employed with the trial-and-error design method. In place of a relatively simple statement of the allowable error, the analytical design procedure employs a more or less elaborate *performance index*. The objective of the performance index is to encompass in a single number a quality measure for the performance of the system. Examples of performance indices are the *integral-square error* for transient signals and *mean-square error* for stochastic signals. In addition to the statement of the performance index to be used, the specifications must include a statement of the required value that the index must have for the system to be considered satisfactory. The other respect in which the specifications differ is on the matter of stability. The analytical design procedure requires no explicit statement concerning the degree of stability of the over-all control system. All solutions for the compensation include the twin requirements that the over-all system be stable and that it be realizable in the sense of having an impulse response that is zero for time less than zero.   The degree of stability is found as part of the solution of the problem and is a function of the other specifications.

One specification necessary to apply the analytical design procedure that is not explicitly used in the trial-and-error procedure concerns the degree of freedom allowed in the compensation.   If there are no fixed elements and if there is no specification for the configuration of the compensation, the design is classed as a *free-configuration problem.* If fixed elements are specified but there is no constraint on the configuration of the compensation the design is described as a *semi-free-configuration problem.*   When fixed elements are specified together with a configuration for the compensation, the design freedom is limited to the adjustment of one or more free parameters in the compensating network.   Such a design is called a *fixed-configuration problem.*

Once the specifications for the design are established, the analytical design procedure is as follows.   The first step is to determine the classification of the problem, that is, whether it is characterized by a free configuration, a semi-free configuration, or a fixed configuration.   If the configuration is free or semi-free, the second step is to use an existing formula for the compensation design or to develop a new formula especially for the problem at hand by employing techniques from the calculus of variations.   The compensation determined by the design equation or formula is the one corresponding to the minimum (or maximum) value of the performance index that can be obtained.

If the configuration is fixed, step two of the design procedure is to express the performance index as a function of the free parameters and to minimize (or maximize) the performance index by suitable adjustment of these parameters.   The values of the parameters found by this procedure correspond to the compensation that gives the performance index the minimum (or maximum) value permitted within the degree of freedom contained in the specifications.

The third step of the design procedure is to check to see that the compensation determined by the preceding step yields a performance index equal to or better than the required value.   If the value of the performance index is satisfactory, the theoretical design is completed and practical realization may begin.   On the other hand, if the value of the performance index is unsatisfactory, this is proof that the specifications cannot be met.   In that event, the problem must be rejected as impossible or else the specifications must be altered.   Table 1.6–2 presents an outline of the analytical design procedure just described.

The analytical design procedure has several advantages over the trial-and-error method, the most important of which is the facility to

Table 1.6–2. Outline of the Analytical Design Procedure

A. Specifications:
   1. Input signal
   2. Desired output
   3. Disturbances
   4. Performance index and required value of same
   5. Fixed elements
   6. Degree of freedom allowed in compensation
B. Design procedure:
   1. Determine the classification of the problem—free, semi-free, or fixed configuration.
   2. If the configuration is free or semi-free, use an appropriate formula for the compensating design. If the configuration is fixed, express the performance index as a function of the free parameters; then minimize (or maximize) the performance index by appropriately adjusting these parameters.
   3. Check to see if the compensation thus determined yields the required value of performance index. If it does, the theoretical design is completed and practical realization may begin. If it does not, the specifications cannot be met and must be altered or else the problem must be rejected as impossible.

detect immediately and surely an inconsistent set of specifications. The designer obtains a "yes" or "no" answer to the question of whether it is possible to fulfill any given set of specifications; he is not left with the haunting thought that if he had tried this or that form of compensation he might have been able to meet the specifications. Another advantage of this design method is that the procedure can be easily modified to restrict the bandwidth or limit the saturation tendencies of a control system to the extent permitted by the design freedom contained in the specifications. By *design freedom* we mean the difference between the specified value of the performance index and the minimum (or maximum) value that can be obtained without violating the specifications and without constraint on either the bandwidth or saturation tendencies. It is often to the designers advantage to absorb this design freedom either wholly or partially by imposing constraints on the system bandwidth or saturation tendencies. A third advantage of the analytical design procedure is its ability to treat with equal ease problems in which the desired output is equal to the input signal as well as problems in which it is not. This advantage is particularly important when noisy input signals are encountered or when the control system is being used as part of a computing device and it is desired to perform mathematical operations on the data component of the input. Last but not least among the advantages of the analytical design procedure is the insight that it gives into the capabilities and limitations of linear systems in general. Even if the reader never employs the analytical design procedure directly, the insight that it gives him into the problem of linear system design materially assists him in employing the trial-and-error design procedure.

Offsetting the above advantages of the analytical design procedure are two important disadvantages. First of all, it is unfortunate that many performance indices which might have engineering usefulness lead to analytically insolvable problems. Thus one is frequently forced to compromise his choice of performance index in order to obtain a solution to the design problem. The other major disadvantage of the analytical design procedure is that, even with performance indices like integral-square and mean-square error, many practical problems lead to involved solutions requiring considerable numerical calculation. In other words, the solving of practical problems can be very laborious and there is the danger that in the solution process the forest will be lost from view because of the large trees.

1.7 CASCADE VERSUS FEEDBACK CONFIGURATIONS; TREATMENT OF DISTURBANCES

In carrying out the analytical design procedure described in the preceding article, it is often convenient to replace the actual control system with its feedback configuration by a cascade combination of compensating and fixed elements. This article discusses this alternate arrangement and its equivalence to the feedback configuration.

Figure 1.7–1 shows a block diagram of the feedback configuration so typical of control systems. The over-all transfer function or system

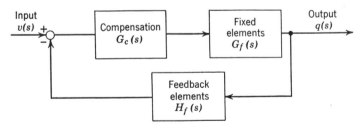

Fig. 1.7–1.   Feedback configuration of control system.

function which relates the output transform $q(s)$ to the input transform $v(s)$ is

$$W(s) = \frac{G_c(s)G_f(s)}{1 + G_c(s)G_f(s)H_f(s)} \tag{1.7-1}$$

Figure 1.7-2 shows a cascade configuration which employs a different compensating network than is used in the feedback configuration and whose transform is represented by the symbol $W_c(s)$. It is desired that this cascade configuration be entirely equivalent to the feedback configuration. The condition for equivalence can be obtained by

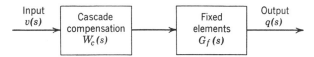

Fig. 1.7–2.   Equivalent cascade configuration of control system.

equating the system functions of the two configurations.   The system function of the cascade configuration is given by

$$W(s) = W_c(s)G_f(s) \qquad (1.7\text{--}2)$$

From this equation and Eq. 1.7–1 we observe that

$$W_c(s) = \frac{G_c(s)}{1 + G_c(s)G_f(s)H_f(s)} \qquad (1.7\text{--}3)$$

in order for the two configurations to have the same over-all transmission characteristics.

The cascade configuration frequently will be used in the preliminary stages of the design of a feedback control system.   As the result of the preliminary work, a solution for $W_c(s)$, or its equivalent in the time domain $w_c(t)$, is obtained in terms of the problem specifications.   As the final step we wish to find an equivalent $G_c(s)$ which will give the same behavior in the feedback configuration as $W_c(s)$ gives in the cascade configuration.   A formula for $G_c(s)$ is obtained by solving Eq. 1.7–3.   The result is

$$G_c(s) = \frac{W_c(s)}{1 - G_f(s)H_f(s)W_c(s)} \qquad (1.7\text{--}4)$$

To the extent that $H_f(s)$ is not rigidly fixed it can be chosen with a view to simplifying the problem of realizing $G_c(s)$.   If $H_f(s)$ has some flexibility, the designer should take advantage of it.

The question now arises as to whether any design freedom has been sacrificed by using the cascade configuration as a preliminary step in the design procedure.   Let us first consider fixed elements $G_f(s)$ which are stable.   One might reason that the feedback configuration could incorporate such compensation as to render the equivalent cascade compensation unstable.   Such a situation could conceivably arise if the fixed elements are non-minimum phase and a right-half-plane zero of the fixed elements is canceled by a corresponding pole of the equivalent cascade compensation. Since the design of the compensation for the cascade configuration will assume such compensation to be stable and realizable in its own right, it would appear that some design freedom has been lost. As a practical matter, however, a system must not become unstable in the face of small parameter variations. Thus the cancellation of a right-half-plane zero in the fixed elements by a corresponding pole in the equivalent cascade compensation will not be allowed. Consequently, the cascade configuration is fully equivalent to the feedback configuration for design purposes as long as the fixed elements are stable.

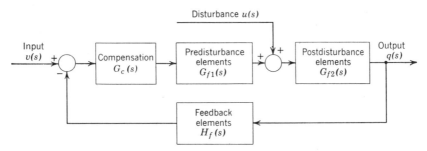

Fig. 1.7–3. Control system with single disturbance.

If the fixed elements are unstable, it would seem immediately evident that the feedback configuration has an advantage over the cascade arrangement since a stable over-all system can be arrived at by using feedback whereas no compensation in the cascade configuration can possibly achieve system stability. Thus it would appear that some design freedom, viz., the ability to deal with unstable fixed elements, has been lost if the cascade configuration is used as a step in the analytical design procedure. Actually, however, no loss of design freedom need be suffered. When dealing with unstable fixed elements and when it is desired to use the cascade configuration as the basis for the compensation design, the first step is to surround the fixed elements by an auxiliary feedback loop arbitrarily compensated with the mere objective of obtaining stability. Then the original fixed elements together with the auxiliary feedback loop can be considered a new set of fixed elements. These new fixed elements are stable, and cascade compensation is entirely feasible. Thus no design freedom need be lost because of unstable fixed elements.

The foregoing considerations concerning the equivalence of the cascade configuration to the feedback configuration has ignored the existence of disturbances. The purpose of the following remarks is to show

how disturbances can be treated within the framework of the cascade configuration of Fig. 1.7–2. Figure 1.7–3 shows a control system with a single disturbance entering the fixed elements. In order to account properly for the disturbance in the equivalent cascade configuration, simply splitting the fixed elements and inserting it there is not sufficient since this would not take into account the effect of the closed loop.

In order to account for the effect of the closed loop on the disturbance, one approach is to move the disturbance outside the closed loop without going through the compensating elements. Figure 1.7–4 indicates how this can be done. In accordance with this figure, we can

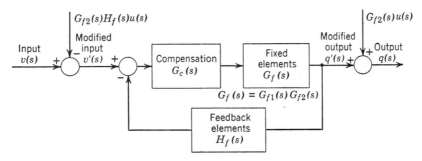

Fig. 1.7–4.   Control system with disturbance moved through postdisturbance elements to periphery.

define a modified input signal $v'(s)$ and a modified output signal $q'(s)$ as follows:

$$v'(s) \triangleq v(s) - G_{f2}(s)H_f(s)u(s) \qquad (1.7\text{–}5)$$

$$q'(s) \triangleq q(s) - G_{f2}u(s) \qquad (1.7\text{–}6)$$

With respect to these modified signals, the feedback configuration is precisely the same as Fig. 1.7–1, in which no disturbance is shown. Corresponding to the modified output signal defined in Eq. 1.7–6, we can define a modified desired output signal as

$$i'(s) \triangleq i(s) - G_{f2}u(s) \qquad (1.7\text{–}7)$$

If the modified output signal is equal to the modified desired output it is apparent from the definitions that the original output will equal the original desired output. As pointed out above, the analytical design procedure involves the minimization (or maximization) of a performance index. With a properly chosen performance index this process will tend to diminish the error between the desired output and the actual output. Thus by using the modified signals defined in Eqs. 1.7–5, 6, and 7, the analytical method may be applied to the design of systems with disturbances in precisely the same way that it can be applied to systems without disturbances. Of course, the actual error is minimized in a slightly different sense when the performance index is applied to the modified signals than when it is applied to the original signals. Usually, however, this difference is not of vital importance since small variations in the way in which the error is minimized generally have small effects on the compensation design.

The above discussion points out one way of handling disturbances in the analytical design of control systems. An alternative approach may sometimes be employed. In this alternative approach the effects of the input signal and the disturbance on the output are considered separately. With the disturbance acting alone, the desired output is normally zero. An error index for the disturbance acting alone can be specified. This index can be constrained to be equal to or less than a specified value in the process of minimizing (or maximizing) the performance index of the system when the input signal alone is acting. This approach will be more easily understood after the discussion of constrained variation given later in this book.

The foregoing articles have given a general picture of the analytical design procedure and where it fits into the control art. The next chapter develops the analytical design method in some detail for the problem of fixed-configuration systems subject to transient input signals and disturbances.

2

ADJUSTMENT OF PARAMETERS
TO MINIMIZE
INTEGRAL-SQUARE ERROR

2.1 STATEMENT OF PROBLEM

In the preceding chapter the idea was introduced of designing a feedback control system so as to minimize (or maximize) a performance index. In this chapter this idea is developed for the following limited class of problems: The input and ideal output signals are transient functions of time; the performance index is the integral-square value of the error between the ideal output and the actual output; and the configuration is fixed, thereby limiting the design freedom to the adjustment of one or more parameters.

The problem of designing a feedback control system for transient signals is an important one. Typical transients are shown in Fig. 2.1–1. Examples of transient signals are the step function, the ramp, the rectangular pulse, the impulse, or in general any non-periodic definite function of time. Transient functions such as the step or the ramp are often used as idealizations of actual input signals. The actual input to a feedback control system may not be transient in character, yet it may contain a section which is responsible for large errors and which can be represented by a transient function. In any event, transient signals offer certain advantages over sinusoidal signals for test purposes since they contain, in general, an infinite number of frequency components rather than just one. Thus a single transient test can yield the same information as a frequency response run which requires a large number of tests with sinusoidal signals of different frequencies.

Next, let us examine the choice of the integral-square error as a performance index. In many applications the performance of feedback

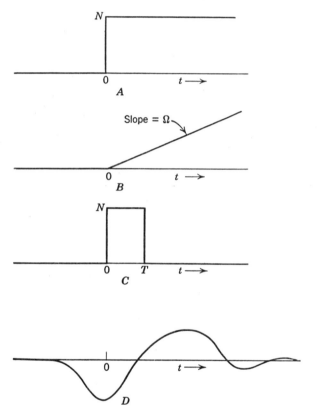

Fig. 2.1–1. Typical transients. (A) Step $N\delta_{-1}(t)$. (B) Ramp $\Omega t\delta_{-1}(t)$. (C) Rectangular pulse $N[\delta_{-1}(t) - \delta_{-1}(t - T)]$. (D) Arbitrary transient.

control systems can be considered either satisfactory, if the errors are below a certain limit, or unsatisfactory, if the errors are above a certain limit. Under these conditions a proper performance index would be the fraction of the time that the errors are outside the allowable tolerance. The smaller this time is, the more satisfactory the performance of the control system. Unfortunately, it is impossible in general to solve analytically the problem of minimizing such a performance index.

However, by minimizing the integral-square error we tend to minimize the duration time of large errors. This comes about because the integral-square error as a performance index gives much stronger emphasis to large errors than to small errors.

Under other circumstances one might wish to minimize the peak error of a control system after a transient disturbance. Minimizing the peak error is also in general an analytically insolvable problem. It is not difficult to see that minimizing the integral-square error will tend to limit the peak error exhibited by a control system provided the problem is such that the peak error can be controlled. There are certain problems in which the peak error is automatically set by the very nature of the specifications. Since the minimization of the integral-square error can be done analytically for a rather general class of signals, its use is justified very frequently as a substitute for performance indices which are more closely associated with the design objectives but which lead to insolvable mathematical problems.

Figure 2.1–2 shows the block diagram of the feedback-control-system configuration under consideration. This is a rather general block diagram in the sense that many other more complex configurations can be manipulated into this form. The hypothesis that the configuration is fixed refers to the form of the system; it is assumed that one or more individual parameter values are subject to adjustment. For example, in a typical problem, the fixed elements and the feedback elements may be completely specified and a form for the compensating elements already chosen. All that remains is to set the values of the gain and time constants in the compensating network. Even though theoretically much opportunity has been sacrificed by fixing the configuration, it often turns out in practice that the adjustment of a few free parameters will improve the performance almost as much as it could be improved if the configuration of the compensating elements were completely free.

In summary, the problem that is considered in this chapter is: Given the input and ideal output signals as transient functions of time and given the configuration of the control system, find the values that the free parameters should have in order to minimize the integral-square error. One approach to solving this problem starts with the Fourier transforms of the input and ideal output signals. The integral-square error is then easily formulated by means of Parseval's theorem. If the transform of the error is a rational function of the complex frequency, the integral-square error can be easily evaluated by means of a table of integrals. When the integral-square error is evaluated, it appears as a function of the free parameters. By using standard

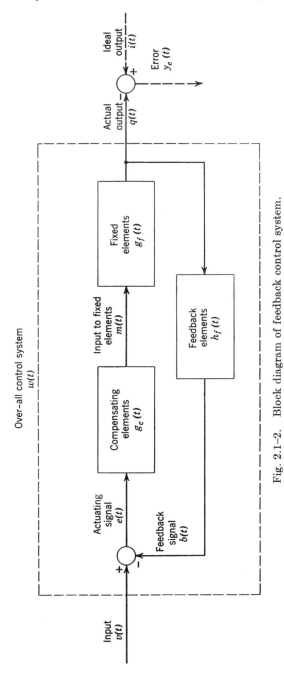

Fig. 2.1-2. Block diagram of feedback control system.

minimization procedures, values for these parameters can be found which minimize this performance index.

2.2   PARSEVAL'S THEOREM

Suppose we wish to know the area beneath the product of two time functions $x_1(t)$ and $x_2(t)$ over the infinite interval of time from minus infinity to plus infinity.   Let this area be denoted by the symbol I (which stands for integral).   Thus

$$I = \int_{-\infty}^{\infty} dt \, x_1(t)x_2(t) \tag{2.2-1}$$

Suppose, in addition, that the time functions are Fourier transformable and have transforms $x_1(s)$ and $x_2(s)$, respectively.   We wish to express the integral I directly in terms of these transforms in order to obviate inverse transforming $x_1(s)$ and $x_2(s)$ when these are given rather than the time functions themselves.   To do this we observe that

$$x_2(t) = \frac{1}{2\pi j} \int_{-j\infty}^{j\infty} ds \, e^{st}x_2(s) \tag{2.2-2}$$

Substitution of this value of $x_2(t)$ into Eq. 2.2–1 yields

$$I = \int_{-\infty}^{\infty} dt \, x_1(t) \frac{1}{2\pi j} \int_{-j\infty}^{j\infty} ds \, e^{st}x_2(s) \tag{2.2-3}$$

Let us now interchange the order of the integrations so that we integrate with respect to time first

$$I = \frac{1}{2\pi j} \int_{-j\infty}^{j\infty} ds \, x_2(s) \int_{-\infty}^{\infty} dt \, e^{st}x_1(t) \tag{2.2-4}$$

By the direct Fourier transform we know that

$$x_1(s) = \int_{-\infty}^{\infty} dt \, e^{-st}x_1(t) \tag{2.2-5}$$

Thus the integral with respect to time on the right side of Eq. 2.2–4 may be evaluated as

$$\int_{-\infty}^{\infty} dt \, e^{st}x_1(t) = x_1(-s) \tag{2.2-6}$$

This permits us to write Eq. 2.2–4 as

$$I = \frac{1}{2\pi j} \int_{-j\infty}^{j\infty} ds \, x_1(-s)x_2(s) \tag{2.2-7}$$

This is the desired expression for the integral I.

An important particular case of the above result occurs when the two time functions involved are identical so that the integral I becomes

$$I = \int_{-\infty}^{\infty} dt \, x^2(t) \tag{2.2–8}$$

We call this integral the integral-square value of the time function $x(t)$. By Eq. 2.2–7 we know this can be expressed as

$$I = \frac{1}{2\pi j} \int_{-j\infty}^{j\infty} ds \, x(-s)x(s) \tag{2.2–9}$$

This result is known as Parseval's theorem.   This theorem represents a very convenient way of expressing the integral-square value of a time function in terms of its transform.

2.3 MINIMIZATION PROCEDURE; EXAMPLE

On the basis of Parseval's theorem we are now in a position to formulate the procedure for minimizing the integral-square error for transient input signals by adjustment of the free parameters.   This procedure involves four steps.   The first step is to express the Fourier transform of the error as a function of the complex frequency s.   This function will involve the free parameters of the system as unknown coefficients. The second step is to express the integral-square error I_y in terms of the error transform $y_e(s)$ by Parseval's theorem; i.e.,

$$I_y = \frac{1}{2\pi j} \int_{-j\infty}^{j\infty} ds \, y_e(-s)y_e(s) \tag{2.3–1}$$

At this stage, provided $y_e(s)$ is a rational function, the integral-square error will appear in the form

$$I_y = \frac{1}{2\pi j} \int_{-j\infty}^{j\infty} ds \, \frac{c(-s)c(s)}{d(-s)d(s)} \tag{2.3–2}$$

where $c(s)$ and $d(s)$ are polynomials in s.   The third step is to evaluate the integral.   Fortunately, definite integrals of this form have been evaluated in terms of the coefficients appearing in the polynomials. A table of these integrals along with an explanation of how they were evaluated is given in Appendix E.   Upon carrying out the integration we have the integral-square error expressed as a function of the free parameters p_1 through p_K.   Symbolically the integral-square error at this stage is expressed as

$$I_y(p_1, p_2, \cdots, p_K)$$

The fourth step of the minimization procedure is to adjust the values of the free parameters in such a way as to minimize the integral-square error.   Formally this can be done in the standard manner of equating the partial derivatives of the integral-square error to zero and solving the resultant set of equations for the values of the parameters.   In symbols this means solving the set of K equations of the form

$$\frac{\partial I_y}{\partial p_k} = 0 \qquad\qquad (2.3\text{--}3)$$

Unfortunately in many practical problems this formal procedure for finding the parameter values that minimize the integral-square error leads to sets of non-linear equations in the parameters which are so complex that straightforward methods of solution do not exist.

If the equations for the parameters obtained by setting the partial derivatives of the integral-square error with respect to the parameters equal to zero are too complex to be solved by analytical methods, we may resort to trial-and-error or successive approximation techniques. However, if such methods are necessary to solve the equations for the parameters, it is probably best to go back to the expression for the integral-square error itself and plot this as a function of one of the parameters, holding the other parameters fixed.   By using a sufficient number of fixed values for these other parameters and making a sufficient number of plots, values can be found for all the parameters that define the minimum value of the integral-square error close enough for engineering purposes.   By working directly with the integral-square error expression we avoid taking the partial derivatives of this expression with respect to each of the free parameters.   Taking these derivatives may be a very difficult and time-consuming chore.

Beyond the above brief statement of the procedure used to minimize the integral-square error little more needs to be said.   This procedure will become quite clear if we consider an example.   For illustrative purposes, consider the problem of designing a positional servo-mechanism.   Take the input signal to be a step function of amplitude N.   The object of a positional servomechanism is to make the output equal to the input; therefore, we shall take the desired output to be identical to the input.   As the fixed elements corresponding to the servomotor, we shall specify an integrator cascaded with a time lag. Physically this is representative of a direct-current servomotor controlled by adjusting the armature current.   Assuming the source supplying the armature current has a voltage proportional to the control signal, and, assuming the armature circuit inductance is negligible, the time lag τ_m is simply the total inertia referred to the motor shaft divided by the electrical damping of the motor. The load torque and the viscous damping effect of the load are taken to be negligible. Since this is a positional servomechanism, it is not unreasonable to take the feedback elements as having a transfer function of unity. Let us use the simplest possible compensation, namely, a pure gain; then the only adjustable parameter is the value of this gain. For this positional servomechanism we wish to find how the integral-square error varies as a function of the gain and what the value of the gain should be to make this error a minimum.

The problem statement can be recapitulated in terms of symbols as follows:

Given.   For the input we have

$$v(t) = N\delta_{-1}(t) \tag{2.3-4}$$

The desired output is

$$i(t) = v(t) \tag{2.3-5}$$

The transfer function for the fixed elements is

$$G_f(s) = \frac{1}{(\tau_m s + 1)s} \tag{2.3-6}$$

The feedback elements are described by

$$H_f(s) = 1 \tag{2.3-7}$$

The compensation is given by

$$G_c(s) = K_v \tag{2.3-8}$$

where K_v is the system velocity constant. Here we have absorbed the gain of the fixed elements with the gain of the compensation so that the product is the velocity constant.

Find.   We desire, first, an expression for the integral-square error as a function of the velocity constant; i.e., in symbols, we seek $I_y(K_v)$. And, second, we ask for the value of the velocity constant for the minimum integral-square error.

Solution.   Inspection of Fig. 2.1–2 allows us to write as a general expression for the error transform

$$y_e(s) = i(s) - W(s)v(s) \tag{2.3-9}$$

From the given data the over-all transfer function for the control system is

$$W(s) = \frac{K_v}{\tau_m s^2 + s + K_v} \qquad (2.3\text{-}10)$$

For the Fourier transform of the input we have

$$v(s) = \frac{N}{s} \qquad (2.3\text{-}11)$$

and the transform of the desired output in view of Eq. 2.3–5 is

$$i(s) = v(s) \qquad (2.3\text{-}12)$$

Thus we can write for the transform of the error

$$y_e(s) = N \frac{\tau_m s + 1}{\tau_m s^2 + s + K_v} \qquad (2.3\text{-}13)$$

By Parseval's theorem the integral-square error can be expressed in the form

$$I_y = \frac{N^2}{2\pi j} \int_{-j\infty}^{j\infty} ds \, \frac{c(-s)}{d(-s)} \frac{c(s)}{d(s)} \qquad (2.3\text{-}14)$$

where

$$c(s) = \tau_m s + 1 \qquad (2.3\text{-}15)$$

and

$$d(s) = \tau_m s^2 + s + K_v \qquad (2.3\text{-}16)$$

The formula for I_2 given in Appendix E is

$$I_2 = \frac{c_1{}^2 d_0 + c_0{}^2 d_2}{2 d_0 d_1 d_2}$$

Substituting the values of the coefficients obtained from Eqs. 2.3–15 and 16 into this expression yields for the integral-square error

$$I_y = N^2 \frac{\tau_m{}^2 K_v + \tau_m}{2 K_v \tau_m} \qquad (2.3\text{-}17)$$

Dividing out by $K_v \tau_m$ simplifies this expression to

$$I_y = \frac{N^2}{2} \left(\tau_m + \frac{1}{K_v} \right) \qquad (2.3\text{-}18)$$

This is the first desired result; it expresses the integral-square error as a function of the velocity constant K_v.

In order to establish the value of the velocity constant which makes the integral-square error a minimum, we must first determine the range of values that are permitted in view of the requirement that the system must be stable. Inspection of the system function given by Eq. 2.3–10 shows us that the system will be stable for all positive values of K_v and unstable for all negative values. By inspection of Eq. 2.3–18 we observe that the value of the velocity constant which minimizes the integral-square error is infinite. This is the second result asked for. Note that, if stability considerations had been ignored, a false value of zero for the integral-square error could be obtained by making K_v equal to $-\tau_m{}^{-1}$. Thus care must be exercised in seeking parameter values which minimize the integral-square error. Only values that correspond to a stable system are allowable. If a parameter should take on a value that corresponds to an unstable system, we know physically that the integral-square error will be infinite. The fact that the expression for the integral-square error (which is obtained by means of the integral table given in the Appendix) is finite for values of the parameters corresponding to instability may be explained by noting the condition postulated in the derivation of these definite integrals. This condition is that $d(s)$ must have all its zeros in the left-half plane. For unstable systems this condition is obviously not met and any value for the integral-square error obtained by means of the integral table is invalid.

Solution of this example has led us to the rather startling conclusion that the gain of the system should be infinite in order to minimize the integral-square error. The damping ratio of a second-order system described by Eq. 2.3–10 is given by

$$\zeta = \frac{1}{2\,(\tau_m K_v)^{1/2}} \tag{2.3–19}$$

and the natural frequency is given by

$$\omega_n = \left(\frac{K_v}{\tau_m}\right)^{1/2} \tag{2.3–20}$$

In terms of these parameters the system function may be expressed as

$$W(s) = \frac{1}{(s^2/\omega_n{}^2) + 2\zeta(s/\omega_n) + 1} \tag{2.3–21}$$

The solution for the error for a step function input and the ideal output equal to the input is given by

$$y_e(t) = \frac{N\delta_{-1}(t)}{(1-\zeta^2)^{1/2}} e^{-\zeta\omega_n t} \cos\left[(1-\zeta^2)^{1/2}\omega_n t - \tan^{-1}\frac{\zeta}{(1-\zeta^2)^{1/2}}\right]$$
$$\tag{2.3–22}$$

In view of the way in which the damping ratio decreases with increasing gain, it may seem surprising that the integral-square error should fall as the gain is increased. However, if we rewrite the expression for the error response to a step input in terms of the parameters τ_m and K_v instead of the damping ratio ζ and natural frequency ω_n, we have

$$y_e(t) = \frac{N\delta_{-1}(t)}{\left(1 - \frac{1}{4\tau_m K_v}\right)^{\frac{1}{2}}} e^{-t/2\tau_m} \cos\left[\left(1 - \frac{1}{4\tau_m K_v}\right)^{\frac{1}{2}}\left(\frac{K_v}{\tau_m}\right)^{\frac{1}{2}} t\right.$$

$$\left. - \tan^{-1} \frac{\frac{1}{2(\tau_m K_v)^{\frac{1}{2}}}}{\left(1 - \frac{1}{4\tau_m K_v}\right)^{\frac{1}{2}}}\right] \qquad (2.3\text{-}23)$$

This expression shows that the envelope of the transient has a time constant fixed by the motor constant τ_m and is independent of the gain K_v. Thus as the gain is increased the solution becomes more and more oscillatory but it is always confined within approximately the same envelope. Figure 2.3–1 illustrates this point. This explains how the integral-square error is always finite irrespective of how large the gain is.

For low values of gain the envelope containing the oscillatory error response actually is somewhat larger than at high values of gain because of the square root factor appearing in the denominator of Eq. 2.3–23. This leads us to expect an increase in the integral-square error as the gain is reduced. On the other hand, for very large values of gain the envelope approaches a constant form corresponding to the exponential in Eq. 2.3–23, and the number of oscillations contained within it become so large that any small group of them appears sinusoidal in form. The mean-square value of a sine wave is equal to one-half of the amplitude squared. This means that we can compute the integral-square value of the error for very large gain as approximately one-half the integral-square value of the envelope. That is,

$$I_y = \frac{1}{2}\int_0^\infty dt\, (Ne^{-t/2\tau_m})^2 \quad \text{for } K_v \to \infty \qquad (2.3\text{-}24)$$

or

$$I_y = \frac{1}{2}N^2\int_0^\infty dt\, e^{-t/\tau_m} \quad \text{for } K_v \to \infty \qquad (2.3\text{-}25)$$

Evaluating the definite integral yields

$$I_y = \tfrac{1}{2}N^2\tau_m \quad \text{for } K_v \to \infty \qquad (2.3\text{--}26)$$

This confirms the value predicted by Eq. 2.3–18.

In most practical problems, raising a gain toward infinity will cause the system to become unstable and make the integral-square error

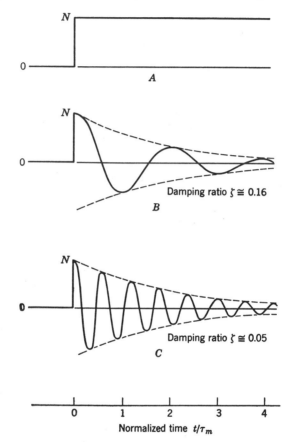

Fig. 2.3–1.   Error response of second-order system to input step.   (A) input. (B) Error response for $\tau_m K_v \cong 10$.   (C) Error response for $\tau_m K_v \cong 100$.

infinite.   Thus the result of this example is rather unusual and can be explained by the simplicity of the fixed elements represented by Eq. 2.3–6.   Such an idealization for the fixed elements is generally inapplicable at very large gains.   One way of restricting the range of parameter variation so that the idealization of the fixed elements is reasonable is to specify the natural frequency of this system and then ask how the parameters should be adjusted to minimize the integral-square error. Here we must let both the motor time constant τ_m and the velocity constant K_v be free. Equation 2.3–18 can be rewritten in terms of the damping ratio and the natural frequency as

$$I_y = \frac{N^2}{2\omega_n}\left(\frac{1}{2\zeta} + 2\zeta\right) \qquad (2.3\text{–}27)$$

It is easily shown that the damping ratio ζ should be set equal to one-half in order to make this expression a minimum. This result was first pointed out by A. C. Hall (see reference H.1). A damping ratio of one-half is a reasonable result for a second-order system.

The integral-square error minimization procedure outlined above and illustrated by this example is appropriate as long as the transform of the error $y_e(s)$ can be expressed as a rational function. If the transform of the error cannot be expressed as a rational function, the foregoing procedure will not work. If the error has a transcendental transform the procedure is not clear. One approach is to approximate the time function so that a rational transform results. A second approach is to approximate the transform of the error by means of rational functions. The third approach is to work entirely in the time domain. The first two approaches are rather obvious since they force the problem into a form in which the design procedure just outlined is satisfactory. The third approach will be discussed briefly in the next section.

2.4   INTEGRAL-SQUARE ERROR IN TERMS OF
TRANSLATION FUNCTIONS

In treating the integral-square error in the time domain the discussion is simplified by introducing two new functions which for the lack of a better name will be called the *autotranslation function* and the *cross-translation function*. Let $x_1(t)$ and $x_2(t)$ denote two arbitrary transient input signals. Then the autotranslation function $I_{11}(\tau)$ is defined as

$$I_{11}(\tau) \triangleq \int_{-\infty}^{\infty} dt\, x_1(t)x_1(t + \tau) \qquad (2.4\text{–}1)$$

and the cross-translation function $I_{12}(\tau)$ is defined as

$$I_{12}(\tau) \triangleq \int_{-\infty}^{\infty} dt\, x_1(t)x_2(t + \tau) \qquad (2.4\text{–}2)$$

These functions characterize the signals x_1 and x_2. The characterization is not unique, however; ordinarily there are a number of different

x_1 and x_2 functions that can give rise to the same translation functions. It is immediately evident from the definition that the autotranslation function is an even function of the shift parameter τ.   Symbolically

$$I_{11}(-\tau) = I_{11}(\tau) \tag{2.4-3}$$

This can be seen by replacing τ by $-\tau$ in Eq. 2.4–1 and changing the variable of integration from t to $t - \tau$.   In a similar manner it can be shown that for the cross-translation function an interchange of subscripts can be offset by changing the sign of the argument, that is,

$$I_{21}(-\tau) = I_{12}(\tau) \tag{2.4-4}$$

The principal reason for introducing the translation functions is to simplify the writing of expressions that involve definite integrals of the products of transient signals.

In order to illustrate the derivation of a cross-translation function for a specific pair of transient signals, let us refer to Fig. 2.4–1. $x_1(t)$ is a rectangular pulse as shown in curve A. $x_2(t)$ is a single saw tooth as shown in curve B.   Using the definition of the cross-translation function given by Eq. 2.4–2 and inserting the values for $x_1(t)$ and $x_2(t)$ given in the figure allow us to write for the cross-translation function

$$
\begin{aligned}
I_{12}(\tau) &= 0 && \text{for } \tau \le 0 \\[6pt]
&= N^2 \int_{-\tau}^{0} dt \left(1 - \frac{t + \tau}{T} \right) && 0 < \tau \le T \\[6pt]
&= N^2 \int_{-T}^{T-\tau} dt \left(1 - \frac{t + \tau}{T} \right) && T < \tau \le 2T \quad (2.4\text{-}5) \\[6pt]
&= 0 && \tau > 2T
\end{aligned}
$$

Evaluation of the definite integrals yields

$$
\begin{aligned}
I_{12}(\tau) &= 0 && \text{for } \tau \le 0 \\[6pt]
&= N^2 \left[\tau - \frac{\tau^2}{2T} \right] && 0 < \tau \le T \\[6pt]
&= N^2 \left[2(T - \tau) + \frac{\tau^2}{2T} \right] && T < \tau \le 2T \\[6pt]
&= 0 && \tau > 2T
\end{aligned}
\tag{2.4-6}
$$

This function is plotted as curve C of the figure.   In a similar way we may compute the cross-translation function $I_{21}(\tau)$; the result is curve

D shown in the figure.   The relation of curves C and D graphically illustrates the meaning of Eq. 2.4–4.

Having introduced the notion of the translation functions, we are now in a position to proceed with the evaluation of the integral-square

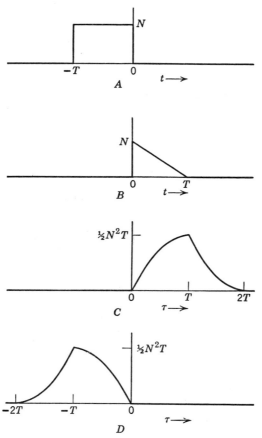

Fig. 2.4–1.   Example of cross-translation function. $(A)\ x_1(t)\ =\ N[\delta_{-1}(t + T)\ -$ $\delta_{-1}(t)]$. $(B)\ x_2(t)\ =\ N[\delta_{-1}(t)\ -\ \delta_{-1}(t - T)]\left(1 - \dfrac{t}{T}\right)\cdot$ $(C)\ I_{12}(\tau)$. $(D)\ I_{21}(\tau)$.

error in the time domain.   The autotranslation function of the error is given by

$$I_{yy}(\tau) = \int_{-\infty}^{\infty} dt\ y_e(t)y_e(t + \tau) \qquad (2.4–7)$$

It is evident that the integral-square error may be obtained by setting τ equal to zero in the above expression.   That is,

$$I_y = I_{yy}(0) \qquad (2.4–8)$$

Figure 2.1–2 shows the error to be

$$y_e(t) = i(t) - q(t) \qquad (2.4\text{–}9)$$

where $i(t)$ is the ideal output and $q(t)$ is the actual output of the control system. Inserting this expression for the error into Eq. 2.4–7 yields

$$I_{yy}(\tau) = \int_{-\infty}^{\infty} dt\, i(t)i(t+\tau) - \int_{-\infty}^{\infty} dt\, i(t)q(t+\tau)$$
$$- \int_{-\infty}^{\infty} dt\, q(t)i(t+\tau) + \int_{-\infty}^{\infty} dt\, q(t)q(t+\tau) \qquad (2.4\text{–}10)$$

By making use of the definitions of the translation functions given by Eqs. 2.4–1 and 2.4–2 this equation may be written in the form

$$I_{yy}(\tau) = I_{ii}(\tau) - I_{iq}(\tau) - I_{qi}(\tau) + I_{qq}(\tau) \qquad (2.4\text{–}11)$$

Here $I_{ii}(\tau)$ is the autotranslation function of the ideal output; $I_{iq}(\tau)$ and $I_{qi}(\tau)$ represent cross-translation functions between the desired and actual output signals; and $I_{qq}(\tau)$ stands for the autotranslation function of the actual output signal. The actual output of the system can be written as the convolution of the system weighting function and the input signal; that is,

$$q(t) = \int_{-\infty}^{\infty} dt_1\, w(t_1)v(t - t_1) \qquad (2.4\text{–}12)$$

Thus the cross-translation function between the desired output and the actual output can be written as

$$I_{iq}(\tau) = \int_{-\infty}^{\infty} dt\, i(t) \int_{-\infty}^{\infty} dt_1\, w(t_1)v(t + \tau - t_1) \qquad (2.4\text{–}13)$$

Interchanging the order of integration so that we integrate first with respect to time t yields

$$I_{iq}(\tau) = \int_{-\infty}^{\infty} dt_1\, w(t_1) \int_{-\infty}^{\infty} dt\, i(t)v(t + \tau - t_1) \qquad (2.4\text{–}14)$$

Making use of the definition of the cross-translation function between the desired output and the input allows us to simplify this expression to

$$I_{iq}(\tau) = \int_{-\infty}^{\infty} dt_1\, w(t_1) I_{iv}(\tau - t_1) \qquad (2.4\text{–}15)$$

Similarly,

$$I_{qi}(\tau) = \int_{-\infty}^{\infty} dt \int_{-\infty}^{\infty} dt_1\, w(t_1)v(t - t_1)i(t + \tau) \qquad (2.4\text{–}16)$$

which simplifies to

$$I_{qi}(\tau) = \int_{-\infty}^{\infty} dt_1\, w(t_1) I_{vi}(\tau + t_1) \qquad (2.4\text{–}17)$$

The autotranslation function of the actual output can be written as

$$I_{qq}(\tau) = \int_{-\infty}^{\infty} dt \int_{-\infty}^{\infty} dt_1\, w(t_1)v(t - t_1) \int_{-\infty}^{\infty} dt_2\, w(t_2)v(t + \tau - t_2)$$

$$(2.4-18)$$

and this reduces to

$$I_{qq}(\tau) = \int_{-\infty}^{\infty} dt_1\, w(t_1) \int_{-\infty}^{\infty} dt_2\, w(t_2) I_{vv}(\tau + t_1 - t_2) \quad (2.4-19)$$

Substituting the translation functions given by Eqs. 2.4–15, 17, and 19 into Eq. 2.4–11 yields

$$I_{yy}(\tau) = I_{ii}(\tau) - \int_{-\infty}^{\infty} dt_1\, w(t_1) I_{iv}(\tau - t_1) - \int_{-\infty}^{\infty} dt_1\, w(t_1) I_{vi}(\tau + t_1)$$

$$+ \int_{-\infty}^{\infty} dt_1\, w(t_1) \int_{-\infty}^{\infty} dt_2\, w(t_2) I_{vv}(\tau + t_1 - t_2) \quad (2.4-20)$$

By setting $\tau = 0$ in this expression, an equation for the integral-square error is obtained; by Eq. 2.4–4, the second and third terms of the equation for the integral-square error are equal. Therefore, we can write for the integral-square error

$$I_y = I_{ii}(0) - 2 \int_{-\infty}^{\infty} dt_1\, w(t_1) I_{vi}(t_1)$$

$$+ \int_{-\infty}^{\infty} dt_1\, w(t_1) \int_{-\infty}^{\infty} dt_2\, w(t_2) I_{vv}(t_1 - t_2) \quad (2.4-21)$$

This is the desired result for the integral-square error evaluated in the time domain.

The minimization procedure in the time domain is as follows. The weighting function $w(t)$ is evaluated as a function of the free parameters. The translation functions are evaluated for the given input and desired output signals. By carrying out the integrations indicated in Eq. 2.4–21 the integral-square error is obtained as a function of the free parameters. This function is then minimized either by analytical or trial-and-error procedures. Unfortunately, for most practical problems involving weighting functions and signals possessing irrational transforms, the foregoing procedure can be carried out only numerically. This comes about because of the complex way in which the free parameters are involved in the weighting functions.

An interesting check on the validity of Eq. 2.4–20 can be obtained by Fourier transforming both sides and evaluating the integral-square error in terms of the transform of the autotranslation function of the error. Obviously the result should check the previous result obtained by means of Parseval's theorem. The Fourier transform of a translation function $I_{12}(\tau)$ is denoted by $I_{12}(s)$.   That is,

$$I_{12}(s) \triangleq \int_{-\infty}^{\infty} d\tau \, e^{-s\tau} I_{12}(\tau) \qquad (2.4\text{--}22)$$

Transforming the second term of the right member of Eq. 2.4–20 yields

$$\int_{-\infty}^{\infty} d\tau \, e^{-s\tau} \int_{-\infty}^{\infty} dt_1 \, w(t_1) I_{iv}(\tau - t_1)$$
$$= \int_{-\infty}^{\infty} dt_1 \, e^{-st_1} w(t_1) \int_{-\infty}^{\infty} d\tau \, e^{-s(\tau - t_1)} I_{iv}(\tau - t_1) \qquad (2.4\text{--}23)$$

where the order of integration has been interchanged on the right side and the exponential has been factored so as to have arguments that agree with the variables of integration.   Regarding $\tau - t_1$ rather than τ as the variable of integration in the first integral makes it possible to evaluate the two integrals independently of one another so that this transform becomes

$$\int_{-\infty}^{\infty} d\tau \, e^{-s\tau} \int_{-\infty}^{\infty} dt_1 \, w(t_1) I_{iv}(\tau - t_1) = W(s) I_{iv}(s) \qquad (2.4\text{--}24)$$

Making use of the fact that

$$I_{iv}(s) = I_{vi}(-s) \qquad (2.4\text{--}25)$$

which follows from Eq. 2.4–4 and transforming the remaining terms allow us to write as the transform of Eq. 2.4–20

$$I_{yy}(s) = I_{ii}(s) - W(s) I_{vi}(-s) - W(-s) I_{vi}(s) \\ + W(-s) W(s) I_{vv}(s) \qquad (2.4\text{--}26)$$

The integral-square error is equal to the inverse transform of the transform of the autotranslation function of the error evaluated at $\tau = 0$. In terms of symbols this means

$$I_y = \frac{1}{2\pi j} \int_{-j\infty}^{j\infty} ds \, I_{yy}(s) \qquad (2.4\text{--}27)$$

Substitution of the value of the transform of the autotranslation function of the error given by Eq. 2.4–26 into this equation gives us an expression for the integral-square error evaluated in the frequency domain.   This expression appears considerably different than that of Eq. 2.3–1, which was obtained by means of Parseval's theorem.

In order to resolve the difference in appearance of the two results for the integral-square error evaluated in the frequency domain, let us express the transform of a translation function in terms of the transforms of the signals that it characterizes.   Substituting the value of the cross-translation function given by Eq. 2.4–2 into the expression for the transform given by Eq. 2.4–22 yields

$$I_{12}(s) = \int_{-\infty}^{\infty} d\tau \, e^{-s\tau} \int_{-\infty}^{\infty} dt \, x_1(t) x_2(t + \tau) \qquad (2.4\text{--}28)$$

Interchanging the order of integration gives us

$$I_{12}(s) = \int_{-\infty}^{\infty} dt \, e^{st} x_1(t) \int_{-\infty}^{\infty} d\tau \, e^{-s(t+\tau)} x_2(t + \tau) \qquad (2.4\text{--}29)$$

The integral with respect to τ yields the transform $x_2(s)$ of the signal $x_2(t)$. The integral with respect to t gives us the transform $x_1(s)$ corresponding to the signal $x_1(t)$ except for a change in sign of the complex frequency variable. Thus we conclude that the transform of a cross-translation function is equivalent to

$$I_{12}(s) = x_1(-s) x_2(s) \qquad (2.4\text{--}30)$$

Making use of this fact we can write Eq. 2.4–26 as follows:

$$I_{yy}(s) = i(-s)i(s) - W(s)v(s)i(-s) - W(-s)v(-s)i(s)$$
$$+ W(-s)W(s)v(-s)v(s) \qquad (2.4\text{--}31)$$

This is equivalent to

$$I_{yy}(s) = [i(-s) - W(-s)v(-s)][i(s) - W(s)v(s)] \qquad (2.4\text{--}32)$$

which in turn is equivalent to

$$I_{yy}(s) = y_e(-s)y_e(s) \qquad (2.4\text{--}33)$$

Substitution of this value of the transform of the autotranslation function of the error into Eq. 2.4–27 returns us to Eq. 2.3–1. Thus the expression for the integral-square error in terms of the transform of the autotranslation function is equivalent to the result previously obtained by means of Parseval's theorem.

The reader should be warned that the translation functions for many commonly encountered transient signals are infinite since their defining integrals do not converge. Examples are the autotranslation functions for the step function and for the ramp. Under these conditions the Fourier transforms also do not exist. As an example, if one attempts to evaluate the integral-square error for the example given in Art. 2.3 by means of Eq. 2.4–21, the result will be indeterminant in the form

$$I_y = \infty - 2\infty + \infty \qquad (2.4\text{--}34)$$

A similar situation will be obtained if one attempts to evaluate the integral-square error for this example by means of Eq. 2.4–27. When such situations arise the judicious introduction of convergence factors in the form of decaying exponentials, which in the limit decay infinitely slowly, will frequently permit a solution to be obtained.

In conclusion, the evaluation of the integral-square error in the time domain can be done. However, it is ordinarily necessary to resort to numerical techniques for evaluating the integrals because of the complex way in which the free parameters are involved. Whenever the Fourier transform of the error is a rational function, it is preferable to use Parseval's theorem to evaluate the integral-square error. In Chapter 6 recourse will be had to the time-domain approach in connection with the problem of minimizing the integral-square error when the configuration is free or semi-free.

2.5 NORMALIZATION

This article discusses normalization techniques which are useful in handling practical problems. For all but the simplest problems it is ordinarily easier to employ the numerical values of the fixed parameters rather than letter symbols. As soon as numbers are introduced into a problem it is desirable to so arrange the expression that the numbers come in as time constants, that is, as ratios of system parameters designed to have the dimensions of time. Frequently, it is found that the time constants which define the dynamic behavior of the system are either large or small compared to unity. If the time constants are not centered around unity it is desirable to go one step further and normalize the time scale so that the important fixed parameters have normalized values in the neighborhood of unity. Doing this allows us to avoid having to carry powers of 10 through the calculations.

It frequently happens that it is desirable to apply the normalization process to transforms of time functions rather than to time functions themselves. We need, therefore, to know how to find for a time function the Fourier transform with respect to the normalized time from the Fourier transform with respect to un-normalized time. How to do this is readily evident if one considers the definition of a Fourier transform. Let $F(s)$ represent the Fourier transform with respect to time t of the function $f(t)$. By the definition of a Fourier transform this means

$$F(s) = \int_{-\infty}^{\infty} dt \; e^{-st} f(t) \tag{2.5-1}$$

Let $G(\lambda)$ represent the Fourier transform with respect to normalized time μ of the function $g(\mu)$. Again by the definition of the Fourier transform we have

$$G(\lambda) = \int_{-\infty}^{\infty} d\mu \, e^{-\lambda\mu} g(\mu) \qquad (2.5\text{-}2)$$

The function of normalized time and the function of ordinary time are really one and the same provided a relationship between the two time scales is established. Let the relationship between the two time scales be defined by

$$\mu = t/\tau_b \qquad (2.5\text{-}3)$$

Here τ_b may carry any dimensions whatsoever but ordinarily either it will have the same dimensions as ordinary time t (in which event the normalized variable μ will be dimensionless), or it will carry units like seconds over minutes (in which event the normalized variable μ will carry dimensions). Symbolically, the relationship of the two functions is expressed as follows:

$$g(\mu) = [f(t)] \quad \text{with } t = \tau_b\mu \qquad (2.5\text{-}4)$$

Replacing t by $\tau_b\mu$ in Eq. 2.5–1 yields

$$F(s) = \int_{-\infty}^{\infty} \tau_b \, d\mu \, e^{-s\tau_b\mu} f(\tau_b\mu) \qquad (2.5\text{-}5)$$

But, by Eq. 2.5–4, we have

$$f(\tau_b\mu) = g(\mu) \qquad (2.5\text{-}6)$$

Let the normalized complex frequency λ be related to the un-normalized complex frequency s by

$$\lambda = \tau_b s \qquad (2.5\text{-}7)$$

Making use of Eqs. 2.5–6 and 7 permits Eq. 2.5–5 to be written in the form

$$F(s) = \tau_b \int_{-\infty}^{\infty} d\mu \, e^{-\lambda\mu} g(\mu) \qquad (2.5\text{-}8)$$

By Eq. 2.5–2 the integral on the right side is by definition the normalized Fourier transform $G(\lambda)$. Thus

$$F(s) = \tau_b G(\lambda) \qquad (2.5\text{-}9)$$

Consequently, if we wish to find the normalized transform from the un-normalized transform, we must use the following rule:

$$G(\lambda) = \frac{1}{\tau_b} [F(s)] \quad \text{with } s \text{ replaced by } \frac{\lambda}{\tau_b} \qquad (2.5\text{-}10)$$

We may summarize the above discussion as follows: If in a transform of a time function s is replaced by λ/τ_b and the result is divided by τ_b, we obtain the transform of the time function with respect to t/τ_b. Inverse transformation of this transform with respect to λ yields the original time function except that t/τ_b is the independent variable instead of t. Although this result has been derived for the Fourier transform, it also holds for the Laplace transform.

It should be noted carefully that the above procedure for normalizing the transform of a time function does not apply to the normalization of a transfer function or a system function. Transfer functions may be looked upon as ratios of transforms of time functions and therefore the factors $1/\tau_b$ which appear as the result of normalization in the numerator and the denominator of the ratio cancel. Thus the rule in normalizing a transfer function is simply to replace s by λ/τ_b. There is no division by the normalization base τ_b.

As an example of how to normalize transforms, consider the following function of time

$$f(t) = \delta_{-1}(t)e^{-at} \qquad (2.5\text{--}11)$$

The transform of this time function is

$$F(s) = \frac{1}{s + \alpha} \qquad (2.5\text{--}12)$$

Application of the normalization rule expressed by Eq. 2.5–10 yields

$$G(\lambda) = \left(\frac{1}{\tau_b}\right) \frac{1}{\dfrac{\lambda}{\tau_b} + \alpha} \qquad (2.5\text{--}13)$$

This simplifies to

$$G(\lambda) = \frac{1}{\lambda + \alpha\tau_b} \qquad (2.5\text{--}14)$$

Inverse transformation with respect to λ gives us

$$g(\mu) = \delta_{-1}(\mu)e^{-\alpha\tau_b\mu} \qquad (2.5\text{--}15)$$

This obviously checks with the original time function given in Eq. 2.5–11.

The question now arises as to how we compute by means of Parseval's theorem the integral-square value of a time function when we know the normalized value of its Fourier transform. It will be recalled that

Parseval's theorem states

$$I = \frac{1}{2\pi j} \int_{-j\infty}^{j\infty} ds\, x(-s)x(s) \tag{2.2-9}$$

where I is the integral-square value of the time function $x(t)$. Now in accordance with the normalization rule, $x(\lambda)$ is given by

$$x(\lambda) = \frac{1}{\tau_b}[x(s)] \quad \text{with } s \text{ replaced by } \frac{\lambda}{\tau_b} \tag{2.5-16}$$

Thus, $x(s)$ is given by

$$x(s) = \tau_b[x(\lambda)] \quad \text{provided } \lambda = \tau_b s \tag{2.5-17}$$

Substituting this value of $x(s)$ into Eq. 2.2-9 and replacing ds by $d\lambda/\tau_b$ yields

$$I = \frac{1}{2\pi j} \int_{-j\infty}^{j\infty} \frac{d\lambda}{\tau_b}[\tau_b x(-\lambda)][\tau_b x(\lambda)] \tag{2.5-18}$$

This reduces to

$$I = \frac{\tau_b}{2\pi j} \int_{-j\infty}^{j\infty} d\lambda\, x(-\lambda)x(\lambda) \tag{2.5-19}$$

Note that the integral-square value I in the above equation is always taken with respect to un-normalized time. Equation 2.5-19 simply states that the application of Parseval's theorem to the normalized transform of a time function yields the integral-square value of that time function provided the integral is multiplied by the normalization base τ_b.

The determination of the integral-square value of a time function from its normalized transform is easily illustrated. Let the time function be

$$x(t) = N\delta_{-1}(t)e^{-\alpha t} \tag{2.5-20}$$

Then, by comparison with the example just given above, the normalized transform of this time function is

$$x(\lambda) = \frac{N}{\lambda + \alpha\tau_b} \tag{2.5-21}$$

Application of the rule stated in Eq. 2.5-19 yields

$$I = \frac{\tau_b}{2\pi j} N^2 \int_{-j\infty}^{j\infty} d\lambda\, \frac{1}{(-\lambda + \alpha\tau_b)(\lambda + \alpha\tau_b)} \tag{2.5-22}$$

Using the formula for I_1 given in the table of integrals of Appendix E yields

$$I = \frac{N^2}{2\alpha} \tag{2.5-23}$$

This result can be checked easily by direct integration of $x^2(t)$.

2.6 USE OF CONSTRAINTS

A design for a feedback control system which is obtained by minimizing (or maximizing) a performance index may be unsatisfactory in practice because of departures from linearity caused by excessive signal magnitudes. The design theory discussed in this book applies to linear mathematical models. The usefulness of this theory is determined by how closely the mathematical model agrees with the physical system under consideration. If, by the very act of minimizing or maximizing a performance index, the signals in the parts of the mathematical model corresponding to the fixed elements of the control system are driven to such high peak values that the mathematical model is no longer a valid approximation, then the design theory is certainly of restricted usefulness. This article discusses a technique for maintaining the validity of the mathematical model in spite of saturation tendencies. The technique is to control in some measure the offending signal levels through the use of constraints introduced into the procedure for optimizing the performance index.

For a specific illustration of how saturation would be caused in a physical system if it were designed on the basis of a linear mathematical model without regard to the peak values of the signals in the model, let us return to the example of Art. 2.3. Here we found that minimizing the integral-square error of a second-order system when driven by a step function input led to very large values of gain. If we consider the implications of large gain on the peak torque required from the servomotor, we immediately see a difficulty. In this system, since there is no load torque, the torque demanded from the servomotor is used exclusively to accelerate the inertia of the output member. Thus the peak torque required of the servomotor is proportional to the peak acceleration of the output. Figure 2.3–1 shows how the error response becomes more and more oscillatory as the velocity constant of the system is increased. It is evident from this figure that the peak output acceleration becomes larger and larger as the gain is increased. The output, although not plotted in this figure, is easily visualized as the input minus the error. If the gain is made large enough, a point is reached at which the peak acceleration of the output exhibited in the linear model exceeds that which may be physically obtained from the servomotor of the actual system. At this point the linear model ceases to be a valid basis for design. Either we must employ a non-linear mathematical model, in which case the design theory discussed in this book is of no use, or we must modify our design procedure so that, although based on linear theory, the possibility of saturation is recognized.

The most direct approach for avoiding saturation in a system subjected to a transient input signal is to limit the peak values of those signals in the linear model that correspond to signals in the physical system that are likely to cause saturation. Limiting the peak value of a signal requires that it be expressed as a function of the free parameters of the system. If this can be done, then in principle it is a simple matter to restrict the adjustment of the free parameters so that the peak value is held constant while the integral-square error is minimized. However, it is impractical to express the peak value of a signal as a function of the free parameters except for first- and second-order systems. For a higher-order system the problem of finding the roots of the characteristic equation makes it either impractical or impossible to solve for a transient signal except by numerical methods which require specific values for all the parameters. Hence for a higher-order system it is not feasible to express the peak value of a signal as a function of the free parameters. Thus, for a higher-order system we are forced to control the peak value of a signal likely to cause saturation by indirect means.

Frequently, the integral-square value of a signal likely to cause saturation can be expressed as a function of the free parameters of the system. When this can be done, it is then possible to limit the integral-square value of this signal while minimizing the integral-square error. If constraining the integral-square value of a signal to some degree controls its peak value, then a useful design procedure for avoiding saturation is available. Because the integral-square value of a signal gives large weight to large values, it is intuitively evident that some degree of control of the peak value will be obtained by this technique. How strong the control is depends on the nature of the system and the particular signal in question. In some systems no control results; in others, an entirely satisfactory degree of control may be obtained.

The foregoing discussion has shown that practical benefits may be derived from minimizing the integral-square error subject to constraints on one or more signals in the form of limits on their integral-square values. We now turn our attention to the procedures for implementing a constrained minimization. The most direct procedure is to express the integral-square error and the integral-square values of the saturation signals as functions of the free parameters. The saturation signal constraints are in the form of integral-square-value functions which are specified to be equal to or less than prescribed numerical limits. Adjusting the free parameters to minimize the integral-square error without regard to these constraints will presumably cause violation of one or more of them. By focusing attention on the critical constraints, a number of free parameters equal to the number of the constraints can be solved for in terms of the remaining free parameters. Thus the effect of the constraints is to reduce the number of free parameters available for minimizing the integral-square error.

Actual elimination of any free parameters by means of the constraint relations may be impractical or impossible because of the complex manner in which they enter into the integral-square-value functions. If this is so, one approach is to adjust the free parameters by trial and error in such a way that the constraints are satisfied and the integral-square error is minimized. In most practical problems only a few free parameters are involved, usually not more than three. By selecting one of the free parameters as a principal variable, the integral-square error can be plotted as a function of this parameter for various fixed values of the other parameters. Similar plots can be made for the integral-square values of the saturation signals. It is then a relatively simple matter to find those combinations of values of the free parameters that satisfy the constraints. By trial and error the various combinations are checked in the integral-square error plots to find those that correspond to a minimum.

A second, more refined approach to the problem of integral-square-error minimization, when the constraint relations are so complex that they cannot be readily used to eliminate free parameters, is the method introduced by Lagrange. Unfortunately, this method usually offers little advantage over the trial-and-error approach. Occasionally, however, it is useful in the fixed configuration problem, and we shall need it very definitely when we come to free and semi-free configurations. We shall, therefore, introduce it at this point.

The technique of Lagrange for minimizing a function subject to one or more constraints is discussed in the textbooks on advanced calculus and applied mathematics (for example, see references F.7 and H.3). The problem treated by Lagrange is stated as follows: Let $f(x_1, \cdots x_n)$ be the function that is to be maximized or minimized subject to the constraint that another function $g(x_1, \cdots x_n)$ shall equal a constant g_0. Then, according to Lagrange, the desired values of the variables x_1

through x_n may be obtained by maximizing or minimizing the synthetic function $F = f + \rho g$, where ρ is a constant called the *Lagrangian multiplier*. After maximizing or minimizing this synthetic function, we effectively have the variables x_1 through x_n determined as functions of the Lagrangian multiplier ρ. Thus, ρ can be adjusted to make the constraint function g take on its specified value g_0. The advantage of Lagrange's technique is that it eliminates any necessity for solving the constraint equations to eliminate a free parameter. The method can be extended to any number of constraints by simply adding terms to the synthetic function. Thus in general the independent variables x_1 through x_n are found by maximizing or minimizing the function $F = f + \rho_1 g_1 + \rho_2 g_2 \cdots + \rho_m g_m$ where the ρ's are the Lagrangian multipliers and the g's are the functions to be constrained.

A simple example of the Lagrange technique is the minimization of the area of a right circular cylinder of radius r and length L when it is required that the cylinder contain a volume V_0. The volume V of the right circular cylinder is given by

$$V = \pi r^2 L \tag{2.6-1}$$

and the surface area A is given by

$$A = 2\pi r L + 2\pi r^2 \tag{2.6-2}$$

Using the Lagrange technique the function to be minimized is

$$F = A + \rho V \tag{2.6-3}$$

Using the expressions for the volume and surface area given by Eqs. 2.6–1 and 2.6–2 permits us to write for F

$$F = 2\pi r L + 2\pi r^2 + \rho \pi r^2 L \tag{2.6-4}$$

To accomplish the minimization we set the partial derivatives with respect to r and L equal to zero.

$$\frac{\partial F}{\partial r} = 2\pi L + 4\pi r + 2\rho \pi r L = 0 \tag{2.6-5}$$

$$\frac{\partial F}{\partial L} = 2\pi r + \rho \pi r^2 = 0 \tag{2.6-6}$$

By the second equation the radius r is equal either to zero or $-2/\rho$. Obviously the second value for r is the only useful result. Placing this value in Eq. 2.6–5 and solving for L shows that L should be equal to $-4/\rho$. Introduction of the values of r and L as functions of ρ into

Eq. 2.6–1 shows that ρ must have the value

$$\rho = -2^{1/3}\pi^{1/3}V_0^{-1/3} \tag{2.6–7}$$

Using the values of r and L thus determined in Eq. 2.6–2 shows that the minimum surface area is given by

$$A_{\min} = 3 \cdot 2^{1/3}\pi^{1/3}V_0^{2/3} \tag{2.6–8}$$

The conclusion that the radius should be one-half the length in order to produce minimum surface area is a well-known result usually obtained by more elementary methods in introductory courses in calculus.

We now turn to a justification of Lagrange's procedure for three independent variables x, y, and z. We seek values of x, y, and z that make the function $f(x, y, z)$ stationary under the constraint that $g(x, y, z)$ is constant. A point at which a function is stationary is a point for which the partial derivatives of the function are equal to zero; it is a point at which the function has a maximum value, a minimum value, or a saddle point. We can think of the variables x, y, and z as functions of another variable ϵ for purposes of exploring for a stationary point. Then at a stationary point of the function f we have the condition

$$\frac{df}{d\epsilon} = 0 \tag{2.6–9}$$

In addition, because we are requiring the function g to be constant, we have the additional condition

$$\frac{dg}{d\epsilon} = 0 \tag{2.6–10}$$

These derivatives can be expressed as

$$\frac{df}{d\epsilon} = \frac{\partial f}{\partial x}\frac{dx}{d\epsilon} + \frac{\partial f}{\partial y}\frac{dy}{d\epsilon} + \frac{\partial f}{\partial z}\frac{dz}{d\epsilon} \tag{2.6–11}$$

$$\frac{dg}{d\epsilon} = \frac{\partial g}{\partial x}\frac{dx}{d\epsilon} + \frac{\partial g}{\partial y}\frac{dy}{d\epsilon} + \frac{\partial g}{\partial z}\frac{dz}{d\epsilon} \tag{2.6–12}$$

Using the fact that the derivative of the function g with respect to ϵ is zero allows us to solve Eq. 2.6–12 for the derivative of x with respect to ϵ. Doing this yields

$$\frac{dx}{d\epsilon} = -\frac{\dfrac{\partial g}{\partial y}\dfrac{dy}{d\epsilon} + \dfrac{\partial g}{\partial z}\dfrac{dz}{d\epsilon}}{\dfrac{\partial g}{\partial x}} \tag{2.6–13}$$

According to this equation we do not have complete freedom in the choice of the x, y, z variables as functions of ϵ. Since the partial derivatives of the function g with respect to x, y, and z are fixed by the definition of the g function, the slope of x as a function of ϵ is immediately determined when y and z as function of ϵ are chosen. This reflects the fact that we really have two degrees of freedom in this minimization problem since the constraint may be regarded as tying down one of the variables x, y, or z as a function of the other two. Substitution of the value of $dx/d\epsilon$ determined by Eq. 2.6–13 into Eq. 2.6–11 yields

$$\frac{df}{d\epsilon} = \left[-\frac{\left(\frac{\partial f}{\partial x}\right)}{\left(\frac{\partial g}{\partial x}\right)} \frac{\partial g}{\partial y} + \frac{\partial f}{\partial y} \right] \frac{dy}{d\epsilon} + \left[-\frac{\left(\frac{\partial f}{\partial x}\right)}{\left(\frac{\partial g}{\partial x}\right)} \frac{\partial g}{\partial z} + \frac{\partial f}{\partial z} \right] \frac{dz}{d\epsilon} \qquad (2.6\text{–}14)$$

Because y and z as functions of ϵ are arbitrary, the slopes $dy/d\epsilon$ and $dz/d\epsilon$ are also arbitrary. The condition for a stationary value of f given by Eq. 2.6–9 is that the derivative of f with respect to ϵ at the solution point should vanish. For this to occur the bracketed quantities in Eq. 2.6–14 must vanish at the solution point; but at a solution point the partial derivatives of f and g with respect to x are both definite numbers and their ratio is constant. Of course, this constant is not known until the solution point is known. Lagrange's contribution lies in his recognition that the solution for the desired stationary point may be facilitated by exploiting the constancy in the neighborhood of the solution point of this unknown ratio. The ratio itself is called the Lagrangian multiplier for which we use the symbol ρ. Using the Lagrangian multiplier, the fact that the bracketed quantities in Eq. 2.6–14 must vanish can be expressed as

$$\frac{\partial}{\partial y} (f + \rho g) = 0 \qquad (2.6\text{–}15)$$

$$\frac{\partial}{\partial z} (f + \rho g) = 0 \qquad (2.6\text{–}16)$$

The definition of the Lagrangian multiplier as the negative ratio of the partial derivative of f with respect to x over the partial derivative g with respect to x can be rewritten in the form

$$\frac{\partial}{\partial x} (f + \rho g) = 0 \qquad (2.6\text{–}17)$$

Equations 2.6–15, 16, and 17 determine the solution-point values of x, y, and z as functions of the unknown multiplier ρ. Evaluating the function g for these solution-point values and setting it equal to its prescribed constant value allows us to determine the multiplier ρ.

Let us now examine the meaning of Eqs. 2.6–15, 16, and 17 which determine the location of the stationary point. These equations are precisely those that we would have found if we were seeking an unconstrained stationary point for the function $F = f + \rho g$. Thus by the Lagrange technique a maximization or minimization problem with a constraint is converted to one without a constraint. Although the above derivation has been carried out for three variables and one constraint, the method can be extended to handle any number of variables and any number of constraints. Additional constraints are taken care of by adding more ρg terms. Additional variables are taken care of by increasing the number of partial derivative conditions.

2.7 EXAMPLES EMPLOYING A CONSTRAINT

In order to illustrate the technique of normalization and the method of employing constraints, let us reconsider the example of Art. 2.3. This example dealt with the adjustment of the velocity constant of a positional servomechanism so as to minimize the integral-square error. The servomotor was characterized by a single integration and a motor time lag τ_m. The input signal is a step function of amplitude N, and the desired output is equal to the input. Let us now examine the effect of limiting the integral-square acceleration of the output member on the solution for minimum integral-square error.

The acceleration of the output member will be denoted by $q_s(t)$. The subscript s stands for saturation signal. Thus for this problem

$$q_s(t) \triangleq \frac{d^2q(t)}{dt^2} \tag{2.7-1}$$

We shall use the symbol I_s to designate the integral-square value of the saturation signal; that is,

$$I_s \triangleq \int_{-\infty}^{\infty} dt\, q_s^{\,2}(t) \tag{2.7-2}$$

Using the normalized form of Parseval's theorem, we have

$$I_s = \frac{\tau_m}{2\pi j} \int_{-j\infty}^{+j\infty} d\lambda\, q_s(-\lambda)q_s(\lambda) \tag{2.7-3}$$

where τ_m is selected as the normalization base. The frequency domain equivalent of Eq. 2.7–1 is

$$q_s(s) = s^2 q(s) \qquad (2.7\text{--}4)$$

Since the output transform is equal to the system function multiplied by the transform of the input, this equation can be written as

$$q_s(s) = s^2 W(s) v(s) \qquad (2.7\text{--}5)$$

Application of the normalization rules of Art. 2.5 allows us to write

$$q_s(\lambda) = \frac{\lambda^2}{\tau_m^2} W(\lambda) v(\lambda) \qquad (2.7\text{--}6)$$

where

$$\lambda = \tau_m s \qquad (2.7\text{--}7)$$

Rewritten in normalized form, Eq. 2.3–10 gives us for $W(\lambda)$

$$W(\lambda) = \frac{K}{\lambda^2 + \lambda + K} \qquad (2.7\text{--}8)$$

where

$$K \triangleq \tau_m K_v \qquad (2.7\text{--}9)$$

Normalizing the transform of the input signal given by Eq. 2.3–11 yields

$$v(\lambda) = N/\lambda \qquad (2.7\text{--}10)$$

Substituting into Eq. 2.7–6 the values for $W(\lambda)$ and $v(\lambda)$ given by Eq. 2.7–8 and 10 gives

$$q_s(\lambda) = \frac{NK}{\tau_m^2} \left[\frac{\lambda}{\lambda^2 + \lambda + K} \right] \qquad (2.7\text{--}11)$$

Consequently the integral-square acceleration is given by

$$I_s = \frac{N^2 K^2}{\tau_m^3} \left[\frac{1}{2\pi j} \int_{-j\infty}^{j\infty} d\lambda \, \frac{c(-\lambda)c(\lambda)}{d(-\lambda)d(\lambda)} \right] \qquad (2.7\text{--}12)$$

where

$$c(\lambda) = \lambda \qquad (2.7\text{--}13)$$

$$d(\lambda) = \lambda^2 + \lambda + K \qquad (2.7\text{--}14)$$

Evaluation of the integral by means of the formula for I_2 given in the table of integrals in Appendix E yields

$$I_s = \frac{N^2 K^2}{2\tau_m^3} \qquad (2.7\text{--}15)$$

In terms of the un-normalized gain or velocity constant, this is

$$I_s = \frac{N^2 K_v{}^2}{2\tau_m} \qquad (2.7\text{--}16)$$

This equation expresses the integral-square value of the output acceleration in terms of the system parameters.

In Art. 2.3 the value of the integral-square error in terms of the system parameters was found to be

$$I_y = \frac{N^2}{2}\left(\tau_m + \frac{1}{K_v}\right) \qquad (2.3\text{--}18)$$

We now wish to minimize this integral-square error subject to the condition that the integral-square acceleration of the output member shall be equal to or less than a specified limit I_{sm}. Symbolically, the condition is expressed as

$$I_s \le I_{sm} \qquad (2.7\text{--}17)$$

The integral-square acceleration is a monotonically increasing function of the velocity constant. The integral-square error is a monotonically decreasing function of the same parameter. With the motor time constant fixed, this means that the velocity constant should be increased until the integral-square acceleration satisfies the condition 2.7–17 with the equals sign. In this way the integral-square error is minimized to the extent permitted by the limit on the integral-square acceleration. Using the equals sign in condition 2.7–17 and substituting the value of the integral-square acceleration given by Eq. 2.7–16 produce an equation that can be solved for the velocity constant. The solution is

$$K_v = \left(\frac{2\tau_m I_{sm}}{N^2}\right)^{\frac{1}{2}} \qquad (2.7\text{--}18)$$

We insert this value for the velocity constant into Eq. 2.3–18 to obtain

$$\frac{I_y}{N^2} = \frac{\tau_m}{2} + 2^{-\frac{3}{2}}\tau_m{}^{-\frac{1}{2}}\left(\frac{I_{sm}}{N^2}\right)^{-\frac{1}{2}} \qquad (2.7\text{--}19)$$

as an expression for the integral-square error as a function of the motor time constant and the limit imposed on the integral-square value of the output acceleration. Figure 2.7–1 illustrates how the integral-square error increases with decreasing limit on the integral-square acceleration. Curve A is drawn for a motor time constant of 0.10 second and curve B, 0.01 second. Both curves A and B approach lower limits on the integral-square error as the integral-square acceleration increases indefinitely. Because there is only one free parameter in this example, the introduction of a constraint on the integral-square-output acceleration has effectively removed all freedom for adjustment.

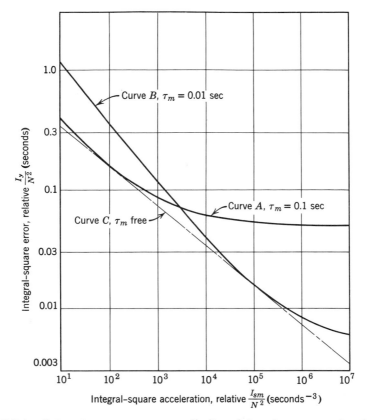

Fig. 2.7–1. Integral-square error versus limit on integral-square acceleration of output.

Let us now introduce an additional degree of freedom into this problem by assuming that the designer has control over the motor time constant and may specify it to have any value whatsoever. This is the opposite extreme from the original problem statement in which the designer was assumed to have no control over the motor time constant. In actual practice the designer has a limited degree of control over a motor time constant. He can usually make it larger than some minimum value.

With two free parameters we can now illustrate Lagrange's technique for minimizing a function subject to constraints. By Lagrange's technique we can minimize the integral-square error subject to the condition

$$I_s = I_{so} \qquad (2.7\text{--}20)$$

where I_{so} is any specified constant. After the values of the free parameters that minimize the integral-square error are found as functions of this constant, its value can be moved through the range permitted by condition 2.7–17. Since the integral-square error is a function of this constant, the minimizing value in the allowed range can be determined.

Using Lagrange's technique, we minimize the function

$$I_y + \rho I_s = \frac{N^2}{2}\left(\tau_m + \frac{1}{K_v} + \rho\frac{K_v{}^2}{\tau_m}\right) \qquad (2.7\text{--}21)$$

proceeding as if there were no constraint. ρ is the undetermined Lagrangian multiplier. Taking the partial derivatives of this function with respect to τ_m and K_v yields

$$\frac{\partial}{\partial\tau_m}(I_y + \rho I_s) = \frac{N^2}{2}\left(1 - \rho\frac{K_v{}^2}{\tau_m{}^2}\right) \qquad (2.7\text{--}22)$$

$$\frac{\partial}{\partial K_v}(I_y + \rho I_s) = \frac{N^2}{2}\left(-\frac{1}{K_v{}^2} + 2\rho\frac{K_v}{\tau_m}\right) \qquad (2.7\text{--}23)$$

Setting the partial derivatives equal to zero gives us two equations involving the free parameters.

$$\frac{\tau_m{}^2}{K_v{}^2} = \rho \qquad (2.7\text{--}24)$$

$$\frac{\tau_m}{K_v{}^3} = 2\rho \qquad (2.7\text{--}25)$$

Upon solving these equations for the free parameters, we have

$$K_v = 2^{-1/2}\rho^{-1/4} \qquad (2.7\text{--}26)$$

$$\tau_m = 2^{-1/2}\rho^{1/4} \qquad (2.7\text{--}27)$$

Using these values in conjunction with Eqs. 2.7–16 and 20 results in

$$2^{-3/2}N^2\rho^{-3/4} = I_{so} \qquad (2.7\text{--}28)$$

Solution for ρ yields

$$\rho^{1/4} = 2^{-1/2}N^{2/3}I_{so}{}^{-1/3} \qquad (2.7\text{--}29)$$

Using this value in Eqs. 2.7–26 and 27 permits us to write

$$K_v = \left(\frac{I_{so}}{N^2}\right)^{\frac{1}{3}} \qquad (2.7\text{--}30)$$

and

$$\tau_m = \frac{1}{2}\left(\frac{I_{so}}{N^2}\right)^{-\frac{1}{3}} \qquad (2.7\text{--}31)$$

Placing these values in Eq. 2.3–18 gives for the integral-square error

$$I_y = \tfrac{3}{4}N^{\frac{2}{3}}(I_{so})^{-\frac{1}{3}} \qquad (2.7\text{--}32)$$

In passing it should be noted that Lagrange's technique was hardly necessary for this problem since Eq. 2.7–16 can be readily solved for either of the free parameters. Solving for τ_m and setting the integral-square acceleration in accordance with Eq. 2.7–20 yield

$$\tau_m = \frac{N^2 K_v{}^2}{2I_{so}} \qquad (2.7\text{--}33)$$

Inserting this value of τ_m into the expression for the integral-square error produces the following function of the velocity constant:

$$I_y = \frac{N^2}{2}\left(\frac{N^2}{2I_{so}}K_v{}^2 + \frac{1}{K_v}\right) \qquad (2.7\text{--}34)$$

Differentiating yields

$$\frac{dI_y}{dK_v} = \frac{N^2}{2}\left(\frac{N^2}{I_{so}}K_v - \frac{1}{K_v{}^2}\right) \qquad (2.7\text{--}35)$$

Setting the derivative equal to zero and solving for K_v gives us Eq. 2.7–30. Placing this value for K_v back in Eq. 2.7–34 returns us to Eq. 2.7–32.

The integral-square error given by Eq. 2.7–32 is a monotonically decreasing function of the constraint I_{so} imposed on the integral-square acceleration. Therefore, the least value of the integral-square error will be obtained when the constraint is made equal to the limit I_{sm} placed on the integral-square acceleration. Thus we write

$$\frac{I_y}{N^2} = \frac{3}{4}\left(\frac{I_{sm}}{N^2}\right)^{-\frac{1}{3}} \qquad (2.7\text{--}36)$$

as the expression for the minimum integral-square error as a function of the limit imposed on the integral-square value of the output acceleration when both the motor time constant and the velocity constant are free parameters. Curve C in Fig. 2.7–1 shows how the integral-square error varies as a function of the limit imposed on the integral-square acceleration. Note how this curve is always below or tangent to the curves obtained when the motor time constant was fixed. This result agrees with the intuitive argument that, the greater the number of free parameters there are, the smaller the minimum integral-square error should be. The way the system physically takes advantage of the additional degree of freedom is indicated by the damping ratio. The damping ratio and the natural frequency for the second-order system, previously given by Eqs. 2.3–19 and 20, take on the values

$$\zeta = 2^{-\frac{1}{2}} \tag{2.7-37}$$

$$\omega_n = 2^{\frac{1}{2}} \left(\frac{I_{sm}}{N^2} \right)^{\frac{1}{3}} \tag{2.7-38}$$

when the free parameters have their optimum values. The damping ratio is constant in this case, whereas previously, when the motor time constant was fixed, the damping ratio decreased with increasing gain.

The purpose behind controlling the integral-square acceleration is to control indirectly the peak acceleration. Because of the simplicity of the second-order system, it is possible to express the peak acceleration very simply in terms of the free parameters. We may, therefore, minimize the integral-square error subject to a constraint on the peak acceleration. The peak acceleration will be designated by the symbol q_{sp}. The peak acceleration occurs at zero time and is easily shown to be

$$q_{sp} = N \frac{K_v}{\tau_m} \tag{2.7-39}$$

Solving for τ_m yields

$$\tau_m = \frac{N K_v}{q_{sp}} \tag{2.7-40}$$

Introducing this value of τ_m into the expression for the integral-square error gives

$$I_y = \frac{N^2}{2} \left(\frac{N}{q_{sp}} K_v + \frac{1}{K_v} \right) \tag{2.7-41}$$

Differentiating with respect to the velocity constant K_v results in

$$\frac{dI_y}{dK_v} = \frac{N^2}{2} \left(\frac{N}{q_{sp}} - \frac{1}{K_v^2} \right) \tag{2.7-42}$$

Setting the derivative equal to zero and solving for the velocity constant give us

$$K_v = \left(\frac{q_{sp}}{N}\right)^{\frac{1}{2}}$$ (2.7–43)

The motor time constant then becomes

$$\tau_m = \left(\frac{N}{q_{sp}}\right)^{\frac{1}{2}}$$ (2.7–44)

and consequently the integral-square error is

$$\frac{I_y}{N^2} = \left(\frac{q_{sp}}{N}\right)^{-\frac{1}{2}}$$ (2.7–45)

For this situation the damping ratio and the natural frequency are given by

$$\zeta = \frac{1}{2}$$ (2.7–46)

$$\omega_n = \left(\frac{q_{sp}}{N}\right)^{\frac{1}{2}}$$ (2.7–47)

Notice that the damping ratio is slightly smaller when the peak acceleration is used as a constraint rather than the integral-square acceleration.

In concluding this example, let us answer the question, "What does the departure from the optimum adjustment caused by indirectly controlling the peak acceleration through a constraint imposed on the integral-square acceleration cost in terms of increased integral-square error?" The peak acceleration for the non-optimum adjustment is given by

$$\frac{q_{sp}}{N} = 2\left(\frac{I_{sm}}{N^2}\right)^{\frac{2}{3}}$$ (2.7–48)

This is obtained by inserting into Eq. 2.7–39 the values of the free parameters given by Eqs. 2.7–30 and 31 with the constraint I_{so} equal to the limit I_{sm}. Elimination of I_{sm} from Eqs. 2.7–36 and 48 yields

$$\frac{I_y}{N^2} = 3 \cdot 2^{-\frac{3}{2}} \left(\frac{q_{sp}}{N}\right)^{-\frac{1}{2}}$$ (2.7–49)

This gives the integral-square error as a function of the peak acceleration when the parameters are adjusted with the integral-square acceleration as the constraint. Comparison of Eqs. 2.7–45 and 2.7–49 shows the integral-square error to be increased about 6 percent over the value obtained by constraining the peak acceleration directly.

This result tends to give us confidence in the idea of placing constraints on integral-square values of quantities as an indirect means of controlling peak values in problems where direct control is either analytically impossible or impractical.

2.8   CONCLUSION

We now summarize the results of this chapter.   The analytical design theory is developed for fixed-configuration systems that are subjected to transient input signals.   This is done by showing how to minimize the integral-square error through parameter adjustment. Parseval's theorem is the device used to formulate the integral-square error in the frequency domain.   The concept of the translation function is introduced in the process of expressing the integral-square error in the time domain.   A procedure for normalizing the time scale of a problem is worked out as an aid in handling numerical calculations. Finally, we show the use of constraints for introducing practical considerations like saturation into designs based on linear mathematical models.   In this connection Lagrange's technique for introducing constraints in minimization problems is presented.

Our next step is to develop the analytical design theory for fixed-configuration systems that are subject to stochastic (random) input signals.   This will be done in Chapter 4 after some of the properties of stochastic signals are introduced in Chapter 3.

3

STOCHASTIC
SIGNALS

3.1 STOCHASTIC PROCESSES; CHARACTERIZATIONS
OF STOCHASTIC SIGNALS

The word *stochastic* is used by mathematicians and physicists to describe processes in which there is an element of chance. It is derived directly from the Greek word στοχαστικόσ. In Aristotle's ethics this word is used in the sense of "able to guess." Apparently, the mathematicians have adopted this word on the basis that, if there is a need to guess, there is an implied element of chance. In Webster's *New International Dictionary* the word stochastic is defined as conjectural. We, therefore, observe that the technical meaning of the word does not exactly agree with its dictionary definition.

Many writers use the term "random process" in the same sense as "stochastic process." In the discussion that follows we shall talk of processes and signals which are not purely random but which contain a degree of randomness. For this reason we prefer the word "stochastic."

Figure 3.1–1 contrasts sample wave forms of a stochastic signal and a predictable signal. If the experiment of sampling the process generating the stochastic signal were repeated, we would obtain a new wave form differing from the first in fine detail but yet exhibiting some simi-

larities in its broad features.   Ocean waves are another example of a
stochastic signal.   Why is it necessary to talk about these somewhat
nebulous stochastic signals?   The answer to this question lies in the
fact that the input signals to a control system frequently are not completely predictable like a sine wave or a particular transient.   Indeed,
stochastic signals are more frequently encountered in control system
designs than predictable signals.   However, it has not been through
oversight that predictable signals have received so much emphasis up
to now.   It is frequently possible to arrive at reasonable designs by
using test signals of the predictable class to represent the salient features of an actual signal which is stochastic in nature.   An example of

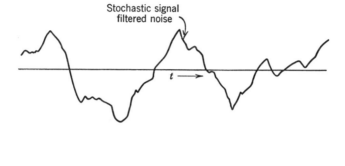

Stochastic signal
filtered noise

$t \longrightarrow$

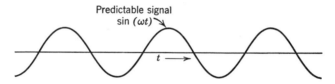

Predictable signal
$\sin (\omega t)$

$t \longrightarrow$

Fig. 3.1–1.   Comparison of typical stochastic and predictable signals.

this is the use of a few carefully chosen sinusoids to represent the
stochastic disturbing moments caused by wave action in the problem of
ship stabilization.   On the other hand we do meet situations in which
it is very difficult to represent the actual stochastic signals by predictable functions.   As one example, consider the design of an auto-
matic-tracking fire-control system.   Here the radar sighting device
does not measure the true pointing error, but only an approximation
thereto.   The difference between the true pointing error and what the
radar measures is often termed radar noise.   Usually radar noise is
very difficult to approximate with a few sinusoids or other simple
functions.   Another example is the drafting of textile fibers.   In the
process of drafting, a loose elongated bundle of fibers (termed a sliver)

is stretched out to form a thread.   The thickness of the thread, in some instances, is used as an input signal to control the drafting process with the objective of holding the thickness more constant.   The disturbance to this process is the variation in the number and thickness of the individual fibers present in the various cross sections of the sliver. It is evident that this type of disturbance is stochastic in nature and difficult to approximate with wholly predictable functions.

The foregoing discussion has indicated the importance of stochastic signals in control system design.   So far, we have talked of stochastic signals loosely as generated by processes containing an element of chance.   In order to proceed further, we must sharpen our concepts concerning such signals.   Modern physics, particularly quantum mechanics, teaches us that all physical processes are discontinuous and indeterminate when examined in detail.   The laws of classical mechanics are replaced by statistical laws concerning the probabilities of events.   As an example, we usually think of the voltage wave produced by a vacuum tube oscillator as being a continuous smooth function.   However, we know that, if we examine the wave microscopically, it will be relatively rough looking because of shot noise in the tubes used to generate the oscillation.   After a little reflection, it is not difficult to persuade ourselves that all signals are stochastic in nature.   Whereas we may at first think that a stochastic signal is a relatively abstract concept compared with a sine wave or a step function, in reality just the reverse is true; the sine wave, the step function, and predictable signals in general represent abstractions from reality. However, just like Euclidean geometry, they are useful abstractions.

A stochastic signal, because it is generated by a process containing an element of chance, cannot be represented graphically in the same way that a sine wave can.   At a particular future time we cannot say that a stochastic signal will have a specified value.   In contrast to a predictable signal, all that we can say concerning the value of a stochastic signal at a particular future time is what the probability of its lying in a specified range of values will be.   We thus see that the concept of *function* is vastly different for stochastic signals from that for wholly predictable signals.   For a predictable variable the idea of function implies a definite dependence of the variable upon its argument.   For each value of the argument we associate one, or at the most, a few, values of the variable.   With stochastic functions, we cannot uniquely associate any values of the variable with a particular value of the argument.   All that we can do is to associate certain probability distributions with particular values of the argument.   In a certain sense, wholly predictable signals are the limiting case of stochastic signals in which the probability distributions have been heavily peaked so that the uncertainty concerning the location of the variable for a particular value of the argument is zero. At first sight a stochastic variable may seem so vague as to make an analytical discussion impossible. However, we shall see that analysis for stochastic signals can be carried on in terms of probability density functions and other statistical characterizations such as the average value, the root-mean-square (rms) value or mean-square value, and the correlation functions.

In view of its statistical nature, a stochastic signal is often conveniently treated as a member of a family of signals, each generated by an identical process. This family of signals is termed an *ensemble*. The concept of ensemble for stochastic signals corresponds to the concept of population in statistics. Characterizations of a stochastic signal generally relate to the ensemble, not to a particular signal in the ensemble. Thus, when we speak of a stochastic signal as having certain properties, we usually mean that the ensemble has these properties. In general, it is impossible to think of a particular stochastic signal as having any properties whatsoever (with the possible exception of the feature of being void of properties). In the next section we shall discuss an important exception to this general rule.

3.2 PROBABILITY-DENSITY FUNCTIONS; ERGODIC HYPOTHESIS

In this article we describe the *probability-density functions* which represent the most fundamental characterization of an ensemble of stochastic signals. As we shall see, an infinite set of these probability-density functions is required to describe completely a stochastic process. In much of the work of this book, however, only the first two probability-density functions will be employed. We shall also see that simplifications can be made when the statistics of the process are independent of time; in this event, the process is termed stationary.

In order to grasp the concept of probability density, let us imagine that we construct a mechanism for generating a stochastic signal. In order to produce an ensemble of these signals, we build a number of identical copies of this mechanism. By attaching an oscillograph to each of the mechanisms we record N oscillograms of the stochastic signals belonging to this ensemble. The oscillograms are arranged as shown in Fig. 3.2–1. The first probability-density function may be approximated as the ratio of the fraction of the number of signals lying in the range between v_1 and $v_1 + \Delta v_1$ at time t_1 to the range Δv_1. A more precise definition of the first probability-density function can be given in terms of two numbers.   Let

$$N \triangleq \text{the total number of signals in the ensemble} \quad (3.2\text{--}1)$$

and

$$\Delta N_1(v_1, t_1, \Delta v_1; N)$$
$$\triangleq \text{the number of signals with values between } v_1 \text{ and } v_1$$
$$+ \Delta v_1 \text{ at time } t_1 \quad (3.2\text{--}2)$$

Then the first probability-density function is defined as

$$p_1(v_1, t_1) \triangleq \lim_{\substack{N \to \infty \\ \Delta v_1 \to 0}} \frac{\left[\dfrac{\Delta N_1(v_1, t_1, \Delta v_1; N)}{N}\right]}{\Delta v_1} \quad (3.2\text{--}3)$$

The first probability density is a function of the location v_1 of the range used in defining the fraction $\Delta N_1/N$. This location has two coordinates.   One coordinate is the location v_1 of the range Δv_1 along

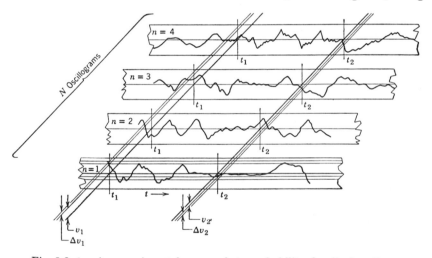

Fig. 3.2–1.   An experimental approach to probability density functions.

the signal scale; the other coordinate is the location t_1 of the range Δv_1 along the time scale.   Intuitively, we should expect the fraction $\Delta N_1/N$ to be proportional to Δv_1 as Δv_1 becomes very small.   Division of the fraction $\Delta N_1/N$ by Δv_1 should therefore produce in the limit as Δv_1 approaches zero a function that is independent of Δv_1.

As an example of the usefulness of the first probability-density function, consider the problem of computing the average value of a stochastic signal.   In general, a single sample of a stochastic signal drawn from an ensemble does not have a meaningful average value taken with respect to time.   To obtain a meaningful average value for a stochastic function, we must average across the ensemble at a particular time.   Thus the average value will be a function of the time at which the average is taken.   We shall indicate an ensemble average by a wiggle bar in order to distinguish it from an average with respect to time, which is indicated by a straight bar.   Let us designate a particular time at which the ensemble average is to be taken as t_1.   Let us indicate the signal values across the ensemble as shown in Fig. 3.2–1 as v_{1n} where the 1 indicates time t_1 and the n the number of the oscillogram.   Then the ensemble average is defined by

$$\widetilde{v(t_1)} \triangleq \lim_{N \to \infty} \frac{v_{11} + v_{12} + \cdots + v_{1N}}{N} \tag{3.2–4}$$

However, the expression for the ensemble average given by Eq. 3.2–5 below is entirely equivalent to that defined by Eq. 3.2–4

$$\widetilde{v(t_1)} = \int_{-\infty}^{\infty} dv_1 \, v_1 \, p_1(v_1, t_1) \tag{3.2–5}$$

This can be seen by grouping the signals v_{1n} of Eq. 3.2–4 according to signal level.   For example, all the v_{1n} lying in the range between v_1 and $v_1 + \Delta v_1$ could be grouped together.   The fraction of these signals to the total is, in the limit, $dv_1 \, p_1(v_1, t_1)$.   Weighting each signal value by its fractional frequency of occurrence and summing yield Eq. 3.2–5 in the limit.

The second probability-density function is next defined.   Refer to Fig. 3.2–1.   Let

$$\Delta N_2(v_1, t_1, \Delta v_1; v_2, t_2 \, \Delta v_2; N) \triangleq \text{the number of signals with}$$
$$\text{values between } v_1 \text{ and } v_1 + \Delta v_1 \text{ at time } t_1 \text{ and also} \tag{3.2–6}$$
$$\text{with values between } v_2 \text{ and } v_2 + \Delta v_2 \text{ at time } t_2$$

Then the second probability-density function is defined as

$$p_2(v_1, t_1; v_2, t_2) \triangleq \lim_{\substack{N \to \infty \\ \Delta v_1 \to 0 \\ \Delta v_2 \to 0}} \frac{\left[\dfrac{\Delta N_2(v_1, t_1, \Delta v_1; v_2, t_2, \Delta v_2; N)}{N} \right]}{\Delta v_1 \Delta v_2} \tag{3.2–7}$$

We thus see that the second probability density depends on four quantities.   Of these, v_1 and t_1 locate the first range Δv_1, and v_2 and t_2 locate the second range Δv_2 used in defining the fraction of signals in question.   As before, for small Δv_1 and Δv_2 we expect the fraction of signals to be proportional to these quantities.   It is evident that the second probability-density function gives a more detailed picture of the ensemble of stochastic signals than the first. In fact, the first probability-density function can be derived from the second by

$$p_1(v_1, t_1) = \int_{-\infty}^{\infty} dv_2 \, p_2(v_1, t_1; v_2, t_2) \qquad (3.2\text{-}8)$$

This expression follows directly from the definition given by Eq. 3.2–7.

Higher-order probability-density functions can be defined by extension of the expressions for the first and second probability-density functions. The stochastic process is defined in more and more detail as the order of the probability-density function increases. Lower-order functions are related to higher-order functions by an equation similar to Eq. 3.2–8. This equation is

$$p_k(v_1, t_1; \cdots; v_k, t_k) = \int_{-\infty}^{\infty} dv_{k+1} \int_{-\infty}^{\infty} \cdots$$
$$\int_{-\infty}^{\infty} dv_n \, p_n(v_1, t_1; \cdots; v_n, t_n) \quad (3.2\text{-}9)$$

This equation summarizes an important feature of the probability-density functions. Another important fact is that the area underneath the first probability-density function for any given time is unity; that is,

$$\int_{-\infty}^{\infty} dv_1 \, p_1(v_1, t_1) = 1 \qquad (3.2\text{-}10)$$

This simply says that we are certain the signal lies somewhere within the range minus infinity to plus infinity.

So far we have been discussing stochastic processes in a manner general enough to include those in which the statistics vary with time. Processes with time-varying statistics are termed *non-stationary*. A simple example of a non-stationary process is an ensemble of mechanisms indicated in Fig. 3.2–2. To exemplify the way in which the statistics of this process might vary with time, Fig. 3.2–3 shows a possible first probability-density variation with time. The signal coming into the potentiometer is stationary but the signal coming out is non-stationary. Initially the potentiometer is near the top so that the output signal is high, and as time goes on the arm of the potentiometer is moved toward zero. Thus we should expect earlier probability-density functions to have a broader spread than later ones. Let us now turn our attention to stationary stochastic processes.

A *stationary process* may be defined as one for which the probability-density functions are unchanged when the time origin is shifted. The first probability-density function becomes time invariant, the second becomes dependent only on the difference between t_1 and t_2, and so on.

This means that the number of time coordinates for a particular probability density is one less in the stationary case than in the non-stationary case. Since the probability-density functions are independent of the time origin, it would appear that the statistics of a

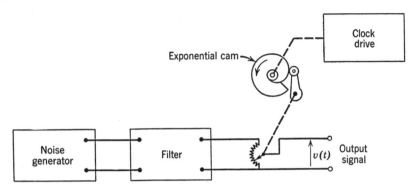

Fig. 3.2–2.   A mechanism for generating a non-stationary stochastic signal.

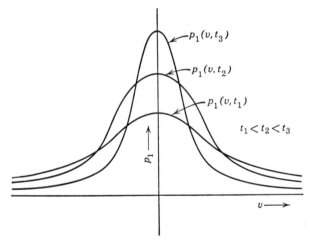

Fig. 3.2–3.   Possible first probability-density variation for non-stationary process.

stationary process are completely revealed by examination of a single oscillogram of infinite length.   Defining

$T \triangleq$ the total time range through which the time t_1 for signal value v_1 is swept   (3.2–11)

$\Delta T_1(v_1, \Delta v_1, T) \triangleq$ the total time during which the signal at time t_1 lies between v_1 and $v_1 + \Delta v_1$ as   (3.2–12) t_1 moves through T

we may define the first probability-density function as

$$p_1(v_1) \triangleq \lim_{\substack{T \to \infty \\ \Delta v_1 \to 0}} \frac{\left[\dfrac{\Delta T_1(v_1, \Delta v_1, T)}{T} \right]}{\Delta v_1} \qquad (3.2\text{--}13)$$

Here we think of the first probability density as approximated by the ratio to Δv_1 of the fraction of the time that the signal lies between the limits v_1 and $v_1 + \Delta v_1$ for the oscillogram of Fig. 3.2–1 labeled $n = 1$. Similarly let us define

$\Delta T_2(v_1, \Delta v_1, \tau_1, v_2, \Delta v_2, T) \triangleq$ the total time during which the signal at time t_1 lies between v_1 and $v_1 + \Delta v_1$ and also at time $t_2 = t_1 + \tau_1$ lies between v_2 and $v_2 + \Delta v_2$ as t_1 moves through T \qquad (3.2–14)

so that the second probability-density function becomes

$$p_2(v_1, v_2, \tau_1) \triangleq \lim_{\substack{T \to \infty \\ \Delta v_1 \to 0 \\ \Delta v_2 \to 0}} \frac{\left[\dfrac{\Delta T_2(v_1, \Delta v_1, \tau_1, v_2, \Delta v_2, T)}{T} \right]}{\Delta v_1 \Delta v_2} \qquad (3.2\text{--}15)$$

We now have two ways of obtaining probability-density functions for a stationary process. One way is by inspection of an ensemble of oscillograms, using Eqs. 3.2–3 and 3.2–7, etc. The other way is to examine a single oscillogram of infinite length and use Eqs. 3.2–13, 3.2–15, etc. The interesting question now arises, "Do the probability-density functions computed by these two methods agree?" We intuitively believe that they do. This assumption is dignified by the name *ergodic hypothesis*. Actually, there is in general no proof of the equivalence. As engineers, however, we choose to employ the ergodic hypothesis as long as it continues to gives reasonable results. So far we have not been in trouble because of using it.

Another aspect of the ergodic hypothesis concerns the relation between time averages and ensemble averages. According to this hypothesis, time averages are equivalent to ensemble averages. Thus we may compute the average values of a stationary function either by Eq. 3.2–4 or by the time average as given by

$$\overline{v(t)} = \lim_{T \to \infty} \frac{1}{2T} \int_{-T}^{T} dt\, v(t) \qquad (3.2\text{--}16)$$

An expression of the form of Eq. 3.2 5 for the average value of a stationary signal will yield the ensemble average or the time average, depending upon which definition of probability density is used. Because, according to the ergodic hypothesis, these probability densities are the same, it matters little which we use.

3.3   CORRELATION FUNCTIONS; METHODS OF DETERMINATION

In the work that follows we shall see that the probability-density functions of a stochastic signal do not usually enter the analysis directly. Rather, we shall employ functions closely related to the second probability-density function. These functions are called correlation functions.

The *autocorrelation function* is defined, in general, as the ensemble average of the product of the signal at a specified time multiplied by the value of the same signal at a time τ units in advance of the specified time. In symbols we have the autocorrelation function φ_{vv} expressed as

$$\varphi_{vv}(t_1, \tau) \triangleq \overline{v(t_1)v(t_1 + \tau)} \tag{3.3-1}$$

Here t_1 is the specified time at which the ensemble average is made. The ensemble average of the product can be computed in a manner analogous to Eq. 3.2–5 for the average value of the function. Because we are concerned with the product of the function at two different times t_1 and $t_1 + \tau$, the second probability density will be involved. Thus we have as a formula for the autocorrelation function

$$\varphi_{vv}(t_1, \tau) = \int_{-\infty}^{\infty} dv_1 \int_{-\infty}^{\infty} dv_2 \, v_1 v_2 p_2(v_1, t_1; v_2, t_1 + \tau) \tag{3.3-2}$$

When the signal with which we are concerned is stationary the autocorrelation function is simplified since it becomes independent of the time at which the ensemble average of the product is taken. Thus the autocorrelation function depends only upon the shift parameter τ. Furthermore, by the ergodic hypothesis we may compute the autocorrelation function by means of a time average rather than an ensemble average so that

$$\varphi_{vv}(\tau) = \overline{v(t)v(t + \tau)} \tag{3.3-3}$$

An equivalent expression for this time average is given by

$$\varphi_{vv}(\tau) = \lim_{T \to \infty} \frac{1}{2T} \int_{-T}^{T} dt \, v(t)v(t + \tau) \tag{3.3-4}$$

A function analogous to the autocorrelation function for a single signal is the *cross-correlation function* for a pair of signals. The general definition for a cross-correlation function is the ensemble average of the product of the first signal at a specified time multiplied by the value of the second signal at the specified time advanced by a shift of τ units. In symbols we have

$$\varphi_{vu}(t_1, \tau) \triangleq \overline{v(t_1)u(t_1 + \tau)} \qquad (3.3\text{-}5)$$

This ensemble average is equivalent to

$$\varphi_{vu}(t_1, \tau) = \int_{-\infty}^{\infty} dv_1 \int_{-\infty}^{\infty} du_2\, v_1 u_2 p_2(v_1, t_1; u_2, t_1 + \tau) \qquad (3.3\text{-}6)$$

where the second probability density multiplied by the elementary area $dv_1\, du_2$ is the probability of finding v between v_1 and $v_1 + dv_1$ at time t_1 and u between u_2 and $u_2 + du_2$ at time $t_1 + \tau$. It should be noted that the second probability density for cross-correlation functions relates to an ensemble of pairs of oscillograms. A single mechanism generating one of the pairs of oscillograms generates both signals simultaneously. The product involved in the ensemble average is always the product of the pair of signals generated by a single mechanism. It is perfectly possible for the mechanism to contain two independent sources of signal for u and v. In this event the second probability-density function in Eq. 3.3–6 is simply the product of the individual first probability densities. When the signal is stationary, the expressions for the cross-correlation function corresponding to Eqs. 3.3–3 and 3.3–4 are

$$\varphi_{vu}(\tau) = \overline{v(t)u(t + \tau)} \qquad (3.3\text{-}7)$$

$$\varphi_{vu}(\tau) = \lim_{T \to \infty} \frac{1}{2T} \int_{-T}^{T} dt\, v(t)u(t + \tau) \qquad (3.3\text{-}8)$$

It is useful to observe certain properties of the autocorrelation function for the stationary case. We notice that changing the sign of τ in Eq. 3.3–3 does not change the average value of the product so that the autocorrelation function is an even function. In symbols we have

$$\varphi_{vv}(\tau) = \varphi_{vv}(-\tau) \qquad (3.3\text{-}9)$$

Another important property of the autocorrelation function for the stationary case is obtained from the inequality

$$[v(t) \pm v(t + \tau)]^2 \geq 0 \qquad (3.3\text{-}10)$$

This is equivalent to

$$v^2(t) + v^2(t + \tau) \pm 2v(t)v(t + \tau) \geq 0 \qquad (3.3\text{--}11)$$

Taking the time average on both sides and dividing by 2 yields

$$\varphi_{vv}(0) \pm \varphi_{vv}(\tau) \geq 0 \qquad (3.3\text{--}12)$$

Now $\varphi_{vv}(0)$ is known to be a positive quantity. When $\varphi_{vv}(\tau)$ is positive, the negative sign of Eq. 3.3–12 tells us that it cannot be larger than $\varphi_{vv}(0)$. On the other hand, when $\varphi_{vv}(\tau)$ is negative, the positive sign in Eq. 3.3–12 tells us that the magnitude of $\varphi_{vv}(\tau)$ cannot exceed $\varphi_{vv}(0)$. Thus we have the relation

$$\left|\varphi_{vv}(\tau)\right| \leq \varphi_{vv}(0) \qquad (3.3\text{--}13)$$

Like the autocorrelation function the cross-correlation function has certain general properties for stationary signals. From Eq. 3.3–7 we observe that

$$\varphi_{vu}(\tau) = \varphi_{uv}(-\tau) \qquad (3.3\text{--}14)$$

It is to be noted that the cross-correlation function is not an even function. Another property of the cross-correlation function is that its magnitude is always less than or equal to the product of the rms values of the individual signals. In equation form this is

$$\left|\varphi_{vu}(\tau)\right| \leq \sqrt{\varphi_{vv}(0)\varphi_{uu}(0)} \qquad (3.3\text{--}15)$$

This property follows from the inequality

$$\left[\frac{v(t)}{\sqrt{\varphi_{vv}(0)}} \pm \frac{u(t + \tau)}{\sqrt{\varphi_{uu}(0)}}\right]^2 \geq 0 \qquad (3.3\text{--}16)$$

Let us conclude our discussion of general properties of correlation functions by considering their asymptotic behavior for large τ. If a pair of stochastic signals $v(t)$ and $u(t)$ containing no periodic components are cross-correlated, we observe that

$$\varphi_{vu}(t_1, \tau) \rightarrow [\overline{v(t_1)}][\overline{u(t_1 + \tau)}] \text{ as } \tau \rightarrow \infty \qquad (3.3\text{--}17)$$

provided the signals approach statistical independence for large τ, a condition almost implicit in the concept of a stochastic signal. In other words, if the second probability density approaches the product of the first probability densities for large τ, the cross-correlation function approaches the product of the average values of the signals evaluated at t_1 and $t_1 + \tau$, respectively. For a stationary signal this means the autocorrelation function approaches the square of the mean value of signal as τ approaches infinity.

A stochastic signal may contain a periodic component. For example suppose that

$$v(t) = x(t) + A \cos (\omega t + \theta)$$

where $x(t)$ is a stationary stochastic signal (without a periodic component). Then the autocorrelation function of such a signal becomes

$$\varphi_{vv}(\tau) = \varphi_{xx}(\tau) + \overline{x(t+\tau)A \cos (\omega t + \theta)} + \overline{x(t)A \cos [\omega(t+\tau) + \theta]}$$
$$+ \overline{A^2 \cos (\omega t + \theta) \cos [\omega(t+\tau) + \theta]}$$

This reduces to

$$\varphi_{vv}(\tau) = \varphi_{xx}(\tau) + \frac{A^2 \cos \omega\tau}{2} \qquad (3.3\text{--}18)$$

Now as τ approaches infinity $\varphi_{xx}(\tau)$ approaches $\overline{x(t)}^2$, a constant. This means that the presence of a sinusoidal component in a stochastic signal can be detected by observing the autocorrelation function for large values of the shift parameter. If such a component is present, an autocorrelation function will oscillate rather than settle to a constant value as τ approaches infinity. These considerations can be extended to non-sinusoidal periodic components and to cross-correlation functions.

So far we have given a number of expressions for the correlation functions and have discussed a few of their properties. This information is useful in deriving the correlation functions from theoretical considerations. The question now arises as to how to compute the correlation functions when we have experimental data available. So far, most of the experimental data treated by correlation techniques have been for stationary signals. We shall therefore give procedures for computing correlation functions from experimental data for stationary processes. The procedures to be followed when the process is non-stationary will be evident from discussion of the stationary case and the ensemble average definitions of the correlation functions. It should be noted that the amount of experimental data required to treat a non-stationary problem is vastly greater than that required to treat a stationary problem.

An approximate numerical procedure for computing correlation functions is as follows. Starting with oscillograms of the pair of signals in question, decide on a suitable length of record for computing the autocorrelation function on a time average basis. Divide this length into J equal intervals of length ΔT. From the values of the functions at the boundaries of these intervals, construct a quantized approximation to each in accordance with the equations

$$v(t) \cong \sum_j v[j\Delta T]\{\delta_{-1}[t - j\Delta T] - \delta_{-1}[t - (j+1)\Delta T]\} \qquad (3.3\text{–}19)$$

$$u(t + \tau) \cong \sum_k u[(k + m)\,\Delta T]\{\delta_{-1}[t - k\Delta T]$$

$$- \delta_{-1}[t - (k+1)\Delta T]\} \qquad (3.3\text{–}20)$$

Here in the second equation we have let τ be represented by $m\Delta T$

$$\tau = m\Delta T \qquad (3.3\text{–}21)$$

where m is an integer. The length of the interval ΔT is established on the basis that the variation of $v(t)$ or $u(t)$ should be small during an interval. From the approximate expressions for the signals, it follows that the cross-correlation function may be approximated by

$$\varphi(m\Delta T) \cong \frac{1}{J} \sum_j v[j\Delta T]u[(j + m)\Delta T] \qquad (3.3\text{–}22)$$

This is evident when we observe that all the products for j not equal to k are zero. Therefore, the double summation becomes a single summation.

Another procedure for computing correlation functions from experimental data is to employ a special form of analogue computer. A schematic of such a computer is shown in Fig. 3.3–1. Here a dual trace oscillogram of the pair of signals to be correlated is caused to travel beneath a pair of styli which are positioned to track the signals. The stylus for $v(t)$ positions the disk of integrator number one so that for a differential displacement of the oscillogram the rotation of the disk is $v(t)\,dt$ within a constant of proportionality. The stylus which tracks the signal $u(t)$ is displaced τ units so that its motion represents $u(t + \tau)$. This motion drives the disk of integrator number two so that its rotation for a differential displacement of the oscillogram represents the product $v(t)u(t + \tau)\,dt$. A counter placed on the disk of integrator 1 will accumulate the integral of $v(t)$. The counter connected to the disk of integrator 2 will accumulate the integral of $v(t)u(t + \tau)$. By dividing the reading of the second counter by the length of the run and adjusting for the constants of proportionality, the value of the correlation function is obtained.

An analogue computer as described above has been used to compute correlation functions from experimental data. It has the obvious disadvantage that manual tracking of the data is required and the manual tracking operation must be repeated for each value of τ for which the correlation function is wanted. Obvious improvements are possible. For example, the signal data could be put on magnetic tape and caused to position servos. The servomechanisms operating from the tape data position the integrator disks. In this way manual tracking would

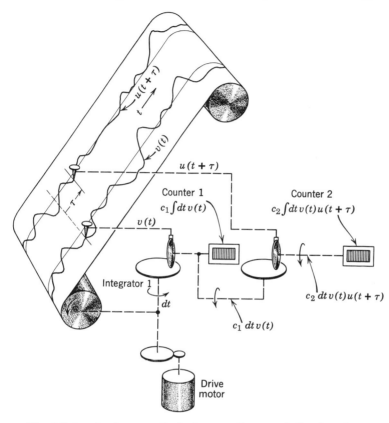

Fig. 3.3-1. Analogue method of computing correlation functions.

be avoided. However, with the digital computing equipment available, the currently preferred method at the M.I.T. Servomechanisms Laboratory is to use a numerical procedure rather than analogue means.

3.4 EXAMPLE OF DERIVATION OF CORRELATION FUNCTIONS FROM THEORETICAL CONSIDERATIONS

The human mind may conceive stochastic functions in a manner entirely analogous to the way in which it conceives predictable functions.   A predictable function may be defined in terms of a geometrical figure.   For example, the function $y = \sin \theta$ may be defined in terms of a right triangle in which θ is an acute angle and y is the ratio of the side opposite the angle θ to the hypotenuse.   We may think of the right triangle as a "process" which defines the function $y = \sin \theta$. In a similar way a stochastic function can be defined in terms of a process used to generate it.   In this article we shall show by means of examples how stochastic functions can be defined.   We shall also show

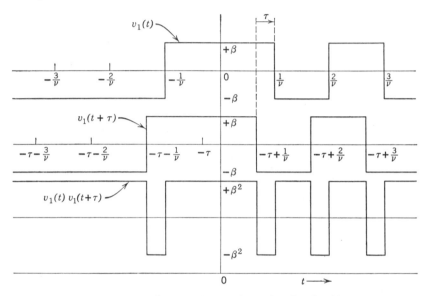

Fig. 3.4–1.   Sample of wave forms for signal $v_1(t)$.

how autocorrelation functions can be computed for stochastic functions by means of theoretical arguments starting from the defining process.

In general, for stationary stochastic signals, there are two principal ways of computing correlation functions: one is by consideration of the ensemble; the other is by consideration of the time average.   Sometimes a hybrid method employing both ensemble and time averaging is used.   It is important to make the correct choice of method for computing the correlation function in order to proceed as expeditiously and as simply as possible to the result.   Experience is the best teacher of how to make this choice.   Until experience is gained, the best procedure seems to be to try one method and, if that does not work, to try the other, and thereby determine by trial and error which method is the easier one.

As our first example of the derivation of an autocorrelation function from theoretical considerations, let us consider the stochastic function $v_1(t)$ defined as follows. Throughout an infinite range of time we postulate a sequence of *event points* uniformly spaced at a frequency ν. The function $v_1(t)$ is constant between event points and has the value $+\beta$ or $-\beta$. At each event point the value of the function is determined for the period until the next event point is reached by a random process such that the values $+\beta$ and $-\beta$ occur with equal likelihood. Figure 3.4–1 shows a sample of the wave form which $v_1(t)$ could exhibit. One way of drawing the graph of $v_1(t)$ is to flip a coin for each event point. If the coin comes up heads, assign to $v_1(t)$ the value $+\beta$. If the coin comes up tails, assign to $v_1(t)$ the value $-\beta$.

In order to find the autocorrelation function for $v_1(t)$ as defined above, we shall employ a time average. First let us consider $0 \leq |\tau| < 1/\nu$. Figure 3.4–1 is drawn for this case (with τ positive). We notice that the product of $v_1(t)v_1(t + \tau)$ is always $+\beta^2$ over an interval of time during each period equal to the length of the period minus the magnitude of τ. Over the remaining time in each period the product is either $+\beta^2$ or $-\beta^2$. It is $+\beta^2$ if the function does not change value at the event point. It is $-\beta^2$ if it does change value at the event point. Since it is equally likely for no change to occur as for a change to occur, the average value for the remaining time in each period is zero. We may, therefore, write:

$$v_1(t)v_1(t + \tau) = \beta^2 \quad \text{for fraction } \frac{\left(\dfrac{1}{\nu}\right) - |\tau|}{\left(\dfrac{1}{\nu}\right)} \text{ of the time} \quad (3.4\text{–}1)$$

$$v_1(t)v_1(t + \tau) = +\beta^2 \quad \text{for fraction } \frac{1}{2}\frac{|\tau|}{\left(\dfrac{1}{\nu}\right)} \text{ of the time}$$

$$\qquad\qquad (3.4\text{–}2)$$

$$= -\beta^2 \quad \text{for fraction } \frac{1}{2}\frac{|\tau|}{\left(\dfrac{1}{\nu}\right)} \text{ of the time}$$

Thus, the autocorrelation function which is the time average of the product is given by

$$\varphi_{vv1}(\tau) = \beta^2(1 - \nu|\tau|) \quad \text{for} \quad 0 \leq |\tau| < \frac{1}{\nu} \qquad (3.4\text{–}3)$$

We next consider $|\tau| \geq \dfrac{1}{\nu}$. Here the product $v_1(t)v_1(t + \tau)$ involves the multiplication of values of $v_1(t)$ during one period by values of $v_1(t)$ from portions of two different periods (except when the magnitude of τ is equal to an integral number of periods in which situation the multiplication would involve values from the whole of a single different period). Since the value of $v_1(t)$ in one period is equally likely to have the same or opposite sign as the value in any different period, it follows that

$$
\begin{aligned}
v_1(t)v_1(t + \tau) &= +\beta^2 \quad \text{for the fraction } \tfrac{1}{2} \text{ of the time} \\
&= -\beta^2 \quad \text{for the fraction } \tfrac{1}{2} \text{ of the time}
\end{aligned}
\tag{3.4-4}
$$

Taking the time average of the product as the autocorrelation function yields

$$
\varphi_{vv1}(\tau) = 0 \quad \text{for } |\tau| \geq \frac{1}{\nu}
\tag{3.4-5}
$$

Equations 3.4–3 and 3.4–5 together define the autocorrelation function throughout the complete range of τ. Figure 3.4–2 illustrates the auto-

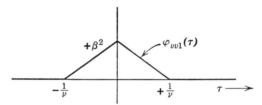

Fig. 3.4–2.   Autocorrelation function for stochastic signal $v_1(t)$.

correlation function determined by these two equations. This concludes our first example.

3.5   THE POISSON DISTRIBUTION

In the preceding example the event points are uniformally spaced in time. In the next example the event points are distributed in a particular random fashion in time. Before we can take up this example it is necessary to discuss the particular random distribution used.

Figure 3.5–1 shows a sample of a random distribution of event points. The particular random distribution to be considered is defined by three hypotheses. The first hypothesis states that the probability of finding any specified number of event points in a specified interval of time is independent of the location of that interval and is independent of what has happened in any other interval whether near or far away. By the second hypothesis the probability of finding just one event point in an interval ΔT approaches a constant times the length of the interval as ΔT approaches zero. Expression 3.5–1 summarizes the second hypothesis:

$$P(1, \Delta T) \to \nu \Delta T \quad \text{as } \Delta T \to 0 \qquad (3.5\text{–}1)$$

In this expression the symbol $P(1, \Delta T)$ stands for the probability of finding one event point in the interval ΔT. The symbol ν is the constant of proportionality. This constant will be shown to be equal to the average frequency of occurrence of the event points. The third

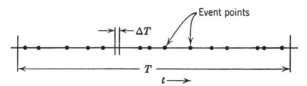

Fig. 3.5–1. Sample of a random distribution of event points.

hypothesis is that the probability of finding more than one event point in the interval ΔT is of higher order than ΔT as ΔT approaches zero. This hypothesis is summarized in expression 3.5–2.

$$P(n, \Delta T) \text{ is of higher order than } \Delta T \text{ as } \Delta T \to 0 \quad \text{for } n > 1 \quad (3.5\text{–}2)$$

Starting with the three hypotheses, we proceed to find an expression for the probability of finding a specified number of event points in a specified interval of time.

To illustrate the procedure to be followed in finding the probability distribution of the event points, we first consider zero event points in an interval T. We imagine the interval T to be broken down into a number of subintervals ΔT. The only way in which zero event points can occur in the interval T is for each of the subintervals ΔT to contain zero event points. Since, in accordance with the first hypothesis, the occurrence of event points in any one subinterval is independent of the occurrence of event points in any other subinterval, the probability of finding zero event points in the interval T is the product of the probabilities of finding zero event points in each of the subintervals in T. This fact is stated in the equation

$$P(0, T) = P(0, \Delta T)^{T/\Delta T} \qquad (3.5\text{–}3)$$

Here the ratio of T to ΔT represents the number of subintervals. Now it is a certainty that there is some number of event points in the interval ΔT where that number lies between zero and infinity. That is, the sum of the probabilities of the mutually exclusive events of finding exactly zero event points, one event point, two event points, three event points, etc., in the interval ΔT is equal to one. Thus we can express the probability of finding zero event points in the interval ΔT as

$$P(0, \Delta T) = 1 - P(1, \Delta T) - P(2, \Delta T) - P(3, \Delta T) \cdots \quad (3.5\text{--}4)$$

As the interval ΔT approaches zero this expression becomes

$$P(0, \Delta T) \rightarrow 1 - \nu\Delta T \quad \text{as } \Delta T \rightarrow 0 \qquad (3.5\text{--}5)$$

This follows from expressions 3.5–1 and 3.5–2 stating the second and third hypotheses. As a consequence of expression 3.5–5, Eq. 3.5–3 becomes

$$P(0, T) \rightarrow (1 - \nu\Delta T)^{T/\Delta T} \quad \text{as } \Delta T \rightarrow 0 \qquad (3.5\text{--}6)$$

In calculus it is shown that

$$(1 - \nu\Delta T)^{T/\Delta T} \rightarrow e^{-\nu T} \quad \text{as } \Delta T \rightarrow 0 \qquad (3.5\text{--}7)$$

Therefore, we have as the probability of finding zero event points in the interval T

$$P(0, T) = e^{-\nu T} \qquad (3.5\text{--}8)$$

We now extend the reasoning used in the preceding paragraph to the more complicated case of finding the probability that n event points

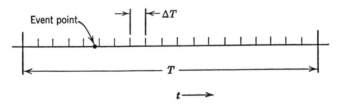

Fig. 3.5–2. One way for a single event point to occur in the interval T.

occur in the interval T. If n is equal to one, there is a number of ways for the one event point to occur in the interval T; this number is equal to the number of subintervals contained in T. The individual ways of finding one event point in T are: one event point in the first subinterval and zero event points in all succeeding subintervals; one event point in the second subinterval and zero event points in each of the other subintervals; and so forth. One of these ways is illustrated in Fig. 3.5–2. Since these ways are mutually exclusive events and since the probability of each way is equal, we see that

$$P(1, T) = \frac{T}{\Delta T} P(1, \Delta T)[P(0, \Delta T)]^{(T-\Delta T)/\Delta T} \qquad (3.5\text{–}9)$$

When n is larger than one, the ways in which n event points can occur in the interval T become more numerous. First there are the ways in which one event point occurs in n subintervals and zero event points occur in the remaining subintervals. Of these, there are a number equal to the number of combinations of n subintervals that can be formed from the total number of subintervals $T/\Delta T$. Next, there are the ways in which two event points occur in one subinterval and one event point occurs in each of $n - 2$ subintervals. Of these there are a number equal to the number of combinations of $n - 1$ subintervals contained in the total number of subintervals multiplied by $n - 1$ to account for the ways in which the subinterval containing two event points can be selected from the $n - 1$ subintervals. Also, we have the remaining ways involving two event points in m subintervals, one event point in $n - 2m$ subintervals and zero event points in the remaining subintervals plus all the other ways up to $n - 2m$ event points in one subinterval. In addition, there are the other ways involving three event points in one or more subintervals, four event points in one or more subintervals, etc. The probability of finding n event points in the interval T can be written as

$$P(n, T) = \frac{\left(\dfrac{T}{\Delta T}\right)!}{n!\left(\dfrac{T}{\Delta T} - n\right)!} [P(1, \Delta T)]^n [P(0, \Delta T)]^{(T-n\Delta T)/\Delta T}$$

$$+ \frac{\left(\dfrac{T}{\Delta T}\right)!}{(n-2)!\left[\dfrac{T}{\Delta T} + (1-n)\right]!} \{P(2, \Delta T)[P(1, \Delta T)]^{n-2}$$

$$[P(0, \Delta T)]^{[T-(n-1)\Delta T]/\Delta T}\} + \cdots \qquad (3.5\text{–}10)$$

In accordance with expression 3.5–5, we have

$$[P(0, \Delta T)]^{(T-n\Delta T)/\Delta T} \to (1 - \nu\Delta T)^{(T-n\Delta T)/\Delta T} \quad \text{as } \Delta T \to 0 \quad (3.5\text{–}11)$$

It follows as an extension from expression 3.5–7 that

$$(1 - \nu\Delta T)^{(T-n\Delta T)/\Delta T} \to e^{-\nu T} \quad \text{as } \Delta T \to 0 \qquad (3.5\text{–}12)$$

In accordance with expression 3.5–1

$$P(1, \Delta T) \to \nu \Delta T \quad \text{as } \Delta T \to 0 \tag{3.5-13}$$

We note that

$$\frac{\left(\dfrac{T}{\Delta T}\right)!}{\left(\dfrac{T}{\Delta T} - n\right)!} \to \left(\frac{T}{\Delta T}\right)^n \quad \text{as } \Delta T \to 0 \tag{3.5-14}$$

In accordance with the third hypothesis, expression 3.5–2, the second and all succeeding terms in Eq. 3.5–10 approach zero. We therefore conclude that

$$P(n, T) = \frac{(\nu T)^n}{n!} e^{-\nu T} \tag{3.5-15}$$

When the probability of finding n event points in the interval T is given by Eq. 3.5–15, we say that the event points are Poisson distributed. Figure 3.5–3 graphically depicts the Poisson distribution given by Eq. 3.5–15. This distribution is a discrete function of the variable n and a continuous function of the variable T. One example of a physical process described by a Poisson distribution is the arrival of electrons at the plate of a vacuum tube in which the average plate current is constant. Another example of a physical process described by a Poisson distribution is the disintegration of the atoms of a radioactive element (provided the radioactive element is continuously replenished so as to maintain constant mass).

In order to illustrate how the Poisson distribution is handled in computations, let us compute the average frequency of event points. To do this consider a number A of intervals each of length T. Let a_n represent the number of these intervals containing exactly n event points. An approximation to the average frequency $\bar{f}$ is given by the total number of event points in the A intervals divided by the total length of the A intervals. The total number of event points can be expressed as the sum of the number of intervals containing one event point plus two times the number of intervals containing two event points plus three times the number of intervals containing three event points and so on. The ratio becomes a better and better approximation of the average frequency as the number of intervals increases indefinitely. Thus the average frequency is given by

$$\bar{f} \to \frac{1a_1 + 2a_2 + 3a_3 + \cdots}{AT} \quad \text{as } A \to \infty \tag{3.5-16}$$

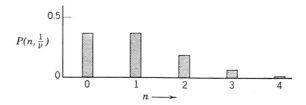

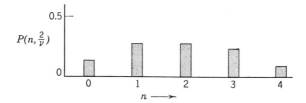

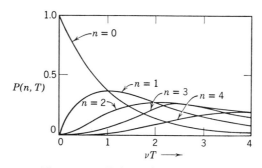

Fig. 3.5–3. Poisson distribution.

From the frequency definition of probability, it is known that

$$\frac{a_n}{A} \to P(n, T) \quad \text{as } A \to \infty \tag{3.5-17}$$

Therefore the average frequency is

$$\bar{f} = \frac{\displaystyle\sum_{n=1}^{\infty} nP(n, T)}{T} \tag{3.5-18}$$

Using the expression for the Poisson distribution given by Eq. 3.5–15 in the above equation yields:

$$\bar{f} = \frac{1}{T} \sum_{n=1}^{\infty} \frac{n(\nu T)^n}{n!} \cdot e^{-\nu T} \tag{3.5-19}$$

Replacing n over $n!$ by 1 over $(n-1)!$ and factoring outside the summation sign (νT) times the exponential yield:

$$\bar{f} = \nu e^{-\nu T} \sum_{j=0}^{\infty} \frac{(\nu T)^j}{j!} \quad \text{where } j = n - 1 \qquad (3.5\text{--}20)$$

But

$$\sum_{j=0}^{\infty} \frac{(\nu T)^j}{j!} = e^{\nu T} \qquad (3.5\text{--}21)$$

Therefore,

$$\bar{f} = \nu \qquad (3.5\text{--}22)$$

Thus we see that the average frequency is equal to ν, the proportionality constant of the first hypothesis, expression 3.5–1. This is what we would intuitively expect.

3.6 ANOTHER EXAMPLE OF A DERIVATION OF AN AUTOCORRELATION FUNCTION

As our second example of the derivation of an autocorrelation function from theoretical considerations, we consider a signal in which the event points are randomly distributed. This is in contrast to our first example, in which the event points are periodically spaced in time. The statement of the second example is as follows:

Given. The signal $v_2(t)$ is a rectangular wave with values $+\beta$ or $-\beta$ and with zero crossings located at event points which are Poisson distributed with an average frequency ν. Figure 3.6–1 shows some samples of wave forms for the signal $v_2(t)$. These samples may be thought of as drawn from the ensemble for $v_2(t)$.

Find. In terms of the given information we wish to find the autocorrelation function $\varphi_{vv2}(\tau)$ of the signal $v_2(t)$.

Solution. This example is most conveniently treated through the ensemble definition of the autocorrelation function. From the given data we know that the process is stationary since there is nothing in the Poisson distribution that depends on time. Thus the autocorrelation function will be independent of the time at which it is evaluated. In Art. 3.3 the autocorrelation function is defined as the ensemble average of the product of the signal at time t multiplied by the value of the signal at time $t + \tau$.   In symbols for the stationary case we have, from definition 3.3–1,

$$\varphi_{vv2}(\tau) = \overline{v_2(t)v_2(t + \tau)} \tag{3.6–1}$$

Let us consider a large number A of signals drawn from the ensemble of all the signals defined by the given data.   Let us further consider,

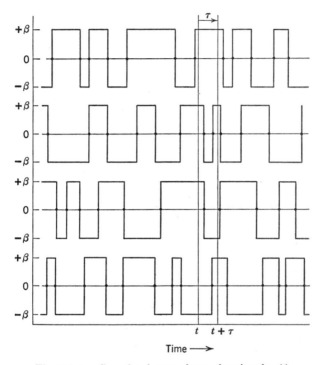

Fig. 3.6–1.   Sample of wave forms for signal $v_2(t)$.

for the time being, that τ is greater than zero as shown in Fig. 3.6–1. From this figure we notice that

$$\begin{aligned}
v_2(t)v_2(t + \tau) &= +\beta^2 \quad \text{for } n \text{ in } \tau \text{ even} \\
&\quad -\beta^2 \quad \text{for } n \text{ in } \tau \text{ odd}
\end{aligned} \tag{3.6–2}$$

where "n in τ" means "number n of event points in the interval τ." We classify the signals by the number of event points contained in the interval τ and let a_n represent the number of signals of the total number A which contain exactly n event points in the interval τ.   Then the ensemble average of the product is given by

$$\overset{\overbrace{\hspace{3cm}}}{v_2(t)v_2(t+\tau)} \rightarrow \frac{[(a_0 + a_2 + a_4 + \cdots) - (a_1 + a_3 + a_5 + \cdots)]\beta^2}{A}$$

$$(3.6\text{--}3)$$

as $A \rightarrow \infty$. But we know that

$$\frac{a_n}{A} \rightarrow P(n, \tau) \tag{3.6--4}$$

as $A \rightarrow \infty$. Therefore, the ensemble average of the product can be expressed as

$$\overset{\overbrace{\hspace{3cm}}}{v_2(t)v_2(t+\tau)} = \beta^2 \left[\sum_{n \text{ even}} P(n, \tau) - \sum_{n \text{ odd}} P(n, \tau) \right] \tag{3.6--5}$$

Using Eq. 3.6–1 for the autocorrelation function and Eq. 3.5–15 for the Poisson distribution allows us to write

$$\varphi_{vv2}(\tau) = \beta^2 e^{-\nu\tau} \left[1 - \nu\tau + \frac{(\nu\tau)^2}{2!} - \frac{(\nu\tau)^3}{3!} + \cdots \right] \tag{3.6--6}$$

Since the infinite series in brackets sums to $e^{-\nu\tau}$ we have

$$\varphi_{vv2}(\tau) = \beta^2 e^{-2\nu\tau} \tag{3.6--7}$$

The foregoing discussion assumed that τ was positive. For τ negative a similar argument can be given. However, it is simpler to recall the even property of the autocorrelation function in the stationary case (see Eq. 3.3–9). Using the even property, we see immediately from Eq. 3.6–7 that the autocorrelation function for all values of τ is specified by

$$\varphi_{vv2}(\tau) = \beta^2 e^{-2\nu|\tau|} \tag{3.6--8}$$

We notice from this equation that the autocorrelation function rapidly decreases as the magnitude of the shift parameter τ increases. At a value of τ equal to one over the average frequency, the autocorrelation function has already decreased to slightly less than 14 per cent of its maximum value. This completes our second example of the computation of correlation functions from theoretical considerations.

3.7 CAMPBELL'S THEOREM

In this article we consider the problem of finding the autocorrelation function of a signal that is built up from a series of pulses of arbitrary shape. The pulses are assumed to be of finite duration and to have their starting points Poisson distributed in time. Signals of this type are usually encountered when each impulse in a stochastic train of impulses causes a transient to occur in an electrical circuit. As an example we have the shot noise which occurs in an electrical circuit as the result of the arrival of individual electrons at the plate of a vacuum tube embedded therein.

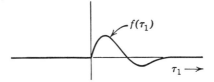

Fig. 3.7–1.   Typical pulse.

Figure 3.7–1 shows a typical pulse $f(\tau_1)$. The signal $v(t)$ is given by

$$v(t) \triangleq \sum_{m=-\infty}^{+\infty} f(t - t_m') \qquad (3.7\text{--}1)$$

where t_m' is the time at which the mth event point occurs. Figure 3.7–2 shows a sample of such a signal. For signals of this type Campbell's theorem shows that the mean-square value of the signal may be

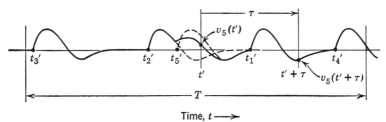

Fig. 3.7–2.   Signal formed from pulses Poisson distributed.

computed from the individual pulse shape and the average value of the signal. Specifically, Campbell's theorem states that

$$\overline{v^2(t)} = \nu \int_{-\infty}^{\infty} d\tau_1 f^2(\tau_1) + \overline{v(t)}^2 \qquad (3.7\text{--}2)$$

where ν is the average frequency of the Poisson-distributed pulses (C.2). An extension (R.3) of Campbell's theorem shows that the autocorrelation function of a signal of this type is

$$\varphi_{vv}(\tau) = \nu \int_{-\infty}^{\infty} d\tau_1 f(\tau_1) f(\tau_1 + \tau) + \overline{v(t)}^2 \qquad (3.7\text{--}3)$$

We now wish to show the validity of Eq. 3.7–3. We shall do this by considering an ensemble of signals and using an ensemble average to compute the autocorrelation function. In order to compute the ensemble average of the autocorrelation product, the signals in the ensemble are examined for a period T long compared to the duration of the elementary pulse $f(\tau_1)$. The period T contains both t' and $t' + \tau$, the times involved in computing the correlation product. These times are indicated in Fig. 3.7–2. Next the signals are classified into subensembles. Each subensemble is formed of the signals that contain in the period T a specified number of event points at which the elementary pulses start. A typical subensemble contains J event points in T. A typical signal in this subensemble is represented by $v_J(t)$ and is given by

$$v_J(t) = \sum_{j=1}^{J} f(t - t_j') \qquad (3.7\text{–}4)$$

This signal is a function of the positions t_j' of the J event points as well as a function of time t. The procedure for determining the autocorrelation function is as follows. First note that the ensemble average of the correlation product $v(t') \, v(t' + \tau)$ is to be computed from the signal values specified at time t' and $t' + \tau$. This product for each signal of a particular subensemble is a function of the locations t_j' of the J event points. This is easily seen from Fig. 3.7–2, which represents a typical signal drawn from the subensemble of signals possessing five event points in the interval T. Note that the index of an event point does not imply the order of its occurrence in time. Figure 3.7–3 represents schematically the correlation product as a function of t_1' and t_2' for the subensemble signals containing two event points in the interval T. To compute the ensemble average of the correlation product we first compute for each subensemble the average of the correlation product for all signals included in the subensemble. We then compute the ensemble average by averaging the subensemble averages. In doing this, proper weight must be given to each individual average to account for the number of signals within its subensemble relative to the total number of signals in the ensemble.

A physical interpretation of the event-point numbering within a particular signal drawn from a subensemble may be helpful. Imagine the process to be an ensemble of radioactive decay experiments. In each experiment the disintegrations of a fixed mass of a radioactive element are detected by a counter and associated circuitry to produce a pulse $f(\tau_1)$ for each disintegration. For a given period T, the records of the output signals can be classified by the number of disintegrations within T. Consider all the experiments in which exactly J disintegrations occurred within T. Prior to the period T we can imagine that in each radioactive mass of these particular experiments certain atoms, J in number, are predestined to disintegrate during the period T. These atoms are arbitrarily numbered 1 through J without knowledge of which will disintegrate first. The time at which each disintegrates is t_j'. It is evident that a particular atom j is just as likely to disintegrate at any one time within T as another. Therefore, the number j associated with

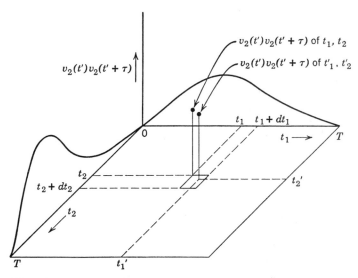

Fig. 3.7–3.   Schematic of $v_2(t')v_2(t' + \tau)$ as a function of t_1 and t_2.

an atom bears no relation to the time at which it disintegrates. Furthermore, the probability that the time t_j' at which an atom disintegrates lies between t_j and $t_j + dt_j$ is simply

$$dP = dt_j/T \qquad (3.7\text{–}5)$$

and is independent of the disintegration times for itself and all the other atoms.

In order to obtain the subensemble average of the correlation product over all possible signals, we simply average all possible values of the product weighted by the probability of occurrence of each value. Referring to Fig. 3.7–3, the infinitesimal probability associated with the product $v_2(t')\, v_2(t' + \tau)$ at t_1' and t_2' is the product of the probability that t_1' lies between t_1 and $t_1 + dt_1$ and the probability that t_2' lies between t_2 and $t_2 + dt_2$. This follows from the independence of t_1' and t_2'. But the correlation product at t_1, t_2 differs from that at t_1', t_2' by an infinitesimal of the first order. Thus one component of the subensemble average is

$$\overline{d[v_2(t')v_2(t'+\tau)]} = \frac{dt_1}{T}\frac{dt_2}{T}[v_2(t')v_2(t'+\tau)]_{t_1,t_2} \qquad (3.7\text{--}6)$$

ignoring infinitesimals higher than the second order. Extending this result to the Jth subensemble yields

$$\overline{d[v_J(t')v_J(t'+\tau)]} = \prod_{j=1}^{J}\frac{dt_j}{T}[v_J(t')v_J(t'+\tau)]_{t_1,t_2,\ldots,t_J} \qquad (3.7\text{--}7)$$

The fact that the correlation product is a function of the locations t_1, $t_2,\cdots,t_J$ of the intervals which contain the event points $t_1',\,t_2',\cdots,$ t_J' is indicated by the subscripts appended to the brackets in both Eqs. 3.7–6 and 3.7–7. Replacing v_J by the right side of Eq. 3.7–4 (with v_J at $t_1',\cdots,t_J'$ replaced by v_J at $t_1,\cdots,t_J$) and adding up the components, we obtain

$$\overline{v_J(t')v_J(t'+\tau)} = \int_0^T\frac{dt_1}{T}\cdots\int_0^T\frac{dt_j}{T}\cdots\int_0^T\frac{dt_J}{T}\sum_{j=1}^J f(t'-t_j)$$
$$\sum_{k=1}^J f(t'+\tau-t_k) \qquad (3.7\text{--}8)$$

The index k is introduced to avoid confusion in the double summation. Interchanging the orders of summation and integration yields

$$\overline{v_J(t')v_J(t'+\tau)} = \sum_{j=1}^J\sum_{k=1}^J\int_0^T\frac{dt_1}{T}\cdots\int_0^T\frac{dt_J}{T}\cdots$$
$$\int_0^T\frac{dt_J}{T}f(t'-t_j)f(t'+\tau-t_k) \qquad (3.7\text{--}9)$$

In the double summation there will be J terms where $j=k$. These terms will be of the form

$$\int_0^T\frac{dt_j}{T}f(t'-t_j)f(t'+\tau-t_j) = \frac{1}{T}\int_{-\infty}^\infty d\tau_1 f(\tau_1)f(\tau_1+\tau) \qquad (3.7\text{--}10)$$

For the other J^2-J terms in the double summation, j will not equal k. These latter terms will be of the form

$$\int_0^T\frac{dt_j}{T}f(t'-t_j)\int_0^T\frac{dt_k}{T}f(t'+\tau-t_k) = \frac{1}{T^2}\left[\int_{-\infty}^\infty d\tau_1 f(\tau_1)\right]^2 \qquad (3.7\text{--}11)$$

The integrations with respect to all variables except t_j in the first case and all variables except t_j and t_k in the second case are carried out first since the integrands are independent of these variables. Each such integration multiplies the remaining integral by unity. Since the period T is long compared to the time that a pulse differs appreciably from zero, and, since t' and $t' + \tau$ are both contained within T, the values of the integrals are independent of t' and $t' + \tau$ and are written as indicated by the right sides of Eqs. 3.7–10 and 3.7–11 with the limits $-\infty$ to $+\infty$ replacing the limits 0 to T. We now write the Jth subensemble average as

$$\overline{v_J(t')v_J(t' + \tau)} = \frac{J}{T} \int_{-\infty}^{\infty} d\tau_1 f(\tau_1)f(\tau_1 + \tau)$$
$$+ \frac{J(J-1)}{T^2}\left[\int_{-\infty}^{\infty} d\tau_1 f(\tau_1)\right]^2 \quad (3.7\text{–}12)$$

The next step is to compute the ensemble average from the subensemble averages. The ratio of the number of signals in the Jth subensemble to the total number of signals in the ensemble is simply the probability of finding J event points in the interval T as given by the Poisson distribution of Eq. 3.5–15. These ratios are weights to be used in averaging the subsemble averages. The ensemble average of the correlation product is therefore

$$\overline{v(t')v(t' + \tau)} = \sum_{J=1}^{\infty} P(J, T)[\overline{v_J(t')v_J(t' + \tau)}] \quad (3.7\text{–}13)$$

Substituting the value of $P(J, T)$ given by Eq. 3.5–15 and the values of the subensemble average given by Eq. 3.7–12 into Eq. 3.7–13 yields

$$\overline{v(t')v(t' + \tau)} = \sum_{J=1}^{\infty} \frac{(\nu T)^J}{J!} e^{-\nu T}\left\{\frac{J}{T}\int_{-\infty}^{\infty} d\tau_1 f(\tau_1)f(\tau_1 + \tau)\right.$$
$$\left. + \frac{J(J-1)}{T^2}\left[\int_{-\infty}^{\infty} d\tau_1 f(\tau_1)\right]^2\right\} \quad (3.7\text{–}14)$$

But

$$\sum_{J=1}^{\infty} \frac{J}{T}\frac{(\nu T)^J}{J!} e^{-\nu T} = \nu \sum_{J=1}^{\infty} \frac{(\nu T)^{J-1}}{(J-1)!} e^{-\nu T}$$
$$= \nu \quad (3.7\text{–}15)$$

and

$$\sum_{J=1}^{\infty} \frac{J(J-1)}{T^2}\frac{(\nu T)^J}{J!} e^{-\nu T} = \nu^2 \sum_{J=1}^{\infty} \frac{(\nu T)^{J-2}}{(J-2)!} e^{-\nu T}$$
$$= \nu^2 \quad (3.7\text{–}16)$$

Thus

$$\overline{v(t')v(t'+\tau)} = v\int_{-\infty}^{\infty} d\tau_1 f(\tau_1)f(\tau_1+\tau) + \left[v\int_{-\infty}^{\infty} d\tau_1 f(\tau_1)\right]^2 \quad (3.7\text{--}17)$$

The last term is the square of the average value of $v(t)$ since v is the average frequency of pulses, and the integral is the area beneath a single pulse. Thus we have proved the validity of Eq. 3.7–3. Since the ensemble average is independent of t', the autocorrelation function depends only on the shift parameter τ. According to the ergodic hypothesis, the ensemble average will be the same as the time average in this stationary situation.

The above derivation of the extended form of Campbell's theorem is an interesting example of the methods used in treating stochastic signals analytically. Such an analysis, as applied to this form of signal, does yield a useful result. However, we should not lose sight of the fact that the vast majority of signals encountered in practice cannot be handled analytically and must have the correlation functions computed by numerical or analogue means as discussed in Art. 3.3.

3.8 CONCLUSION

In this chapter the reader is introduced to the concept of a stochastic signal. He learns how such signals can be characterized in terms of correlation functions. In order to grasp better the fundamental meaning of a stochastic signal we have indicated some of the ways in which probability theory can be applied to derive correlation functions from theoretical considerations. In this connection the concept of a probability density of signal amplitudes is introduced; also employed is the Poisson distribution of event points. However, in practical applications, the correlation functions for stochastic signals are usually obtained by direct application of their definitions to experimentally obtained oscillograms.

Since the theory of random signals is not the main theme of this book, our treatment of probability theory and stochastic processes is necessarily brief. The reader who is interested in pursuing this subject further will find the text book of Laning and Battin (Reference L.05) very helpful. In addition, References J.1, C.7, W.05, and W.3 are useful.

In the next chapter we return to our main theme: analytical design theory. There we apply the concept of a stochastic signal to the problem of adjusting the parameters of a system to minimize the mean-square error.

4

ADJUSTMENT OF PARAMETERS

TO MINIMIZE

MEAN-SQUARE ERROR

4.1 RESPONSE OF A LINEAR SYSTEM TO A STOCHASTIC INPUT SIGNAL

In the preceding chapter we learned of the importance of stochastic signals in the design of feedback control systems. We found that a stochastic signal can be conveniently, but not uniquely, characterized by its autocorrelation function. The relation of one signal to another in a pair of signals we found to be characterized by the cross-correlation function. In this chapter we shall apply our knowledge of stochastic signals to the problem of minimizing the mean-square error of a linear control system by means of parameter adjustments. The configuration of the control system is assumed to be fixed. In order to do this we need to formulate the mean-square error in terms of the system parameters. We shall find it convenient to employ transforms of correlation functions; these transforms are called *power-density spectra*. The first two articles of this chapter discuss the response of a linear system to a stochastic input signal, show why it is convenient to introduce transforms of correlation functions, and show why these transforms are called power-density spectra.

Figure 4.1–1 illustrates a general linear system which is completely described by its weighting function $w(t)$ relating the input $v(t)$ to the output $q(t)$. If $v(t)$ is a stochastic signal, we know that $q(t)$ will likewise be a stochastic signal. We seek the relationship of the autocorrelation function of the output to the autocorrelation function of the

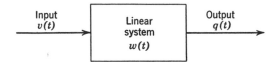

Fig. 4.1-1.   Block diagram of linear system.

input. We know that, by the convolution integral,

$$q(t) = \int_{-\infty}^{\infty} dt_1\, w(t_1)v(t - t_1) \tag{4.1-1}$$

Similarly,

$$q(t + \tau) = \int_{-\infty}^{\infty} dt_2\, w(t_2)v(t + \tau - t_2) \tag{4.1-2}$$

By the definition of the autocorrelation function, we have

$$\varphi_{qq}(\tau) = \lim_{T \to \infty} \frac{1}{2T} \int_{-T}^{T} dt\, q(t)q(t + \tau) \tag{4.1-3}$$

Substituting the values of $q(t)$ and $q(t + \tau)$ given by Eqs. 4.1–1 and 4.1–2 into this equation yields as an expression for the output autocorrelation function

$$\varphi_{qq}(\tau) = \lim_{T \to \infty} \frac{1}{2T} \int_{-T}^{T} dt \int_{-\infty}^{\infty} dt_1\, w(t_1)v(t - t_1)$$

$$\int_{-\infty}^{\infty} dt_2\, w(t_2)v(t + \tau - t_2) \tag{4.1-4}$$

By interchanging the order of the limit process and the other integrations so that we integrate with respect to t first, we have

$$\varphi_{qq}(\tau) = \int_{-\infty}^{\infty} dt_1\, w(t_1) \int_{-\infty}^{\infty} dt_2\, w(t_2)$$

$$\lim_{T \to \infty} \frac{1}{2T} \int_{-T}^{T} dt\, v(t - t_1)v(t + \tau - t_2) \tag{4.1-5}$$

Recalling the definition of the input autocorrelation function, we see that

$$\lim_{T \to \infty} \frac{1}{2T} \int_{-T}^{T} dt\, v(t - t_1)v(t + \tau - t_2) = \varphi_{vv}(\tau + t_1 - t_2) \tag{4.1-6}$$

and this permits us to write

$$\varphi_{qq}(\tau) = \int_{-\infty}^{\infty} dt_1\, w(t_1) \int_{-\infty}^{\infty} dt_2\, w(t_2)\varphi_{vv}(\tau + t_1 - t_2) \quad (4.1\text{--}7)$$

as the autocorrelation function of the output signal expressed in terms of the autocorrelation function of the input signal and the system weighting function. This is an important general relation which holds for any linear system.

In a similar manner, we may derive an expression for the cross-correlation function between the input and output signals. We recall that the cross-correlation function is defined as

$$\varphi_{vq}(\tau) \triangleq \lim_{T \to \infty} \frac{1}{2T} \int_{-T}^{T} dt\, v(t)q(t + \tau) \qquad (4.1\text{--}8)$$

Substituting for $q(t + \tau)$ the right side of Eq. 4.1–2, we obtain

$$\varphi_{vq}(\tau) = \lim_{T \to \infty} \frac{1}{2T} \int_{-T}^{T} dt\, v(t) \int_{-\infty}^{\infty} dt_2\, w(t_2)v(t + \tau - t_2) \quad (4.1\text{--}9)$$

Interchanging the order of integration and carrying out the limit process with respect to T first permit us to write

$$\varphi_{vq}(\tau) = \int_{-\infty}^{\infty} dt_2\, w(t_2)\varphi_{vv}(\tau - t_2) \qquad (4.1\text{--}10)$$

This equation gives us the cross-correlation function between the input and output signals in terms of the autocorrelation function of the input signal and the system weighting function. This relationship is also a very fundamental one for linear systems.

The expressions for the cross-correlation and autocorrelation functions given above may be interpreted physically in a rather simple way. We note from the form of Eq. 4.1–10 that the cross-correlation function between the input and output signals is a simple convolution of the system weighting function and the autocorrelation of the input signal. Thus the cross-correlation function may be interpreted to be the response of the linear system when excited by the autocorrelation function of the input signal. Next we note that, by substituting the expression for the cross-correlation function given by Eq. 4.1–10 into the right side of Eq. 4.1–7, we obtain the following expression for the autocorrelation function of the output signal

$$\varphi_{qq}(\tau) = \int_{-\infty}^{\infty} dt_1\, w(t_1)\varphi_{vq}(\tau + t_1) \qquad (4.1\text{--}11)$$

Thus the autocorrelation function of the output signal may be physi-

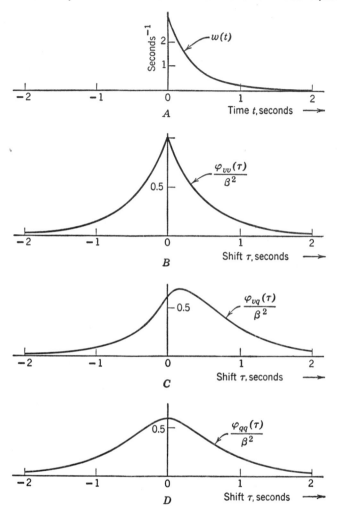

Fig. 4.1–2. Relations among correlation functions in a linear system. (A) System weighting function. (B) Input autocorrelation function. (C) Input-output cross-correlation function. (D) Output autocorrelation function.

cally interpreted as the convolution of the system weighting function with the cross-correlation function provided we understand that τ is running backwards, from positive values through zero and on toward minus infinity. This interpretation follows from the plus sign before the variable of integration t_1 appearing in the argument of the cross-correlation function.

As a specific illustration of these relationships, let us take the input autocorrelation function as

$$\varphi_{vv}(\tau) = \beta^2 e^{-2\nu|\tau|} \tag{4.1-12}$$

From Chapter 3 it will be recalled that this autocorrelation function corresponds to a signal which has values either plus β or minus β and which has its zero crossings Poisson distributed with average frequency ν. Let the system have a weighting function given by

$$w(t) = \frac{1}{\tau_s} e^{-t/\tau_s} \delta_{-1}(t) \tag{4.1-13}$$

which corresponds to a simple first-order lag of τ_s seconds. For this particular input autocorrelation function and weighting function, we find by Eq. 4.1–10 that the cross-correlation between the input and output signals is

$$\varphi_{vq}(\tau) = \beta^2 \frac{e^{2\nu\tau}}{(2\nu\tau_s + 1)} \quad \text{for } \tau < 0$$

$$= \beta^2 \left\{ \frac{e^{-2\nu\tau}}{(-2\nu\tau_s + 1)} - \frac{4\nu\tau_s e^{-\tau/\tau_s}}{[-(2\nu\tau_s)^2 + 1]} \right\} \quad \text{for } \tau \geq 0 \tag{4.1-14}$$

Using this value for the cross-correlation function in Eq. 4.1–11, we obtain as the expression for the output autocorrelation function

$$\varphi_{qq}(\tau) = \frac{\beta^2}{[-(2\nu\tau_s)^2 + 1]} [e^{-2\nu|\tau|} - 2\nu\tau_s e^{-1/\tau_s|\tau|}] \tag{4.1-15}$$

Figure 4.1–2 illustrates the input autocorrelation function, the weighting function, the cross-correlation function, and the output autocorrelation function for $\nu = 1$ inverse second and $\tau_s = \frac{1}{3}$ second. Note that the cross-correlation function between the input and output signals is not an even function of τ. But note that the backward convolution of this cross-correlation function with the system weighting function does yield an even function for the auto-correlation function of the output signal. This is as it should be since autocorrelation functions are guaranteed to be even in view of their definition.

4.2 POWER-DENSITY SPECTRA; RELATIONS IN LINEAR SYSTEMS

The time domain relationships among the correlation functions in linear systems given by Eqs. 4.1–7 and 4.1–10 involve one or more convolutions with the system weighting function. In numerical computation, relationships involving convolution may not be the most convenient to employ. In the event that the weighting function and the correlation functions are Fourier transformable, a corresponding set of relationships in the frequency domain can be derived. These frequency domain relationships do not involve convolution and therefore may be easier to use in numerical computation.

As an illustration of the procedure that is used in deriving frequency domain relationships, consider the Fourier transform of Eq. 4.1–7. Multiplying both sides of this equation by $e^{-s\tau}$ and integrating over the infinite range in τ yield

$$\int_{-\infty}^{\infty} d\tau \, e^{-s\tau} \varphi_{qq}(\tau)$$
$$= \int_{-\infty}^{\infty} d\tau \, e^{-s\tau} \int_{-\infty}^{\infty} dt_1 \, w(t_1) \int_{-\infty}^{\infty} dt_2 \, w(t_2) \varphi_{vv}(\tau + t_1 - t_2) \quad (4.2\text{–}1)$$

For reasons that will become clearer by the end of this article, let us define the frequency function corresponding to a correlation function to be $1/2\pi$ times the Fourier transform of the correlation function. Specifically, as the frequency function corresponding to the input autocorrelation function we define

$$\Phi_{vv}(s) \triangleq \frac{1}{2\pi} \int_{-\infty}^{\infty} d\tau \, e^{-s\tau} \varphi_{vv}(\tau) \quad (4.2\text{–}2)$$

and as the frequency function corresponding to the output autocorrelation function

$$\Phi_{qq}(s) \triangleq \frac{1}{2\pi} \int_{-\infty}^{\infty} d\tau \, e^{-s\tau} \varphi_{qq}(\tau) \quad (4.2\text{–}3)$$

In Eq. 4.2–1 let us interchange the order of integration on the right side so that we integrate with respect to τ first. Doing this and adjusting the argument of the exponential to agree with that of the correlation function yield

$$\int_{-\infty}^{\infty} d\tau \, e^{-s\tau} \varphi_{qq}(\tau) = \int_{-\infty}^{\infty} dt_1 \, e^{st_1} w(t_1) \int_{-\infty}^{\infty} dt_2 \, e^{-st_2} w(t_2)$$
$$\int_{-\infty}^{\infty} d\tau \, e^{-s(\tau+t_1-t_2)} \varphi_{vv}(\tau + t_1 - t_2) \quad (4.2\text{–}4)$$

Recalling that the system function $W(s)$ is the Fourier transform of the weighting function $w(t)$ and employing definitions 4.2–2 and 3 enable us to write

$$\Phi_{qq}(s) = W(-s)W(s)\Phi_{vv}(s) \quad (4.2\text{–}5)$$

as the frequency domain relationship corresponding to Eq. 4.1–7.

Before attempting to interpret Eq. 4.2–5, let us see if we can give a physical meaning to the frequency function corresponding to an auto-correlation function. Consider the frequency function given in Eq. 4.2–2. Since it is defined as the Fourier transform of the autocorrelation function divided by 2π it is evident that the autocorrelation function is obtained from the frequency function by taking the inverse transform and multiplying by 2π. Thus we have

$$\varphi_{vv}(\tau) = \frac{1}{j} \int_{-j\infty}^{j\infty} ds \, e^{s\tau} \Phi_{vv}(s) \qquad (4.2\text{–}6)$$

Since the integration is along the imaginary axis of the s-plane, we may write the inverse transform in terms of the real frequency ω. Doing this yields for the autocorrelation function

$$\varphi_{vv}(\tau) = \int_{-\infty}^{\infty} d\omega \, e^{j\omega\tau} \Phi_{vv}(j\omega) \qquad (4.2\text{–}7)$$

We are frequently interested in the mean-square value of the signal. Since this is the value of the autocorrelation function at $\tau = 0$, we see that the mean-square value is given by

$$\text{Mean-square value of signal } \varphi_{vv}(0) = \int_{-\infty}^{\infty} d\omega \, \Phi_{vv}(j\omega) \quad (4.2\text{–}8)$$

The frequency function $\Phi_{vv}(j\omega)$ is known to be a real function of the frequency ω. This follows from the fact that the autocorrelation function is an even function of τ. To see this, write the exponential appearing in definition 4.2–2 in rectangular form to obtain

$$\Phi_{vv}(j\omega) = \frac{1}{2\pi} \int_{-\infty}^{\infty} d\tau \, \cos \omega\tau \, \varphi_{vv}(\tau) - \frac{j}{2\pi} \int_{-\infty}^{\infty} d\tau \, \sin \omega\tau \, \varphi_{vv}(\tau) \quad (4.2\text{–}9)$$

Since the sine is an odd function of τ and the autocorrelation function is an even function of τ, the integrand of the imaginary part is odd so that the integral over the infinite range is zero. Thus the frequency function $\Phi_{vv}(j\omega)$ is real. Equation 4.2–8 states that the area underneath this frequency function over the infinite frequency range is equal to the mean-square value of this signal. Although derived for an input signal, this important result applies to any signal.

The fact that the area underneath the frequency function $\Phi_{vv}(j\omega)$ is equal to the mean-square value of the signal makes us wonder if the frequency function can be interpreted as a linear density distribution of the mean-square value of the signal along the frequency axis. This interpretation can be checked by postulating a linear system in the form of a very narrow band filter which possesses the system function magnitude characteristic as a function of frequency shown in Fig.

4.2–1.   For real frequencies, Eq. 4.2–5 becomes

$$\Phi_{qq}(j\omega) = W(-j\omega)W(j\omega)\Phi_{vv}(j\omega) \qquad (4.2\text{–}10)$$

For any realizable system, we know that the real part of the system function is an even function of frequency and the imaginary part is an

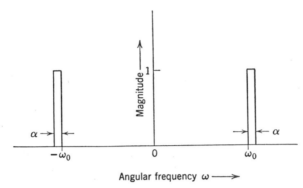

Fig. 4.2–1.   Magnitude characteristic of narrow band filter $|W_0(j\omega)|$.

odd function of frequency.   Thus we know that $W(-j\omega)$ is the conjugate of $W(j\omega)$ so that their product is the square of the magnitude of $W(j\omega)$.   Thus we can write

$$\Phi_{qq}(j\omega) = |W(j\omega)|^2\Phi_{vv}(j\omega) \qquad (4.2\text{–}11)$$

Combining the results of Eqs. 4.2–8 and 4.2–11 allows us to write the mean-square value of the output signal of a linear system in terms of the frequency function of the input signal as follows:

$$\varphi_{qq}(0) = \int_{-\infty}^{\infty} d\omega\, |W(j\omega)|^2\Phi_{vv}(j\omega) \qquad (4.2\text{–}12)$$

If we apply the general result of Eq. 4.2–12 to the particular case of the narrow band filter characteristic shown in Fig. 4.2–1 we have

$$\varphi_{qq0}(0) = \int_{-\infty}^{\infty} d\omega\, |W_0(j\omega)|^2\Phi_{vv}(j\omega) \qquad (4.2\text{–}13)$$

The subscripts zero appearing with the system function and with the output autocorrelation function indicate that we are considering the particular case of the narrow band filter.   Since the narrow band filter has a magnitude characteristic of unity over its pass band and zero outside its pass band (by assumption), the right side of Eq. 4.2–13 simplifies so that we can write

$$\varphi_{qq0}(0) = \int_{-(\omega_0+\alpha)}^{-\omega_0} d\omega\, \Phi_{vv}(j\omega) + \int_{\omega_0}^{\omega_0+\alpha} d\omega\, \Phi_{vv}(j\omega) \qquad (4.2\text{–}14)$$

In the limit as α becomes small, this equation reduces to

$$\varphi_{qq0}(0) = \alpha\Phi_{vv}(-j\omega_0) + \alpha\Phi_{vv}(j\omega_0) \qquad (4.2\text{–}15)$$

The two terms on the right side of this equation are equal to one another since the frequency function $\Phi_{vv}(j\omega)$ is even. Physically, there is no reason to associate more mean-square value of output with the positive frequency portion of $\Phi_{vv}(j\omega)$ than with the negative frequency portion. Therefore, we associate one-half of the mean-square value of the output from a narrow band filter with positive frequencies and one-half with negative frequencies. Thus we see that the mean-square value of output per unit frequency transmitted through a very narrow band filter is simply the value of the frequency function $\Phi_{vv}(j\omega)$ at the pass-band frequency. Since the pass-band frequency is arbitrary, this shows that the mean-square value per unit frequency at any frequency ω, which is associated with the input signal, is identically equal to the value of $\Phi_{vv}(j\omega)$. If the input signal $v(t)$ were a voltage wave impressed upon a 1-ohm resistor, the mean-square value of $v(t)$ would represent the average power dissipated in the resistor. Under this condition, the frequency function $\Phi_{vv}(j\omega)$ would represent the power-density spectrum of the signal. It has become common practice to refer to any frequency function obtained by transforming an autocorrelation function and dividing by 2π as a power-density spectrum even though in reality it is a mean-square-value-density spectrum. Some authors even refer to such frequency functions as power spectra. In this book, we shall refer to the mean-square-value-density spectrum as a power-density spectrum for the sake of brevity even though this is not a precise way of speaking. Occasionally, where no confusion will result, we may even abbreviate this to the single word "spectrum." Frequently, we shall employ the complex variable s in manipulations involving transforms. A frequency function like $\Phi_{vv}(s)$ will still be referred to as a power-density spectrum even though the mean-square-value-density connotation applies only along the imaginary axis.

In order to complete our discussion of the basic relationships among the power-density spectra of signals in linear systems, we must consider the cross-power-density spectrum for the input and output signals. By transforming both sides of Eq. 4.1–10, we obtain the expression

$$\Phi_{vq}(s) = W(s)\Phi_{vv}(s) \qquad (4.2\text{–}16)$$

where

$$\Phi_{vq}(s) \triangleq \frac{1}{2\pi} \int_{-\infty}^{\infty} d\tau\, e^{-s\tau}\varphi_{vq}(\tau) \qquad (4.2\text{–}17)$$

$\Phi_{vq}(s)$ is referred to as the cross-power-density spectrum of the input and output signals even though it is not directly related to the mean-square-value density of either signal. Equation 4.2–16 expresses an important relationship among the power-density spectra of linear systems. It is frequently used to determine the system function $W(s)$ from measurements made upon the input and output signals. The system function is simply the ratio of the cross-power-density spectrum to the input power-density spectrum. It is sometimes possible to use naturally occurring noise or disturbance as the input signal for determining the system function. However, if non-linearities are present or if appreciable errors exist in the determination of the power-density spectra, the system function determined by Eq. 4.2–16 may not be physically realizable. Under these conditions, a physically realizable system function, representing the linear system whose output differs from the actual output by the least possible amount in a mean-square sense, can be derived by the method given in Chapter 5.

4.3 ADDITIONAL RELATIONS AMONG POWER-DENSITY SPECTRA

The preceding article has disclosed the two most basic relationships between the power-density spectra of the input and output signals of a stationary linear system. In this article we shall supplement these basic relationships with three additional relationships which will be useful in subsequent work.

First, let us consider the effect of interchanging the subscripts in a cross-power-density spectrum. We recall from Chapter 3 that the cross-correlation functions are related in the following way:

$$\varphi_{13}(\tau) = \varphi_{31}(-\tau) \tag{4.3–1}$$

Here numerical subscripts are used to designate the signals. By Fourier-transforming both sides of this equation and dividing by 2π, we derive the corresponding relationship among the cross-power-density spectra. Carrying out this operation on the right member yields

$$\frac{1}{2\pi} \int_{-\infty}^{\infty} d\tau \, e^{-s\tau} \varphi_{31}(-\tau) = \Phi_{31}(-s) \tag{4.3–2}$$

where $\Phi_{31}(s)$ is the cross-power-density spectrum corresponding to $\varphi_{31}(\tau)$. This is easily seen by changing the variable of integration in the Fourier transform from τ to say $-\tau_1$. We therefore conclude that the relationship between the cross-power-density spectra corresponding to the cross-correlation functions of Eq. 4.3–1 is

$$\Phi_{13}(s) = \Phi_{31}(-s) \qquad (4.3\text{–}3)$$

Thus, interchanging subscripts in a cross-power-density spectrum can be compensated for by changing the sign of the complex argument.

Next, let us determine the relationship of the cross-power-density spectrum of the outputs from two separate linear systems to the spectrum characterizing the input signals. Figure 4.3–1 illustrates the

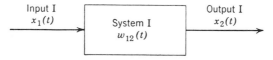

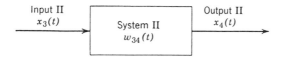

Fig. 4.3–1. Signals in two systems.

situation that we are considering here. The nomenclature is defined in this figure. The cross-correlation function of the output signals is given by

$$\varphi_{24}(\tau) = \lim_{T \to \infty} \frac{1}{2T} \int_{-T}^{T} dt\, x_2(t) x_4(t + \tau) \qquad (4.3\text{–}4)$$

In terms of the inputs, the output of System I is given by

$$x_2(t) = \int_{-\infty}^{\infty} dt_1\, w_{12}(t_1) x_1(t - t_1) \qquad (4.3\text{–}5)$$

and that of System II by

$$x_4(t + \tau) = \int_{-\infty}^{\infty} dt_3\, w_{34}(t_3) x_3(t + \tau - t_3) \qquad (4.3\text{–}6)$$

Substituting these expressions for the system outputs into Eq. 4.3–4, we obtain

$$\varphi_{24}(\tau) = \lim_{T \to \infty} \frac{1}{2T} \int_{-T}^{T} dt \int_{-\infty}^{\infty} dt_1\, w_{12}(t_1)$$
$$\int_{-\infty}^{\infty} dt_3\, w_{34}(t_3) x_1(t - t_1) x_3(t + \tau - t_3) \qquad (4.3\text{–}7)$$

By interchanging the orders of integration and the limit process so that we first integrate with respect to t and take the limit as T approaches infinity, and by recognizing the resultant cross-correlation function of the input signals, we obtain

$$\varphi_{24}(\tau) = \int_{-\infty}^{\infty} dt_1\, w_{12}(t_1) \int_{-\infty}^{\infty} dt_3\, w_{34}(t_3)\varphi_{13}(\tau + t_1 - t_3) \quad (4.3\text{--}8)$$

Transforming both sides of this expression and dividing by 2π yield

$$\Phi_{24}(s) = W_{12}(-s)W_{34}(s)\Phi_{13}(s) \quad (4.3\text{--}9)$$

where $W_{12}(s)$ and $W_{34}(s)$ are the transfer functions of Systems I and II, respectively. This is an important relationship between power-density spectra, since many other relationships can be derived with its aid. For example, Eq. 4.2–5 can be derived by making the two systems identical and setting the inputs equal to each other. Also Eq. 4.2–16 can be derived by assigning the same input to both systems and considering the first system to have a unity transfer characteristic.

We now turn our attention to the power-density spectrum of the sum or difference of the outputs from two different linear systems. Referring to Fig. 4.3–1, let the sum (or difference) of the output signals be $x_5(t)$. Thus

$$x_5(t) \triangleq x_2(t) \pm x_4(t) \quad (4.3\text{--}10)$$

The autocorrelation function of this signal is given by

$$\varphi_{55}(\tau) = \overline{x_5(t)x_5(t+\tau)} \quad (4.3\text{--}11)$$

This can be written as

$$\varphi_{55}(\tau) = \overline{[x_2(t) \pm x_4(t)][x_2(t+\tau) \pm x_4(t+\tau)]} \quad (4.3\text{--}12)$$

which expands into

$$\varphi_{55}(\tau) = \overline{x_2(t)x_2(t+\tau)} \pm \overline{x_2(t)x_4(t+\tau)} \pm \overline{x_4(t)x_2(t+\tau)}$$
$$+ \overline{x_4(t)x_4(t+\tau)} \quad (4.3\text{--}13)$$

Identifying the several correlation functions, we have

$$\varphi_{55}(\tau) = \varphi_{22}(\tau) \pm \varphi_{24}(\tau) \pm \varphi_{42}(\tau) + \varphi_{44}(\tau) \quad (4.3\text{--}14)$$

Transformation of this equation yields, after division by 2π,

$$\Phi_{55}(s) = \Phi_{22}(s) \pm \Phi_{24}(s) \pm \Phi_{42}(s) + \Phi_{44}(s) \quad (4.3\text{--}15)$$

From Eq. 4.2–5 we recognize that

$$\Phi_{22}(s) = W_{12}(-s)W_{12}(s)\Phi_{11}(s)$$
$$\Phi_{44}(s) = W_{34}(-s)W_{34}(s)\Phi_{33}(s)$$

Equation 4.3–9 gives us an expression for $\Phi_{24}(s)$. $\Phi_{42}(s)$ is found in terms of $\Phi_{24}(s)$ by Eq. 4.3–3 and is written as

$$\Phi_{42}(s) = W_{34}(-s)W_{12}(s)\Phi_{31}(s)$$

Therefore we may write the following expression as the power-density spectrum of the sum or difference of the output signals:

$$\begin{aligned}
\Phi_{55}(s) = \; & W_{12}(-s)W_{12}(s)\Phi_{11}(s) \\
\pm \; & W_{12}(-s)W_{34}(s)\Phi_{13}(s) \\
\pm \; & W_{34}(-s)W_{12}(s)\Phi_{31}(s) \\
+ \; & W_{34}(-s)W_{34}(s)\Phi_{33}(s)
\end{aligned} \qquad (4.3\text{–}16)$$

This is another important relationship since it allows us to express the spectrum of the sum or difference of two output signals in terms of the input spectra and the system transfer characteristics.   In the next article we shall apply this result to the computation of the power-density spectrum of the error exhibited by a control system.

4.4 FORMULATION OF MEAN-SQUARE ERROR; MINIMIZATION PROCEDURE

The power-density relations presented in the foregoing articles are the basis for formulating the mean-square error of a control system in

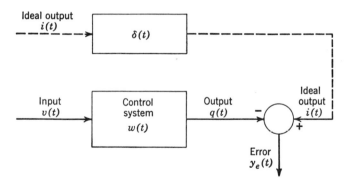

Fig. 4.4–1.   Error as the difference between outputs of two systems.

terms of its parameters.   The mean-square error of a control system, i.e., the mean-square value of the difference between the desired or ideal output and the actual output (Fig. 4.4–1), is identically equal to the value of the autocorrelation function of the error at zero shift.   In equation form this fact is expressed as

$$\overline{y_e^2(t)} = \varphi_{yy}(0) \qquad (4.4\text{–}1)$$

Therefore we shall generally use the symbol $\varphi_{yy}(0)$ to stand for the mean-square error. By Eq. 4.2–8 we know that the mean-square error is also equal to the area beneath the power-density spectrum of the error provided this spectrum is expressed as a function of the real frequency ω. In terms of the complex frequency s, the mean-square error is

$$\varphi_{yy}(0) = \frac{1}{j} \int_{-j\infty}^{j\infty} ds\, \Phi_{yy}(s) \qquad (4.4\text{–}2)$$

This can be seen by setting $\tau = 0$ in Eq. 4.2–6. All that remains is to show how the power-density spectrum of the error is related to the system function which characterizes the control system.

The control system error is defined as

$$y_e(t) = i(t) - q(t) \qquad (4.4\text{–}3)$$

where $i(t)$ is the ideal output and $q(t)$ is the actual output. Inspection of Fig. 4.4–1 indicates how this error may be interpreted as the differences in the output of two linear systems. Since the input and output of the first system are identical, the impulse response of the first system is simply an impulse at $t = 0$. By comparing Fig. 4.3–1 with Fig. 4.4–1 the following identifications can be made:

$$x_1(t) = i(t)$$

$$w_{12}(t) = \delta(t)$$

$$x_3(t) = v(t)$$

$$w_{34}(t) = w(t)$$

Let us now apply Eq. 4.3–16 to the evaluation of the power-density spectrum of the error. To do this, we identify the following equivalences:

$$\Phi_{11}(s) = \Phi_{ii}(s)$$

$$\Phi_{31}(s) = \Phi_{vi}(s)$$

$$\Phi_{13}(s) = \Phi_{iv}(s)$$

$$\Phi_{33}(s) = \Phi_{vv}(s)$$

$$W_{12}(s) = 1$$

$$W_{34}(s) = W(s)$$

Employing these in Eq. 4.3–16 allows us to write as the power-density spectrum of the error

$$\Phi_{yy}(s) = \Phi_{ii}(s) - W(s)\Phi_{vi}(-s) - W(-s)\Phi_{vi}(s)$$
$$+ W(-s)W(s)\Phi_{vv}(s) \quad (4.4\text{--}4)$$

Here we have made use of the fact that $\Phi_{iv}(s) = \Phi_{vi}(-s)$. This formula is one important way of expressing the power-density spectrum of the error in terms of the system function. Given the power-density spectrum $\Phi_{ii}(s)$ of the ideal output, the cross-power-density spectrum $\Phi_{vi}(s)$ between the input and ideal output, and the power-density spectrum $\Phi_{vv}(s)$ of the input, we can evaluate the power-density spectrum $\Phi_{yy}(s)$ of the error as a function of the free parameters of the system function $W(s)$. Substitution of this spectrum into Eq. 4.4–2 gives us the mean-square error as a function of the free parameters. If the system function and the power-density spectra

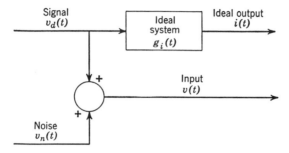

Fig. 4.4–2.   Composition of input as signal plus noise.

are rational functions of s, the table of definite integrals given in Appendix E makes the evaluation of Eq. 4.4–2 very simple to carry out. Under these conditions the resulting expression for the mean-square error will be an explicit function of the coefficients appearing in the rational functions representing the power-density spectra and the system function. If the power-density spectra and the system function are not rational functions, the integral of Eq. 4.4–2 is difficult to evaluate; the most common procedure for handling irrational functions is to approximate them with rational functions.

Frequently the input signal $v(t)$ to a control system is composed of a signal or data component $v_d(t)$ and a noise component $v_n(t)$. Thus

$$v(t) = v_d(t) + v_n(t) \quad (4.4\text{--}5)$$

In this event the desired or ideal output may be related exclusively to the signal component of the input signal as shown in Fig. 4.4–2. Let the transfer characteristic of the hypothetical linear system relating the ideal output to the signal component of the input be denoted by $G_i(s)$. In designating power-density spectra that involve input signal or noise components, subscripts d or n will be used, respectively. The subscript v will still refer to the total input signal. By Eq. 4.3–9 we see that

$$\Phi_{vi}(s) = G_i(s)\Phi_{vd}(s) \tag{4.4–6}$$

Multiplying both sides of Eq. 4.4–5 by $v_d(t + \tau)$, averaging, identifying correlation functions, transforming, and dividing by 2π show us that

$$\Phi_{vd}(s) = \Phi_{dd}(s) + \Phi_{nd}(s) \tag{4.4–7}$$

Equation 4.2–5 allows us to write

$$\Phi_{ii}(s) = G_i(-s)G_i(s)\Phi_{dd}(s) \tag{4.4–8}$$

By means of Eq. 4.3–16, we see that

$$\Phi_{vv}(s) = \Phi_{dd}(s) + \Phi_{nd}(s) + \Phi_{nd}(-s) + \Phi_{nn}(s) \tag{4.4–9}$$

Substituting the equivalents given by Eqs. 4.4–6, 8, 9 into Eq. 4.4–4 and replacing $\Phi_{vd}(s)$ by the right member of Eq. 4.4–7 yields

$$\begin{aligned}
\Phi_{yy}(s) = {} & \begin{bmatrix} G_i(-s)G_i(s) - W(s)G_i(-s) \\ -W(-s)G_i(s) + W(-s)W(s) \end{bmatrix} \Phi_{dd}(s) \\
& + [W(-s)W(s) - W(-s)G_i(s)]\Phi_{nd}(s) \\
& + [W(-s)W(s) - W(s)G_i(-s)]\Phi_{nd}(-s) \\
& + W(-s)W(s)\Phi_{nn}(s) \tag{4.4–10}
\end{aligned}$$

Here we have made use of the fact that $\Phi_{dd}(s)$ is an even function. This result may be simplified by introducing an error transfer characteristic $W_y(s)$ which represents the difference between the ideal transfer function and the actual transfer function. Thus

$$W_y(s) \triangleq G_i(s) - W(s) \tag{4.4–11}$$

In terms of the error transfer characteristic, the power-density spectrum of the error may be expressed as

$$\begin{aligned}
\Phi_{yy}(s) = {} & W_y(-s)W_y(s)\Phi_{dd}(s) + W(-s)W(s)\Phi_{nn}(s) \\
& - W_y(-s)W(s)\Phi_{nd}(-s) - W(-s)W_y(s)\Phi_{nd}(s) \tag{4.4–12}
\end{aligned}$$

This alternate expression for the power-density spectrum of the error is especially important when the cross-correlation between the noise and signal is zero and therefore the cross-power spectrum is zero. Under this condition the error can be thought of as having two components. One component corresponds to the input signal acting through the error transfer characteristic; the other component cor-

Example   125

responds to the noise acting through the transfer characteristic of the control system.

The above discussion has indicated how the mean-square error can be expressed as a function of the free parameters of the control system by first finding the power-density spectrum of the error and then finding the area beneath this spectrum along the imaginary axis. What remains is to show how the error may be minimized by a suitable adjustment of the free parameters. In general, there are two approaches. One is the formal technique of setting the partial derivatives of the mean-square error with respect to the several free parameters equal to zero and solving the resultant set of equations for the desired values of the free parameters. In most practical problems the resultant expressions for the partial derivatives are so complex as to preclude an algebraic solution for the parameter values. An alternate approach is to determine the minimum value of the mean-square error by plotting. This approach is particularly effective when there are only one or two free parameters; many practical problems are of this character. In general, it is seen that the problem of minimizing the mean-square error for stochastic signals is identical to the problem of minimizing the integral-square error for transient signals since the integrals to be evaluated are of the same form. The discussion of the minimization problem given in Chapter 2 for the integral-square error therefore is pertinent to the minimization of the mean-square error also.

The procedure for formulating and minimizing the mean-square error will be made clear by solving some examples. The next article will illustrate the procedure with a simple problem in which formal methods of minimization will be effective.

4.5 EXAMPLE

As our first example of setting a parameter to minimize the mean-square error of a control system, let us consider the problem of adjusting the gain of a positional servomechanism so that it will follow an input signal with the least error in the mean-square sense. The input signal is specified to be a rectangular wave with values plus or minus a constant β and with zero crossings Poisson distributed with an average frequency ν. This input signal has been discussed in Art. 3.6. It is further specified that the input to this positional control system is noise free. In the design of positional servomechanisms, the inputs may be taken to be noise free more often than not. The objective of a positional servomechanism is to reproduce the input signal. Therefore, the desired output is specified to be identical with the input signal. The fixed elements of this servomechanism we shall take to be the servomotor exclusive of a gain factor. The motor is specified to be an integrator cascaded with a time lag τ_m. The feedback network of this servomechanism is specified to have a unity transfer function. The compensating network is specified to be a simple gain whose value is to be chosen by the designer. The gain factor of the fixed elements is lumped with this adjustable gain. This completes the specifications for this design problem. Let us first find the mean-square error as a function of the adjustable gain. After this has been done, let us next determine the value of the gain that minimizes the mean-square error.

Before proceeding to the solution of this problem, let us recapitulate the problem statement in terms of symbols.

Given. For purposes of solving this problem the description of the input signal given in the preceding paragraph may be replaced by the autocorrelation function of this signal. The solution depends only on the autocorrelation function and not on any other signal characteristics. In Article 3.6 the autocorrelation function of this input signal is shown to be

$$\varphi_{dd}(\tau) = \beta^2 e^{-2\nu|\tau|} \qquad (4.5\text{--}1)$$

The fact that the input is noise free can be summarized in the statement

$$v_n(t) = 0 \qquad (4.5\text{--}2)$$

The equality of the desired output and the input signal is stated by

$$i(t) = v_d(t) \qquad (4.5\text{--}3)$$

From the statement that the servomotor is an integrator cascaded with a time lag, we deduce that the fixed elements in this problem are characterized by the transfer function

$$G_f(s) = \frac{1}{(\tau_m s + 1)s} \qquad (4.5\text{--}4)$$

The specification that the feedback network has a unity transfer function is symbolized by

$$H_f(s) = 1 \qquad (4.5\text{--}5)$$

The restriction on the compensating network, namely, that it is a simple adjustable gain, is stated by

$$G_c(s) = K_v \qquad (4.5\text{--}6)$$

Here the subscript v denotes the fact that this gain is the velocity con-

Example   127

stant of the servomechanism. This happens to be so since we have lumped the gain of the servomotor with the gain of the compensating network. The six above equations briefly summarize the given data for this problem.

Find. (1) The mean-square error $\phi_{yy}(0)$ as a function of the adjustable velocity constant, K_v; and (2) K_v for minimum $\phi_{yy}(0)$. This completes the problem statement.

Solution. Since the noise component of the input signal for this problem is zero, all correlation functions that involve noise are zero and therefore the corresponding power-density spectra are zero. Thus, for this particular problem, Eq. 4.4–12 for the power-density spectrum of the error reduces to

$$\Phi_{yy}(s) = W_y(-s)W_y(s)\Phi_{dd}(s) \qquad (4.5\text{–}7)$$

Because the desired output is identical with the input signal, the transfer function $G_i(s)$ which relates the desired output to the input signal is unity. Therefore the error transfer function $W_y(s)$ is simply 1 minus the system function $W(s)$. For this problem the system function is

$$W(s) = \frac{K_v}{\tau_m s^2 + s + K_v} \qquad (4.5\text{–}8)$$

Thus the error transfer function is

$$W_y(s) = \frac{\tau_m s^2 + s}{\tau_m s^2 + s + K_v} \qquad (4.5\text{–}9)$$

The power-density spectrum of the input signal, which is obtained by transforming the autocorrelation function given by Eq. 4.5–1 and dividing by 2π, is found to be

$$\Phi_{dd}(s) = \frac{\beta^2}{\pi} \frac{2\nu}{-s^2 + 4\nu^2} \qquad (4.5\text{–}10)$$

Substitution of the error transfer function given by Eq. 4.5–9 and the power-density spectrum of the input signal given by Eq. 4.5–10 into Eq. 4.5–7 yields as the power-density spectrum of the error

$$\Phi_{yy}(s) = \frac{2\nu\beta^2}{\pi} \frac{c(-s)c(s)}{d(-s)d(s)} \qquad (4.5\text{–}11)$$

where

$$c(s) = \tau_m s^2 + s \qquad (4.5\text{–}12)$$

and

$$d(s) = \tau_m s^3 + (1 + 2\nu\tau_m)s^2 + (K_v + 2\nu)s + 2\nu K_v \quad (4.5\text{–}13)$$

The mean-square error is found from the power-density spectrum of the error signal by means of the integral of Eq. 4.4–2 which is repeated here to maintain continuity.

$$\varphi_{yy}(0) = \frac{1}{j} \int_{-j\infty}^{j\infty} ds \; \Phi_{yy}(s) \qquad (4.4\text{--}2)$$

By means of the formula for I_3 in the table of definite integrals given in the Appendix E, the integral is evaluated for the error power-density spectrum given by Eq. 4.5–11. The result is

$$\varphi_{yy}(0) = 2\nu\beta^2 \; \frac{(K_v + 2\nu)\tau_m + 1}{(K_v + 2\nu + 4\nu^2\tau_m)} \qquad (4.5\text{--}14)$$

This equation expresses the mean-square error as a function of the velocity constant K_v and the other system and signal parameters. It, therefore, constitutes the first desired result.

The above result for the mean-square error as a function of K_v may be written somewhat more neatly in terms of a normalized signal frequency N_ν and a normalized gain K defined as follows:

$$N_\nu \triangleq 2\nu\tau_m \qquad (4.5\text{--}15)$$

and

$$K \triangleq \tau_m K_v \qquad (4.5\text{--}16)$$

In terms of these normalized parameters, the ratio of the mean-square error to the square of the input signal amplitude is expressed as

$$\frac{\varphi_{yy}(0)}{\beta^2} = N_\nu \frac{(N_\nu + 1 + K)}{(N_\nu^2 + N_\nu + K)} \qquad (4.5\text{--}17)$$

Here N_ν and β are fixed for any particular problem specification, and K is subject to the designer's choice.

We now ask, "What value should K have in order to minimize the mean-square error?" Proceeding in a formal manner, we differentiate both sides of Eq. 4.5–17 with respect to K and obtain

$$\frac{d[\varphi_{yy}(0)/\beta^2]}{dK} = N_\nu \frac{N_\nu^2 - 1}{(N_\nu^2 + N_\nu + K)^2} \qquad (4.5\text{--}18)$$

When we attempt to set this derivative equal to zero, we note that no finite value of K will satisfy the resulting equation. Reference to Eq. 4.5–8 shows us that K_v, and hence K, must be greater than or equal to zero in order for the control system to be stable. For K positive, we note that the slope of the mean-square error as a function of K is always negative for N_ν less than 1 and always positive for N_ν greater than 1. For N_ν less than 1, K should be made as large as possible since

Example   129

the smallest value of the function occurs when K is infinite. For N_ν larger than 1, the normalized gain K should be set equal to zero in order to minimize the mean-square error. For N_ν equal to 1, reference

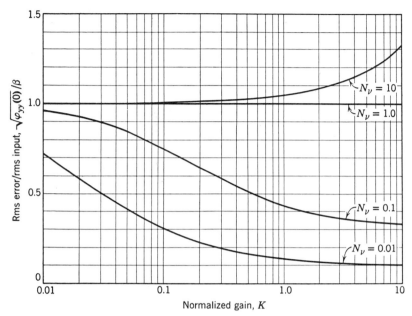

Fig. 4.5–1.   Rms error as a function of gain for second-order system with rectangular-wave input having random zero crossings.

Specifications:

$$\varphi_{ss}(\tau) = \beta^2 e^{-2\nu|\tau|}$$
$$v_n(t) = 0$$
$$i(t) = \nu_s(t)$$

$$G_f(s) = \frac{1}{(\tau_m s + 1)s}$$
$$H_f(s) = 1$$
$$G_c(s) = K_v$$

Note:

$$N\nu \triangleq 2\nu\tau_m$$
$$K \triangleq \tau_m K_v$$

to Eq. 4.5–17 indicates that the value of the mean-square error is independent of the value of the gain K.

Figure 4.5–1 shows graphically how the error varies with gain. Rather than the mean-square error we have chosen to plot the rms error in this figure. This is done in order to make the plotted variable correspond to a quantity that would normally be measured in the laboratory. The rms error as the function of gain is shown for four values of the normalized signal frequency N_ν. In order to cover the large range in gain needed to display these functional relationships, a logarithmic horizontal scale is used. For $N_\nu = 10$, the rms error continuously increases as the gain is increased. This is typical of the behavior of the system when N_ν is greater than 1; under this condition the gain should be made equal to zero to minimize the rms error, that is, the servomechanism should be turned off. The curve for $N_\nu = 1$ corresponds to a critical case in which the rms error is independent of the value of the gain. Under this condition it is also true that the servomechanism may just as well be turned off. For $N_\nu = 0.1$ and 0.01, the servomechanism is able to follow the input signal to some extent. The ability to follow increases with increasing gain and decreasing N_ν. For N_ν less than 1, the least value of the mean-square error always occurs at infinite gain and is equal to the mean-square value of the input signal multiplied by N_ν. However, little benefit is derived from using gains much larger than unity since the rms error decreases very slowly as the normalized gain is increased from 1 toward infinity. In fact, with N_v near zero, setting the normalized gain at 1 instead of infinity makes the rms error only approximately the $\sqrt{2}$ times its minimum value. It should be observed further that the break frequency of the servomotor $1/\tau_m$ must be higher by several orders of magnitude than the average frequency of the zero crossings of the input signal if the servomechanism is to have a usefully small rms error. For example, if the servomotor has a time constant of 0.01 second corresponding to a break frequency of 100 radians per second and the velocity constant is set for 100 corresponding to a normalized gain of unity, the ratio of the rms error to the rms input is 0.063 for an average frequency of zero crossings of 0.1 per second.

By way of further explanation of the rather singular result of this example—namely, that infinite gain should be used in order to minimize the rms error if the servomechanism is able to follow at all—let us examine precisely what takes place as the system gain is made very large. Consider how this control system responds to a single zero crossing of the input as shown in Fig. 4.5–2(A). The error response to this single zero crossing is given by

$$y_e(t) = \frac{2\beta\delta_{-1}(t)}{\left(1 - \dfrac{1}{4\tau_m K_v}\right)^{\frac{1}{2}}} e^{-t/2\tau_m}$$

$$\cos\left\{\left[\left(1 - \frac{1}{4\tau_m K_v}\right)^{\frac{1}{2}}\left(\frac{K_v}{\tau_m}\right)^{\frac{1}{2}}\right]t - \tan^{-1}\left[\frac{\dfrac{1}{2(\tau_m K_v)^{\frac{1}{2}}}}{\left(1 - \dfrac{1}{4\tau_m K_v}\right)^{\frac{1}{2}}}\right]\right\}$$

$$(4.5–19)$$

Example   131

Here t refers to the time elapsed since the occurrence of the zero crossing.   This error response may be obtained by inverse transforming the
right member of Eq. 4.5–9 multiplied by $2\beta/s$, the transform of a step
input of amplitude 2β.   Typical error responses are shown in Figs.
4.5–2(B) and (C).   These error responses correspond to normalized

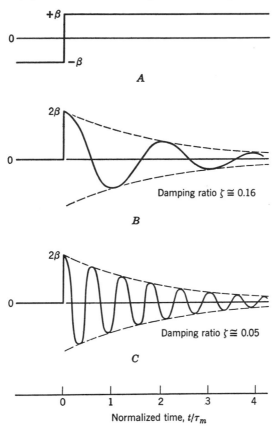

Fig. 4.5–2.   Error response of second-order system to single zero crossing of rectangular wave.   (A) Input.   (B) Error response for $\tau_m K_v \cong 10$.   (C) Error response
for $\tau_m K_v \cong 100$.

gain settings of 10 and 100, respectively.   Notice that the exponential
envelope of the decaying oscillation is independent of the gain setting;
the time constant of this envelope is two times the motor time constant.
As the gain is increased the number of oscillations included within the
envelope in a given period of time increases as the square root of the
gain.   Let us assume that the gain is very large.   The number of
oscillations in the envelope becomes large also, and a point is reached

where the wave form of each oscillation is almost indistinguishable from a sine wave.

Under the condition of $K_v \to \infty$, we may check the limiting value of the mean-square error as follows.   First, compute the integral-square value of the exponential envelope.   Next, correct for the fact that the actual wave form is not an exponential, but is a very slowly decaying oscillation, by multiplying by the ratio of the mean-square value of a sinusoid to the peak-squared value.   This ratio is $\frac{1}{2}$.   The integral-square value of the error response to a single zero crossing is then multiplied by the number of zero crossings occurring in some large period T. Dividing the integral-square value of the error for the period T by the length of that period yields the mean-square error.   Symbolically the first step is represented by

$$\int_{-\infty}^{\infty} dt\; y_e{}^2\;(t) \cong \tfrac{1}{2}(2\beta)^2 \int_0^{\infty} dt\; (e^{-t/2\tau_m})^2 \qquad (4.5\text{--}20)$$

The integral contained in the right member turns out to be

$$\int_0^{\infty} dt\; (e^{-t/2\tau_m})^2 = \tau_m \qquad (4.5\text{--}21)$$

Thus the integral-square value of the error response to a single zero crossing is

$$\int_{-\infty}^{\infty} dt\; y_e{}^2(t) \cong 2\beta^2 \tau_m \qquad (4.5\text{--}22)$$

The average number of zero crossings occurring in a period T is simply the average frequency ν multiplied by T.   Thus the mean-square value of the error is given by

$$\overline{y_e{}^2(t)} \cong \frac{\nu T}{T} \left[\int_{-\infty}^{\infty} dt\; y_e{}^2(t) \right] \qquad (4.5\text{--}23)$$

which reduces to

$$\overline{y_e{}^2(t)} \cong 2\beta^2 \tau_m \nu \qquad (4.5\text{--}24)$$

This is the same value that is given by Eq. 4.5–17 when K is infinite. This may seem surprising in view of the overlapping of the error responses to the individual zero crossings.   However, it must be recalled that the zero crossings are randomly spaced so that the oscillations in the transients are incoherent.

In conclusion, it should be observed that the extreme simplicity of this example leads to the very unusual result of a continuously decreasing rms error with increasing gain.   This phenomenon is intimately associated with the fact that this second-order system never becomes unstable with increasing gain.   If the fixed elements in this problem had been more realistic, the system would be higher than second order and would become unstable with sufficiently high gain. Under these circumstances the gain corresponding to minimum rms error would be finite. For other examples, the reader is referred to the problems at the end of this book and to Reference J.1.

4.6 NORMALIZATION OF POWER-DENSITY SPECTRA

In solving for the mean-square error as a function of one or more parameters, normalization of frequency and time can frequently simplify our calculations. This is particularly so in complicated problems where it is impractical to keep all constants in literal form. In such problems, most of the constants must be expressed numerically in order to prevent excessively involved coefficients from appearing in the expression for the power-density spectrum of the error. This article discusses the normalization procedure that is useful in dealing with power-density spectra.

A power-density spectrum, it will be recalled, is merely the transform of a corresponding correlation function divided by 2π as indicated in the following equation

$$\Phi(s) = \frac{1}{2\pi} \int_{-\infty}^{\infty} d\tau \; e^{-s\tau} \varphi(\tau) \qquad (4.6\text{--}1)$$

Thus the rules discussed in Art. 2.5 for normalizing transforms in general apply directly to the normalization of power-density spectra. Thus, if we define a normalized time μ as

$$\mu \triangleq \frac{\tau}{\tau_b} \qquad (4.6\text{--}2)$$

and a normalized frequency λ as

$$\lambda \triangleq \tau_b s \qquad (4.6\text{--}3)$$

the rule for forming the normalized power-density spectrum from the non-normalized form is

$$\Phi(\lambda) = \frac{1}{\tau_b} [\Phi(s)] \quad \text{with } s \text{ replaced by } \frac{\lambda}{\tau_b} \qquad (4.6\text{--}4)$$

Here τ_b is the base time unit with respect to which we are normalizing. With the normalized spectrum defined in this manner, it follows that

$$\Phi(\lambda) = \frac{1}{2\pi} \int_{-\infty}^{\infty} d\mu \; e^{-\lambda\mu} \varphi(\mu) \qquad (4.6\text{--}5)$$

where $\varphi(\mu)$ is the correlation function expressed in terms of normalized time. The above relations, of course, are true for both ordinary and cross-power-density spectra. All relationships among power spectra such as those given by Art. 4.2 through 4.4 hold equally well for normalized spectra provided the transfer functions are also normalized as discussed in Art. 2.5.

It should be noted that the mean-square value of a function can be determined from the area beneath its normalized power-density spectrum along the imaginary axis provided the integration is carried out with respect to the normalized frequency variable. This is so because we know that the mean-square value of a time function is related to the non-normalized power-density spectrum by

$$\varphi_{11}(0) = \frac{1}{j} \int_{-j\infty}^{j\infty} ds \; \Phi_{11}(s) \qquad (4.6\text{--}6)$$

This can be written as

$$\varphi_{11}(0) = \frac{1}{j} \int_{-j\infty}^{j\infty} \tau_b \, ds \; \frac{\Phi_{11}(s)}{\tau_b} \qquad (4.6\text{--}7)$$

Hence, in view of the rule for forming the normalized power-density spectrum given by Eq. 4.6–4, we have

$$\varphi_{11}(0) = \frac{1}{j} \int_{-j\infty}^{j\infty} d\lambda \; \Phi_{11}(\lambda) \qquad (4.6\text{--}8)$$

Here the subscripts 11 have been used to indicate that the power spectra involved must be the transforms of autocorrelation functions.

The use of normalization will be illustrated in examples from time to time in the rest of this book. It again should be emphasized that normalization is of particular help when numerical quantities are involved. When a problem can be solved entirely in literal form as in the preceding example, there is relatively little to be gained by normalization.

4.7 USE OF CONSTRAINTS; EXAMPLE

In this article we discuss the use of constraints as a technique for recognizing the physical limitations of the fixed elements of a control system. In Art. 2.6 the usefulness of limiting the integral-square value of certain signals was pointed out. The physical components, which in our linear model are represented by the fixed elements with the transfer function $G_f(s)$, are always limited in the range of signal amplitudes that they can accommodate without invalidating their linearized representation. If in the process of minimizing the integral-square or mean-square error we could always be sure of keeping the signals in the fixed elements within their linear ranges, greater confidence could be placed in a design procedure based upon the principle of minimizing a performance index. As pointed out in Art. 2.7, what we would like to do is to control the peak value of signals within the fixed elements so that by design they stay within their linear ranges. For a transient input signal, however, specification of the peak value of a signal implies a general transient solution for that signal; such a solution cannot be obtained for high-order systems and as a matter of fact is impractical to obtain for any system higher than the second order. This difficulty caused us to make a flank attack on the problem through the control of the integral-square value of a signal likely to cause saturation. For many types of transient input signals we intuitively feel that control of the integral-square value of the signal comes close to controlling the peak value of the signal.

For stochastic input signals, the situation is similar to that for transient signals—no direct control of the peak value of a signal within the fixed elements is possible. This arises both from the impossibility of a general transient solution and the statistical nature of the signals. It frequently happens that there is no limit to the peak value of a signal in the linear model of a system. However, by controlling the rms value of the signal, which in the linear model corresponds to a signal in the physical system that could cause saturation by becoming too large, some degree of control of the probability of saturation can be obtained. For example, if, in the design of a control system through the use of a linear model, the rms value of a signal is restricted to approximately one-third of the saturation value of the analogous signal in the physical system, it is often found that the probability of saturation because of this signal is within satisfactory bounds. Thus, in order to avoid difficulties caused by saturation, we are led quite naturally to the idea of controlling the rms or mean-square values of certain signals in the fixed elements of a control system. Further discussion of the physical basis for this approach is given in Art. 7.1 and 7.2.

The procedure for constraining the rms values of one or more signals while minimizing the mean-square error by adjustment of one or more parameters is entirely analogous to the procedure that was followed in Art. 2.6 for minimizing the integral-square error subject to limitations imposed on the integral-square values of one or more signals. First, express the mean-square error as a function of the free parameters using the techniques outlined in the preceding articles. Next, express the mean-square values of the signals that are to be limited as functions of the same free parameters, using the same techniques as are used for mean-square error.   By setting each of these mean-square values equal to or less than its specified limit, constraints are established on the ranges of the values that the free parameters may take on.   Theoretically, the number of constraints is equal to the number of mean-square-value limits imposed on the signals in the fixed elements.   In practice, it usually turns out that only one or two of the inequalities is controlling and the rest are automatically satisfied.   Because the functions involved are usually fairly complicated, it is ordinarily impossible to eliminate a number of free parameters equal to the number of controlling inequalities and then minimize the mean-square error with respect to the remaining free parameters.   Lagrange's technique as explained in Art. 2.6 may be helpful in overcoming this difficulty. Often the most practical approach is to plot the several functions versus one selected parameter with the other parameters held fixed.   By doing this for a number of fixed values of the other parameters it is possible to find gradually the combination of values of the parameters which minimizes the mean-square error and which satisfies the inequalities.   Obviously, if there are more than two or three free parameters, the process becomes very complex.   Sometimes it is possible to approximate the actual functions with simpler functions which are accurate enough over the range of interest; in this way considerable time may be saved in finding a solution.

To illustrate the general notions described above, consider the example discussed in Art. 4.5.   In this situation it will be recalled that minimizing the mean-square error by adjustment of the gain resulted in a solution calling for a large gain and resulting in a highly oscillatory transient response.   In view of the fact that this is the design of a positional servomechanism, an oscillatory response demands high acceleration of the output member.   In many positional servomechanisms the principal torque supplied to the load is that required to accelerate its inertia.   It is therefore natural to limit the peak acceleration of the load as a means of limiting the torque that must be supplied by the servomotor.   Since it is inconvenient to limit the peak value of the acceleration directly, we shall attempt to limit it indirectly by placing a constraint on the mean-square acceleration.   Let the acceleration of the output member be represented by $q_s(t)$, that is,

$$q_s(t) \triangleq \frac{d^2 q(t)}{dt^2} \tag{4.7–1}$$

We ask that the mean-square acceleration be maintained equal to or less than a constant value $\sigma_{sm}{}^2$. In terms of symbols this constraint is expressed as

$$\overline{q_s{}^2(t)} \leq \sigma_{sm}{}^2 \tag{4.7-2}$$

Representing the autocorrelation function of the signal q_s by $\varphi_{ss}(\tau)$ as shown in Eq. 4.7–3

$$\varphi_{ss}(\tau) \triangleq \overline{q_s(t)q_s(t+\tau)} \tag{4.7-3}$$

we observe the mean-square acceleration to be equal to the value of this correlation function at $\tau = 0$. This mean-square value we shall evaluate by taking the area beneath the power-density spectrum of the acceleration signal along the imaginary axis. Since in the frequency domain the acceleration is related to the output by

$$q_s(s) = s^2 q(s) \tag{4.7-4}$$

it follows that the power-density spectrum of the acceleration is related to that of the ouput by

$$\Phi_{ss}(s) = (-s)^2 s^2 \Phi_{qq}(s) \tag{4.7-5}$$

The output spectrum in turn is related to the spectrum of the input signal as follows

$$\Phi_{qq}(s) = W(-s)W(s)\Phi_{dd}(s) \tag{4.7-6}$$

In order to demonstrate the normalization procedure discussed in the preceding article, let us normalize the transfer functions and spectra. Using the motor time constant τ_m as the base gives as the mean-square value of the acceleration

$$\varphi_{ss}(0) = \frac{1}{j} \int_{-j\infty}^{j\infty} d\lambda\, \Phi_{ss}(\lambda) \tag{4.7-7}$$

As a consequence of Eqs. 4.7–5 and 6 the normalized acceleration spectrum is

$$\Phi_{ss}(\lambda) = \frac{\lambda^4}{\tau_m{}^4} W(-\lambda)W(\lambda)\Phi_{dd}(\lambda) \tag{4.7-8}$$

From Eq. 4.5–8 we note that

$$W(\lambda) = \frac{K}{\lambda^2 + \lambda + K} \tag{4.7-9}$$

Applying the normalization procedure for power-density spectra to Eq. 4.5–10 yields

$$\Phi_{dd}(\lambda) = \frac{\beta^2}{\pi}\left(\frac{N_\nu}{-\lambda^2 + N_\nu{}^2}\right) \tag{4.7-10}$$

Here N_ν and K are defined by Eqs. 4.5–15 and 16, respectively. Substituting the values of the system function and power-density spectrum given by the last two equations into Eq. 4.7–8, we find

$$\Phi_{ss}(\lambda) = \frac{\beta^2}{\pi} \frac{N_\nu K^2}{\tau_m{}^4} \frac{c(-\lambda)c(\lambda)}{d(-\lambda)d(\lambda)} \qquad (4.7\text{–}11)$$

where

$$c(\lambda) = \lambda^2 \qquad (4.7\text{–}12)$$

$$d(\lambda) = \lambda^3 + (N_\nu + 1)\lambda^2 + (N_\nu + K)\lambda + N_\nu K \qquad (4.7\text{–}13)$$

Integrating the expression for the acceleration spectrum given by Eq. 4.7–11 with the aid of the table of integrals given in Appendix E, we obtain for the mean-square value of the acceleration as a function of the single free parameter K the following expression:

$$\varphi_{ss}(0) = \frac{\beta^2 N_\nu K^2}{\tau_m{}^4} \left(\frac{N_\nu + K}{N_\nu{}^2 + N_\nu + K} \right) \qquad (4.7\text{–}14)$$

Let us now examine the nature of the functional relationship implied by Eq. 4.7–14.   For small values of the normalized frequency N_ν of the input signal zero crossings, say less than $\frac{1}{10}$, the bracketed quantity in this equation is approximately unity for all N_ν and all K (the worst error in the approximation which occurs for $K = 0$ and $N_\nu = \frac{1}{10}$ is about 9 percent).   We may, therefore, approximate the mean-square acceleration very simply.   Taking the square root we have for the rms acceleration the following approximate expression

$$[\varphi_{ss}(0)]^{\frac{1}{2}} \cong \frac{\beta}{\tau_m{}^2} K(N_\nu)^{\frac{1}{2}} \quad \text{for } N_\nu < 0.1 \qquad (4.7\text{–}15)$$

Since it was pointed out in Art. 4.5 that the positional servomechanism is practically useless except for small values of N_ν, this approximate expression will serve in all cases of interest.   It states that the rms acceleration is proportional to the normalized gain and proportional to the square root of the normalized frequency of the input signal.   Since the rms acceleration is a continuously increasing function of the gain and the rms error as given in Art. 4.5 is a continuously decreasing function of the gain, all that must be done to find the minimum rms error that is possible in the presence of a prescribed rms acceleration is to solve Eq. 4.7–15 for the gain corresponding to the specified limit σ_{sm} on the rms acceleration and substitute this value of the gain into Eq. 4.5–17.

As a general conclusion we see, by inspection of Fig. 4.5–1 and by reflecting on the implications of Eq. 4.7–15, that there is, indeed, no reason to use normalized gains in excess of unity in view of the heavy penalty paid in terms of the rms acceleration and the small improvement that is possible in the rms error.   Figure 4.5–1 with a change in the horizontal scale can be equally well plotted as a *trading curve* relating rms error to rms output acceleration.   This follows from the fact that the rms acceleration is proportional to the gain.   Thus changing the rms acceleration from infinity to $\beta \sqrt{N_\nu}/\tau_m{}^2$ causes only a 41 percent increase in the rms error.   Specifically, for a motor time constant of 0.01 second, an average frequency of zero crossings of 0.1 per second and an amplitude of input signal of 3.16 radians, we find that a reduction of the rms output acceleration from infinity to 1410 radians per second squared increases the rms error from 0.141 to 0.200 radian.

4.8   CONCLUSION

In this chapter analytical design theory is applied to fixed configuration systems which are subject to stochastic input signals.   The response of a linear system in both the time domain and the frequency domain is formulated.   Correlation functions are used in the time domain to represent the signals within the system.   In the frequency domain, power-density spectra are found to be the most convenient characterizations for the signals.   After the response of a linear system to stochastic inputs is formulated in a general way, we turn to the specific problem of finding the mean-square error.   The procedure for adjusting parameters to minimize the mean-square error is shown.   Normalization of the time and frequency scales is developed as an aid for numerical calculations.   Finally, the use of constraints to account for saturation tendencies within the system is pointed out.

Chapter 2 together with this chapter completes our discussion of parameter adjustments in fixed configuration systems for the purpose of minimizing a performance index.   In the next chapter we consider systems of the opposite extreme, namely, systems whose configurations are completely free.

5 ————————————

MINIMIZATION OF
MEAN-SQUARE ERROR,
FREE CONFIGURATION

5.1 STATEMENT OF PROBLEM

In the preceding chapter we considered the problem of minimizing the mean-square error of a control system whose configuration is specified as part of the problem statement. Under these conditions our freedom in system design is limited to adjusting one or more free parameters so that the mean-square error is minimized. In this chapter we consider the somewhat more complex problem of minimizing the mean-square error of a control system whose configuration is completely free. Under these conditions we not only have to choose the parameters but even before they can be chosen we have to determine the configuration that offers the possibility of minimum mean-square error when the parameters are properly adjusted. Obviously we enjoy considerably more freedom in our design under these conditions than under those that prevailed in Chapter 4.

We shall consider first the design problem illustrated in Fig. 5.1–1. Here we have a control system with a stochastic input $v(t)$ which produces an output $q(t)$. As discussed in Chapter 1, we represent this control system by a single over-all weighting function $w(t)$ [or its transform $W(s)$]. In Chapter 1 it was shown that the control system could be reduced to this form even though it actually comprises a number of cascaded elements with one or more feedback paths. Also in Chapter

1, it is shown that disturbances can be considered as merely modifying the input and output signals provided the feedback elements are fixed. In other words the representation of the control system by a single weighting function $w(t)$ is ordinarily possible even though disturbances (multiple inputs) exist in the actual system. As shown in Fig. 5.1–1, the error is the difference between the ideal output $i(t)$ and the actual output $q(t)$. Our objective is to minimize the mean-square value of this error by suitable adjustment of the weighting function $w(t)$. The weighting function that minimizes the mean-square error is a function

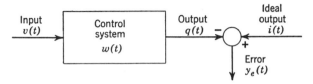

Fig. 5.1–1.   Control system, free configuration.

of the input and the ideal output. As shown in the next article, specification of the input $v(t)$ and the ideal output $i(t)$ makes possible a solution for $w(t)$ that minimizes the mean-square error. As will be seen, $w(t)$ is found in terms of the autocorrelation function of the input and the cross-correlation function between the input and the ideal output.

5.2   AN INTEGRAL EQUATION FOR THE WEIGHTING FUNCTION

This article presents a solution for $w(t)$ in the form of an integral equation. The steps followed in deriving this integral equation are as follows. First the square of the error is expressed in terms of the weighting function, the input, and the ideal output. Next, the expression for the error squared is averaged and in so doing auto- and cross-correlation functions are introduced. At this point we have an expression for the mean-square error in terms of the weighting function $w(t)$, the input autocorrelation function $\varphi_{vv}(\tau)$, the input-ideal-output cross-correlation function $\varphi_{vi}(\tau)$, and the ideal-output autocorrelation function $\varphi_{ii}(\tau)$. Thus we have the mean-square error expressed as a functional of $w(t)$. By employing a standard variational procedure the condition for this functional to be a minimum is developed into an integral equation for the solution $w_m(t)$, i.e., the weighting function that minimizes the mean-square error.

Let us now go through the steps, indicated above, in detail. Referring to Fig. 5.1–1, the error is by definition

$$y_e(t) \triangleq i(t) - q(t) \qquad (5.2\text{--}1)$$

Squaring both sides yields

$$y_e^2(t) = i^2(t) - 2q(t)i(t) + q^2(t) \qquad (5.2\text{-}2)$$

We now relate the output $q(t)$ and the weighting function $w(t)$ by means of the convolution integral

$$q(t) = \int_{-\infty}^{\infty} dt_1\, w(t_1)v(t - t_1) \qquad (5.2\text{-}3)$$

The square of the output is expressed as

$$q^2(t) = \left[\int_{-\infty}^{\infty} dt_1\, w(t_1)v(t - t_1) \right]\left[\int_{-\infty}^{\infty} dt_2\, w(t_2)v(t - t_2) \right] \qquad (5.2\text{-}4)$$

In this equation separate integration variables t_1 and t_2 are used in order to avoid confusion in later manipulations. By substituting the value of $q(t)$ given by Eq. 5.2–3 and the value of $q^2(t)$ given by Eq. 5.2–4 into Eq. 5.2–2 we obtain

$$y_e^2(t) = i^2(t) - 2\left[\int_{-\infty}^{\infty} dt_1\, w(t_1)v(t - t_1) \right] i(t)$$
$$+ \left[\int_{-\infty}^{\infty} dt_1\, w(t_1)v(t - t_1) \right]\left[\int_{-\infty}^{\infty} dt_2\, w(t_2)v(t - t_2) \right] \qquad (5.2\text{-}5)$$

This equation gives us the square of the error in terms of the weighting function, input, and ideal output.

The next step is to average the square of the error. By definition the mean-square error is

$$\overline{y_e^2(t)} \triangleq \lim_{T \to \infty} \frac{1}{2T} \int_{-T}^{T} dt\, y_e^2(t) \qquad (5.2\text{-}6)$$

Using the value of the square of the error given by Eq. 5.2–5 in this expression yields

$$\overline{y_e^2(t)} = \overline{i^2(t)} - 2 \lim_{T \to \infty} \frac{1}{2T} \int_{-T}^{T} dt \int_{-\infty}^{\infty} dt_1\, w(t_1)v(t - t_1)i(t)$$
$$+ \lim_{T \to \infty} \frac{1}{2T} \int_{-T}^{T} dt \int_{-\infty}^{\infty} dt_1\, w(t_1)v(t - t_1)$$
$$\int_{-\infty}^{\infty} dt_2\, w(t_2)v(t - t_2) \qquad (5.2\text{-}7)$$

Recall the definition of the input autocorrelation function

$$\varphi_{vv}(\tau) \triangleq \lim_{T \to \infty} \frac{1}{2T} \int_{-T}^{T} dt\, v(t)v(t + \tau) \qquad (5.2\text{-}8)$$

Similarly the cross-correlation function between the input and the ideal output is

$$\varphi_{vi}(\tau) \triangleq \lim_{T \to \infty} \frac{1}{2T} \int_{-T}^{T} dt\, v(t)i(t + \tau) \qquad (5.2\text{–}9)$$

and the autocorrelation function of the ideal output is

$$\varphi_{ii}(\tau) \triangleq \lim_{T \to \infty} \frac{1}{2T} \int_{-T}^{T} dt\, i(t)i(t + \tau) \qquad (5.2\text{–}10)$$

In the right member of Eq. 5.2–7, let us now interchange the order of integration so that we integrate with respect to t and take the limit as T approaches infinity before we integrate with respect to t_1 and t_2. Doing this and recognizing the correlation functions given by Eqs. 5.2–8 through 10 permit us to write for the mean-square error

$$\overline{y_e^2(t)} = \varphi_{ii}(0) - 2 \int_{-\infty}^{\infty} dt_1\, w(t_1)\varphi_{vi}(t_1)$$
$$+ \int_{-\infty}^{\infty} dt_1\, w(t_1) \int_{-\infty}^{\infty} dt_2\, w(t_2)\varphi_{vv}(t_1 - t_2) \quad (5.2\text{–}11)$$

This equation gives the mean-square error as a functional of the weighting function $w(t)$.

We now wish to determine the system function that minimizes the mean-square error. To do this we shall assume that a solution does exist, and we denote this assumed solution as $w_m(t)$. We next construct a weighting function in accordance with

$$w(t) = w_m(t) + \epsilon w_\epsilon(t) \qquad (5.2\text{–}12)$$

Here $w_m(t)$ is the assumed solution and $w_\epsilon(t)$ is any arbitrary realizable weighting function. ϵ is a parameter which we may vary to test whether $w_m(t)$ is the solution. If $w_m(t)$ is the solution, then any variation of ϵ from zero value for any $w_\epsilon(t)$ that we choose must produce an increase in the mean-square error. In the calculus of variations $\epsilon w_\epsilon(t)$ is referred to as the variation of $w(t)$. Substitution of our specially constructed $w(t)$ into the right member of Eq. 5.2–11 makes the mean-square error a function of the parameter ϵ. In view of the manner in which we have constructed $w(t)$, the mean-square error must be stationary for variations of ϵ about zero. That is, at ϵ equal to zero the derivative of the mean-square error with respect to ϵ must be equal to zero. By setting this derivative equal to zero for ϵ equal to zero, we arrive at a condition for $w_m(t)$ which must be satisfied in order for it to be the solution.

Substituting $w(t)$ given by Eq. 5.2–12 into the right member of Eq. 5.2–11 and differentiating with respect to ϵ yield

$$\frac{d\overline{[y_e^2(t)]}}{d\epsilon} = -2 \int_{-\infty}^{\infty} dt_1 \, w_e(t_1) \varphi_{vi}(t_1)$$

$$+ \int_{-\infty}^{\infty} dt_1 \, w_m(t_1) \int_{-\infty}^{\infty} dt_2 \, w_e(t_2) \varphi_{vv}(t_1 - t_2)$$

$$+ \int_{-\infty}^{\infty} dt_1 \, w_e(t_1) \int_{-\infty}^{\infty} dt_2 \, w_m(t_2) \varphi_{vv}(t_1 - t_2)$$

$$+ 2\epsilon \int_{-\infty}^{\infty} dt_1 \, w_e(t_1) \int_{-\infty}^{\infty} dt_2 \, w_e(t_2) \varphi_{vv}(t_1 - t_2) \quad (5.2\text{–}13)$$

Because of the even property of autocorrelation functions of stationary signals, we know that

$$\varphi_{vv}(t_2 - t_1) = \varphi_{vv}(t_1 - t_2) \quad (5.2\text{–}14)$$

This means that

$$\int_{-\infty}^{\infty} dt_1 \, w_m(t_1) \int_{-\infty}^{\infty} dt_2 \, w_e(t_2) \varphi_{vv}(t_1 - t_2)$$

$$= \int_{-\infty}^{\infty} dt_1 \, w_e(t_1) \int_{-\infty}^{\infty} dt_2 \, w_m(t_2) \varphi_{vv}(t_1 - t_2) \quad (5.2\text{–}15)$$

since we can interchange the order of integration and the labeling of the integration variables of the left member with the result that the only difference between the two sides will be in the sign of the autocorrelation variable. Setting

$$\frac{d\overline{[y_e^2(t)]}}{d\epsilon} = 0 \quad \text{at } \epsilon = 0 \quad (5.2\text{–}16)$$

and using Eq. 5.2–15 in Eq. 5.2–13 yield

$$2 \int_{-\infty}^{\infty} dt_1 \, w_e(t_1) \left[\int_{-\infty}^{\infty} dt_2 \, w_m(t_2) \varphi_{vv}(t_1 - t_2) - \varphi_{vi}(t_1) \right] = 0 \quad (5.2\text{–}17)$$

Now $w_e(t)$ is a realizable weighting function but other than that perfectly arbitrary. Since $w_e(t)$ is a realizable weighting function, it must be zero for values of t less than zero. In view of these facts, the only way in which Eq. 5.2–17 can be satisfied for values of t_1 equal to or greater than zero is for the factor in brackets to be equal to zero. Thus we are led to the condition

$$\int_{-\infty}^{\infty} dt_2 \, w_m(t_2) \varphi_{vv}(t_1 - t_2) - \varphi_{vi}(t_1) = 0 \quad \text{for } t_1 \geq 0 \quad (5.2\text{–}18)$$

The system weighting function that minimizes the mean-square error must satisfy this condition.

Strictly speaking, the $w_m(t)$ that satisfies Eq. 5.2–18 merely produces a stationary value of the mean-square error and does not necessarily ensure a minimum. Physically we know that, if a solution exists at all, it must be that of a minimum since we can easily construct weighting functions that will produce unlimited mean-square error. However, for the sake of completeness we can show that the solution obtained from Eq. 5.2–18 does yield a minimum by considering the second derivative of the mean-square error with respect to ϵ. Differentiating both sides of Eq. 5.2–13 yields

$$\frac{d^2[\overline{y_e{}^2(t)}]}{d\epsilon^2} = 2 \int_{-\infty}^{\infty} dt_1 \, w_\epsilon(t_1) \int_{-\infty}^{\infty} dt_2 \, w_\epsilon(t_2) \varphi_{vv}(t_1 - t_2) \quad (5.2\text{–}19)$$

A physical interpretation of this result is given in Fig. 5.2–1. The second derivative of the mean-square error is simply two times the mean-square value of the filtered input function obtained by passing the input through a system having the weighting function $w_\epsilon(t)$. Since this mean-square signal can never be negative, we have shown that the second derivative of the mean-square system error is always positive. Thus we have shown that the solution from Eq. 5.2–18 corresponds to a minimum.

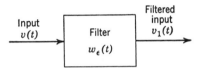

Fig. 5.2–1. Physical interpretation of Eq. 5.2–19.

The solution that we have obtained for $w_m(t)$ is an implicit one in the form of an integral equation. This integral equation is known as the Wiener-Hopf equation. (See Reference W.3.) The original equation discussed by Wiener was in a somewhat less general form. Unfortunately, integral equations are usually somewhat difficult to solve. In the next article we give an example of a solution obtained directly from the integral equation. Later we shall give an explicit solution of the integral equation useful when the correlation functions are transformable.

5.3 EXAMPLE OF SOLUTION OBTAINED FROM INTEGRAL EQUATION

As an example of a solution for a weighting function obtained directly from the integral equation (5.2–18), let us consider a particular problem of prediction. In this problem the input is noise free so that the ideal output is identical in form with the input, but it is advanced in time by a constant amount. Specifically, the problem statement is as follows.

Given. The input $v(t)$ is a rectangular wave with excursion plus or minus a constant value β and with zero crossings Poisson distributed with average frequency ν.

The ideal output $i(t)$ is a wave of the same form as the input except that it leads the input by a constant amount α.

$$i(t) = v(t + \alpha) \qquad (5.3\text{--}1)$$

A negative α corresponds to the ideal output lagging the input. Figure 5.3–1 illustrates the relationship between the input and the ideal output.

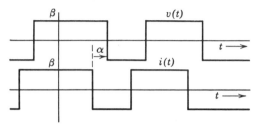

Fig. 5.3–1.   Input and ideal output.

Find.   The system weighting function that produces minimum mean-square error.

Solution.   In order to solve this problem we first make a physical interpretation of the integral equation form of solution given by Eq. 5.2–18.   We may rewrite this equation as

$$\int_{-\infty}^{\infty} dt_1 \, w_m(t_1)\varphi_{vv}(\tau - t_1) = \varphi_{vi}(\tau) \quad \text{for } \tau \geq 0 \qquad (5.3\text{--}2)$$

The left member of this equation is the convolution of the input autocorrelation function with the system weighting function.   Therefore, we may interpret the solving of the integral equation as the finding of a

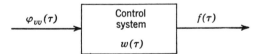

Fig. 5.3–2.   Interpretation of integral equation. $w_m(\tau)$ is $w(\tau)$ which makes $f(\tau) = \varphi_{vi}(\tau)$ for $\tau \geq 0$.

system weighting function that by operating upon the input auto-correlation function produces a function $f(\tau)$ which is equal to the input ideal-output cross-correlation function $\varphi_{vi}(\tau)$ for τ equal to or greater than zero.   For τ less than zero $f(\tau)$ may have any value.   Figure 5.3–2 illustrates this physical interpretation.   In other words, the solving of the integral equation is equivalent to the testing of each individual weighting function in the infinite set of all possible realizable weighting functions in order to select that particular one that produces an $f(\tau)$ equal to the input-ideal-output cross-correlation function for τ equal to or greater than zero. This interpretation of the integral equation is quite general; the particular problem at hand represents an opportunity to apply it.

In order to apply our physical interpretation of the integral equation to the problem under consideration, we must have the input autocorrelation function $\varphi_{vv}(\tau)$ and the cross-correlation function between the input and the ideal output $\varphi_{vi}(\tau)$. The input autocorrelation function is given by

$$\varphi_{vv}(\tau) = \beta^2 e^{-2\nu|\tau|} \tag{5.3-3}$$

This result is derived in Art. 3.6. The definition of the cross-correlation function is repeated as

$$\varphi_{vi}(\tau) \triangleq \lim_{T\to\infty} \frac{1}{2T} \int_{-T}^{T} dt\, v(t)i(t+\tau) \tag{5.2-9}$$

Substituting the value of the ideal output $i(t)$ given by Eq. 5.3–1 into this equation yields

$$\varphi_{vi}(\tau) = \lim_{T\to\infty} \frac{1}{2T} \int_{-T}^{T} dt\, v(t)v(t+\alpha+\tau) \tag{5.3-4}$$

Thus we see that

$$\varphi_{vi}(\tau) = \varphi_{vv}(\tau+\alpha) \tag{5.3-5}$$

The cross-correlation function is identical with the autocorrelation function except for a time advance of α. For the problem at hand, the expression for the cross-correlation function is

$$\varphi_{vi}(\tau) = \beta^2 e^{-2\nu|\tau+\alpha|} \tag{5.3-6}$$

Figure 5.3–3 illustrates the input autocorrelation function and the cross-correlation function between the input and the ideal output.

Let us now consider the case of α positive. As shown in Fig. 5.3–3 the cross-correlation function over the positive time range is an exact replica of the autocorrelation function except for an attenuation factor $e^{-2\nu\alpha}$. If the weighting function were a unit impulse, $f(\tau)$ would be equal to the autocorrelation function. Thus the solution to the integral equation for this case is simply a unit impulse multiplied by an attenuation factor. Analytically we may express the weighting function as

$$w_m(\tau) = e^{-2\nu\alpha}\delta(\tau) \quad \text{for } \alpha \geq 0 \tag{5.3-7}$$

Let us next consider the case of α negative. Here the cross-correlation function lags the autocorrelation function but is of precisely the same form.   If the weighting function is a unit impulse delayed by the lag of the cross-correlation function with respect to the autocorrelation function, then $f(\tau)$ will obviously equal the cross-correlation function for positive time.   Thus

$$w_m(\tau) = \delta(\tau + \alpha) \quad \text{for } \alpha < 0 \qquad (5.3\text{–}8)$$

A word of explanation of the result that we have obtained for the prediction case may be in order.   The input function used in this problem is essentially unpredictable.   Knowing where one zero crossing is does not allow one to know where any other zero crossing will be. In this situation the system that minimizes the mean-square error does not try to predict the future by analyzing the past; it merely says that

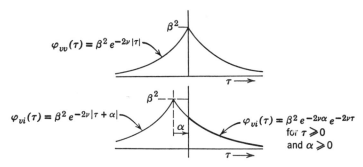

Fig. 5.3–3. Input autocorrelation and input-ideal-output cross-correlation functions.

the immediate future is likely to be much like the present whereas the distant future is likely to be little related to the present.   This situation bears a strong resemblance to the problem of weather forecasting in certain regions of the world such as Boston.

In conclusion, this example is one of the rare situations in which the solution of the integral equation is self-evident.   In most problems the solution of the integral equation will not be so easily obtained.   The next article discusses a formal procedure for solving integral equations of the Wiener-Hopf type through the use of the Fourier transforms. This procedure is applicable to many practical problems provided approximations are used to produce analytic functions for the transforms.   Sometimes, however, it is desirable to stay in the time domain and solve the integral equation directly as was done in this example. In this event, numerical procedures are usually employed to solve the integral equation approximately.

5.4 AN EXPLICIT SOLUTION FORMULA FOR THE WEIGHTING FUNCTION

In this article an explicit solution for the Wiener-Hopf type of integral equation is derived. The general form of this integral equation is:

$$\int_{-\infty}^{\infty} dt_1\, \psi(t_1)\Delta(\tau - t_1) - \Gamma(\tau) = 0 \quad \text{for } \tau \geq 0 \qquad (5.4\text{--}1)$$

A specific example of an integral equation of this type is Eq. 5.2–18, the solution of which yields the system weighting function that minimizes the mean-square error when the system configuration is completely free. $\psi(t)$ in Eq. 5.4–1 corresponds to the system weighting function $w_m(t)$ in Eq. 5.2–18. Likewise, $\Delta(\tau)$ and $\Gamma(\tau)$ in Eq. 5.4–1 correspond to the autocorrelation function $\varphi_{vv}(t)$ and the cross-correlation function $\varphi_{vi}(t)$, respectively. In subsequent portions of this book we shall meet integral equations involving more complex quantities than simple auto- and cross-correlation functions. For this reason less specific notation is introduced in Eq. 5.4–1 than was used in Eq. 5.2–18. The formula for the Fourier transform of $\psi(t)$ which is derived in this article represents an explicit solution generally applicable to all integral equations of the Wiener-Hopf type.

Before proceeding with the detailed solution of Eq. 5.4–1, a few remarks on the method to be followed in the solution are in order. If the left side of Eq. 5.4–1 were equal to zero for all values of τ, we should have an equation known as an "integral equation of the first kind" which could be solved by means of Fourier transforms provided the functions ψ, Δ, and Γ possess Fourier transforms. However, Eq. 5.4–1 cannot be handled so easily since the left side is equal to zero only for τ equal to or greater than zero. Fourier transformation of the left side yields a function of frequency that is not equal to zero as would be true of an integral equation of the first kind. In order to avoid this complication, it is desirable to convert an integral equation from the Wiener-Hopf form to the form of one of the first kind by performing some preliminary operations in the time domain before making the Fourier transformation. In the derivation that follows we first perform the necessary preliminary time domain operations on the Wiener-Hopf equation. Next we recall certain facts relating to the Fourier transform and its inverse. Finally, we transform the modified Wiener-Hopf equation to obtain an explicit solution formula.

As the first step in the time domain operations, we represent $\Delta(\tau)$ as the convolution of a pair of functions designated as $\Delta^-(\tau)$ and $\Delta^+(\tau)$. $\Delta^+(\tau)$ is defined to be zero for τ less than zero, and can have non-zero values only for τ equal to or greater than zero. Similarly, $\Delta^-(\tau)$ is defined to be zero for τ greater than zero so that it can have non-zero values only for τ equal to or less than zero. Thus, we have in equation form

$$\int_{-\infty}^{\infty} dt_2\, \Delta^-(t_2)\Delta^+(\tau - t_2) \triangleq \Delta(\tau) \tag{5.4-2}$$

$$\Delta^+(\tau) \triangleq 0 \quad \text{for } \tau < 0 \tag{5.4-3}$$

$$\Delta^-(\tau) \triangleq 0 \quad \text{for } \tau > 0 \tag{5.4-4}$$

One can think of Eq. 5.4–2 as representing a physical system in which a weighting function $\Delta^+(\tau)$ operates upon an input function $\Delta^-(\tau)$ to produce a response function $\Delta(\tau)$. In view of the definitions of $\Delta^+(\tau)$ and $\Delta^-(\tau)$, it is evident that $\Delta(\tau)$ in Eq. 5.4–2 may have non-zero values for both negative and positive τ. $\Delta(\tau)$ will generally be an even function since the integral equation (5.4–1) results from minimizing functionals analogous to the mean-square error given by Eq. 5.2–11. To obtain integral equations of the Wiener-Hopf type from the minimization of functionals like that given in Eq. 5.2–11, it is essential that $\Delta(\tau)$ be an even function. As will be shown later, the process of obtaining the auxiliary functions $\Delta^+(\tau)$ and $\Delta^-(\tau)$ from the given function $\Delta(\tau)$ involves factoring the transform of $\Delta(\tau)$. For this reason the process of solving a Wiener-Hopf type of integral equation is often referred to as "spectrum factorization." This ingenious technique for handling the Wiener-Hopf equation was devised by Wiener.

By a treatment similar to that for $\Delta(\tau)$, we represent $\Gamma(\tau)$ as the convolution of two auxiliary functions $\Delta^-(\tau)$ and $\gamma(\tau)$. Thus

$$\int_{-\infty}^{\infty} dt_2\, \Delta^-(t_2)\gamma(\tau - t_2) = \Gamma(\tau) \tag{5.4-5}$$

It should be carefully noted that $\gamma(\tau)$ unlike $\Delta^+(\tau)$ may have non-zero values over the complete range of τ.

In terms of the above-defined auxiliary functions, we can now write Eq. 5.4-1 by substituting the left side of Eq. 5.4–2 for $\Delta(\tau)$ and the left side of Eq. 5.4-5 for $\Gamma(\tau)$. Doing this yields

$$\int_{-\infty}^{\infty} dt_1\, \psi(t_1) \int_{-\infty}^{\infty} dt_2\, \Delta^-(t_2)\Delta^+(\tau - t_1 - t_2)$$
$$- \int_{-\infty}^{\infty} dt_2\, \Delta^-(t_2)\gamma(\tau - t_2) = 0 \quad \text{for } \tau \geq 0 \tag{5.4-6}$$

Interchanging the orders of integration, so that we integrate with respect to t_2 last, allows us to write Eq. 5.4–6 in the form

$$\int_{-\infty}^{\infty} dt_2\, \Delta^-(t_2) \left[\int_{-\infty}^{\infty} dt_1\, \psi(t_1)\Delta^+(\tau - t_1 - t_2) - \gamma(\tau - t_2) \right]$$
$$= 0 \quad \text{for } \tau \geq 0 \quad (5.4\text{--}7)$$

Since $\Delta^-(t_2)$ is in general non-zero for t_2 equal to or less than zero, the bracketed terms in Eq. 5.4–7 must be equal to zero when τ is equal to or greater than zero and t_2 is equal to or less than zero. That is,

$$\int_{-\infty}^{\infty} dt_1\, \psi(t_1)\Delta^+(\tau - t_1 - t_2) - \gamma(\tau - t_2)$$
$$= 0 \quad \text{for } \tau \geq 0 \text{ and } t_2 \leq 0 \quad (5.4\text{--}8)$$

Since this equality holds for

$$\tau - t_2 \geq 0 \qquad (5.4\text{--}9)$$

we may replace $\tau - t_2$ by t and write

$$\int_{-\infty}^{\infty} dt_1\, \psi(t_1)\Delta^+(t - t_1) - \gamma(t) = 0 \quad \text{for } t \geq 0 \quad (5.4\text{--}10)$$

In form, this equation appears to be identical with the original Wiener-Hopf equation given by Eq. 5.4–1. However, the first term on the left side of Eq. 5.4–10 is equal to zero for t less than zero since $\Delta^+(t)$ by definition is equal to zero for negative time and $\psi(t)$, which must represent a realizable weighting function, is also equal to zero for negative time. Thus, whereas the left side of Eq. 5.4–1 could differ from zero for τ less than zero by virtue of both terms, the left side of Eq. 5.4–10 can differ from zero for negative time only on account of the second term $\gamma(t)$. We now resolve $\gamma(t)$ into two components $\gamma_+(t)$ and $\gamma_-(t)$ which added together equal $\gamma(t)$ and are defined so that $\gamma_+(t)$ is zero for negative time and $\gamma_-(t)$ is zero for positive time. Symbolically, we have

$$\gamma_+(t) + \gamma_-(t) \triangleq \gamma(t) \qquad (5.4\text{--}11)$$

$$\gamma_+(t) \triangleq 0 \quad \text{for } t < 0 \qquad (5.4\text{--}12)$$

$$\gamma_-(t) \triangleq 0 \quad \text{for } t > 0 \qquad (5.4\text{--}13)$$

Since the left side of Eq. 5.4–10 is non-zero for negative time only on account of $\gamma_-(t)$, we can write

$$\int_{-\infty}^{\infty} dt_1\, \psi(t_1)\Delta^+(t - t_1) - \gamma_+(t) = 0 \quad \text{for all values of } t \quad (5.4\text{--}14)$$

As noted, this equation holds for the complete time range and is therefore an ordinary integral equation of the first kind. We have thus accomplished our objective of modifying the Wiener-Hopf equation so as to make it solvable in the frequency domain.

Before proceeding with the derivation, let us recall a few facts concerning the direct and inverse Fourier transforms. The definition of the direct Fourier transform is:

$$F(s) \triangleq \int_{-\infty}^{\infty} dt \, e^{-st} f(t) \qquad (5.4\text{--}15)$$

Corresponding to this definition, the inverse transform is given by:

$$f(t) = \frac{1}{2\pi j} \int_{-j\infty}^{+j\infty} ds \, e^{st} F(s) \qquad (5.4\text{--}16)$$

The direct transform of a time function which is zero for negative time will have all its poles in the left half-plane (LHP). On the other hand, a time function which is zero for positive time will have a Fourier transform with poles confined to the right half-plane (RHP). A time function that is non-zero for all values of time will transform to a function having poles on both sides of the imaginary axis. These facts concerning the Fourier transform are readily appreciated through consideration of the contour integration method of evaluating the inverse transform. For more information on this matter, see Appendix A of this book. With regard to notation, a departure from the usual custom of using lower-case letters to denote time functions and upper-case letters to denote transforms of time functions will occasionally be necessary. In any event, the argument of the function or the context will always make clear which meaning a particular symbol carries.

We now proceed with the solution of Eq. 5.4–14. Transforming both sides of this equation yields

$$\Psi(s)\Delta^{+}(s) - \gamma_{+}(s) = 0 \qquad (5.4\text{--}17)$$

From this equation we obtain

$$\Psi(s) = \frac{\gamma_{+}(s)}{\Delta^{+}(s)} \qquad (5.4\text{--}18)$$

as an explicit solution for the transform $\Psi(s)$ of the weighting function $\psi(t)$ given by Eq. 5.4–14 and therefore as an explicit solution of Eq. 5.4–1. However, it is necessary for us to show how to obtain $\gamma_{+}(s)$ and $\Delta^{+}(s)$ before this solution can be put to practical use.

Transforming both sides of Eq. 5.4–2 yields

$$\Delta^{-}(s)\Delta^{+}(s) = \Delta(s) \qquad (5.4\text{--}19)$$

In view of Eq. 5.4–3 which defines $\Delta^{+}(\tau)$ as zero for τ less than zero, we know that $\Delta^{+}(s)$ must possess all the poles of $\Delta(s)$ that lie in the left half-plane and none of those that lie in the right half-plane. Because

$\Delta^+(s)$ occurs in the denominator of the right side of Eq. 5.4–18, we know that it can contain no zeros in the right half-plane since $\Psi(s)$ corresponds to a physically realizable system function. Thus we may define $\Delta^+(s)$ as follows:

$$\Delta^+(s) \triangleq \text{any factor of } \Delta(s) \text{ which includes all the poles and} \atop \text{zeros of } \Delta(s) \text{ in the LHP} \qquad (5.4\text{–}20)$$

From this definition and from Eq. 5.4–19, we see that $\Delta^-(s)$ may be defined as

$$\Delta^-(s) \triangleq \frac{\Delta(s)}{\Delta^+(s)} \qquad (5.4\text{–}21)$$

and therefore includes all the poles and zeros of $\Delta(s)$ in the RHP. We have chosen to define $\Delta^+(s)$ and $\Delta^-(s)$ by Eqs. 5.4–20 and 21, respectively, rather than by transformation of $\Delta^+(t)$ and $\Delta^-(t)$ as given by Eqs. 5.4–2, 3, and 4. The transformation definitions are obviously consistent with the time function definitions. We have chosen to define the transforms this way in order to expedite the solution of practical problems. Once the integral equation has been solved in the frequency domain, we wish to avoid going back to the time domain in order to establish the appropriate frequency functions, as would be necessary if we merely defined $\Delta^+(s)$ as the transform of $\Delta^+(t)$, etc.

We now show that $\gamma_+(s)$ can be rather simply expressed in terms of $\gamma(s)$ and $\Delta^-(s)$. Transformation of Eq. 5.4–5 yields

$$\Delta^-(s)\gamma(s) = \Gamma(s) \qquad (5.4\text{–}22)$$

Thus, we have $\gamma(s)$ given by

$$\gamma(s) = \frac{\Gamma(s)}{\Delta^-(s)} \qquad (5.4\text{–}23)$$

and symbolically $\gamma_+(s)$ given by

$$\gamma_+(s) = \left[\frac{\Gamma(s)}{\Delta^-(s)}\right]_+ \qquad (5.4\text{–}24)$$

The meaning to be attached to the symbol appearing on the right side of Eq. 5.4–24 is clear when we consider the defining equations for $\gamma_+(t)$ and $\gamma_-(t)$ given by Eqs. 5.4–11, 12, and 13. Since $\gamma_+(t)$ is zero for t less than zero, we know that its transform can possess poles in the left half-plane only. Likewise, $\gamma_-(s)$ must possess poles in the right half-plane only. Furthermore, since $\gamma_+(s)$ added to $\gamma_-(s)$ must equal $\gamma(s)$ as indicated by the transformation of Eq. 5.4–11, we know that $\gamma_+(s)$ must possess all the poles of $\gamma(s)$ that lie in the left half-plane. We may therefore define the right side of Eq. 5.4–24 as

$$\left[\frac{\Gamma(s)}{\Delta^-(s)}\right]_+ \triangleq \text{component of } \frac{\Gamma(s)}{\Delta^-(s)} \text{ which has all its poles in}$$

the LHP and such that   (5.4–25)

$$\frac{\Gamma(s)}{\Delta^-(s)} - \left[\frac{\Gamma(s)}{\Delta^-(s)}\right]_+ \text{ has all its poles in the RHP}$$

If $\Gamma(s)$ divided by $\Delta^-(s)$ is a rational function, the procedure for obtaining

$$\left[\frac{\Gamma(s)}{\Delta^-(s)}\right]_+$$

is quite clear from this definition. All that we must do is to expand $\Gamma(s)$ over $\Delta^-(s)$ in partial fractions and throw away all the terms corresponding to poles in the right half-plane. In the event that $\Gamma(s)$ over $\Delta^-(s)$ is not rational, we may use the equation

$$\left[\frac{\Gamma(s)}{\Delta^-(s)}\right]_+ = \int_0^\infty dt \, e^{-st} \gamma(t) \qquad (5.4\text{–}26)$$

where

$$\gamma(t) = \frac{1}{2\pi j} \int_{-j\infty}^{+j\infty} ds_1 \, e^{s_1 t} \frac{\Gamma(s_1)}{\Delta^-(s_1)} \qquad (5.4\text{–}27)$$

This equation corresponds to taking the inverse Fourier transform of $\Gamma(s)$ over $\Delta^-(s)$ to obtain the time function $\gamma(t)$, which in general has non-zero values for both positive and negative time. By means of the Laplace transform of Eq. 5.4–26, we obtain the Fourier transform of the time function which is identical with $\gamma(t)$ for t positive and zero for t negative. This is the transform $\gamma_+(s)$ which is the same as

$$\left[\frac{\Gamma(s)}{\Delta^-(s)}\right]_+$$

In terms of the preceding definitions, we may re-express the explicit solution formula of Eq. 5.4–18 as

$$\Psi(s) = \frac{\left[\dfrac{\Gamma(s)}{\Delta^-(s)}\right]_+}{\Delta^+(s)} \qquad (5.4\text{–}28)$$

This is the explicit solution formula for the Wiener-Hopf integral equation given by Eq. 5.4–1. In the following portions of this book we shall feel free to use this explicit solution formula for any integral equation of the Wiener-Hopf type provided the functions $\Delta(\tau)$ and $\Gamma(\tau)$ are Fourier transformable. We may not always use the explicit solution formula even if the Δ and Γ functions are transformable since the functions may be so complex as to make an approximate solution in the time domain a simpler approach.

5.5 EXAMPLES ILLUSTRATING USE OF SOLUTION FORMULA

In this article we shall illustrate the use of the explicit solution formula for the Wiener-Hopf equation which was derived in the preceding section. To do this the solution formula will be used to solve the same problem that was handled in Art. 5.3 through time domain considerations. The reader will recall that this problem is to find the system weighting function (or its transform) that produces minimum mean-square error when the input is a rectangular wave with excursion plus or minus a constant value β and with zero crossings Poisson distributed with average frequency ν. The ideal output is a wave of the same form as the input but advanced in time by a constant amount α. Of course, α may be negative, in which event the ideal output would be lagging the input.

As the first step in solving this problem, we identify the general symbols used in Eq. 5.4–1 with the specific functions used in the problem description. Thus,

$$\psi(t) = w_m(t) \tag{5.5-1}$$

$$\Delta(\tau) = \varphi_{vv}(\tau) \tag{5.5-2}$$

$$\Gamma(\tau) = \varphi_{vi}(\tau) \tag{5.5-3}$$

Since the power-density spectrum of any signal is $1/2\pi$ times the Fourier transform of the autocorrelation function of the signal, it follows that

$$\Delta(s) = 2\pi\Phi_{vv}(s) \tag{5.5-4}$$

where

$\Phi_{vv}(s) \triangleq$ the power-density spectrum of the input signal $\qquad$ (5.5–5)

Similarly, a cross-power density spectrum may be defined as $1/2\pi$ times the Fourier transform of a cross-correlation function. Thus

$$\Gamma(s) \triangleq 2\pi\Phi_{vi}(s) \tag{5.5-6}$$

where

$\Phi_{vi}(s) \triangleq$ the cross-power density spectrum of the input and
ideal output signals   (5.5–7)

By transforming the autocorrelation function given by Eq. 5.3–3 and
the cross-correlation function given by Eq. 5.3–6, we find

$$\Phi_{vv}(s) = \frac{\beta^2}{\pi} \frac{2\nu}{-s^2 + 4\nu^2} \tag{5.5–8}$$

$$\Phi_{vi}(s) = \frac{\beta^2}{\pi} \frac{2\nu e^{\alpha s}}{-s^2 + 4\nu^2} \tag{5.5–9}$$

Thus we have

$$\Delta(s) = \beta^2 \frac{4\nu}{-s^2 + 4\nu^2} \tag{5.5–10}$$

$$\Gamma(s) = \beta^2 \frac{4\nu e^{\alpha s}}{-s^2 + 4\nu^2} \tag{5.5–11}$$

The next step in solving this problem is to factor $\Delta(s)$. Since this factorization is unique only within a constant, we may associate any constant we please with $\Delta^+(s)$. It is easily seen that the choice of this constant in no way affects the solution for the system function. It is usually convenient to make $\Delta^+(s)$ as simple in form as possible. Identifying $\Delta^+(s)$ with the factor of $\Delta(s)$ that has all the poles and zeros that lie in the left half-plane, we have

$$\Delta^+(s) = \frac{1}{s + 2\nu} \tag{5.5–12}$$

Consequently,

$$\Delta^-(s) = \beta^2 \frac{4\nu}{-s + 2\nu} \tag{5.5–13}$$

Therefore, the ratio of $\Gamma(s)$ to $\Delta^-(s)$ is given by

$$\frac{\Gamma(s)}{\Delta^-(s)} = \frac{e^{\alpha s}}{s + 2\nu} \tag{5.5–14}$$

Since this ratio is a transcendental function, we shall evaluate $[\Gamma(s)/\Delta^-(s)]_+$ by means of Eqs. 5.4–26 and 5.4–27. Applying Eq. 5.4–27 yields

$$\gamma(t) = \frac{1}{2\pi j} \int_{-j\infty}^{j\infty} ds_1 \, e^{s_1 t} \left(\frac{e^{\alpha s_1}}{s_1 + 2\nu} \right) \tag{5.5–15}$$

Combining the exponentials gives

$$\gamma(t) = \frac{1}{2\pi j} \int_{-j\infty}^{j\infty} ds_1 \frac{e^{s_1(t+\alpha)}}{s_1 + 2\nu} \qquad (5.5\text{-}16)$$

This integral is evaluated by a contour integration, using a left half-plane contour provided $t + \alpha$ is equal to or greater than zero. The value of the integral over the left-half-plane semicircle is zero for $t + \alpha \geq 0$. This means $\gamma(t)$ is equal to the sum of the residues in the poles of the integrand which lie in the left half-plane. Since the residue in the single pole at $s_1 = -2\nu$ is $e^{-2\nu(t+\alpha)}$ we have

$$\gamma(t) = e^{-2\nu(t+\alpha)} \quad \text{for } t \geq -\alpha \qquad (5.5\text{-}17)$$

For $t + \alpha$ less than zero we must use a right-half-plane contour in order to have the integral over the semicircle vanish; and, since there are no poles in the right half-plane, it follows that

$$\gamma(t) = 0 \quad \text{for } t < -\alpha \qquad (5.5\text{-}18)$$

Figure 5.5–1 illustrates the form of $\gamma(t)$ for α positive and negative.

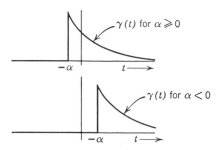

Fig. 5.5-1. $\gamma(t)$ versus t.

An expression for $\gamma(t)$ which holds for the complete time range is

$$\gamma(t) = \delta_{-1}(t + \alpha)e^{-2\nu(t+\alpha)} \qquad (5.5\text{-}19)$$

where $\delta_{-1}(t)$ is the unit step function.

We now may evaluate $[\Gamma(s)/\Delta^-(s)]_+$ by Eq. 5.4–26 as

$$\left[\frac{\Gamma(s)}{\Delta^-(s)}\right]_+ = \int_0^\infty dt\, e^{-st}\delta_{-1}(t + \alpha)e^{-2\nu(t+\alpha)} \qquad (5.5\text{-}20)$$

Taking the constant exponential factor outside the integral yields

$$\left[\frac{\Gamma(s)}{\Delta^-(s)}\right]_+ = e^{-2\nu\alpha} \int_0^\infty dt\, e^{-(s+2\nu)t}\delta_{-1}(t + \alpha) \qquad (5.5\text{-}21)$$

In carrying out the integration, two cases must be distinguished; one for α equal to or greater than zero and one for α less than zero. For the first case we have

$$\left[\frac{\Gamma(s)}{\Delta^-(s)}\right]_+ = -e^{-2\nu\alpha}\frac{e^{-(s+2\nu)t}}{s+2\nu}\bigg|_0^\infty \quad \text{for } \alpha \geq 0 \qquad (5.5\text{-}22)$$

which reduces to

$$\left[\frac{\Gamma(s)}{\Delta^-(s)}\right]_+ = \frac{e^{-2\nu\alpha}}{s+2\nu} \quad \text{for } \alpha \geq 0 \qquad (5.5\text{-}23)$$

On the other hand, the second case gives

$$\left[\frac{\Gamma(s)}{\Delta^-(s)}\right]_+ = -e^{-2\nu\alpha}\frac{e^{-(s+2\nu)t}}{s+2\nu}\bigg|_{-\alpha}^\infty \quad \text{for } \alpha < 0 \qquad (5.5\text{-}24)$$

which is equivalent to

$$\left[\frac{\Gamma(s)}{\Delta^-(s)}\right]_+ = \frac{e^{\alpha s}}{s+2\nu} \quad \text{for } \alpha < 0 \qquad (5.5\text{-}25)$$

In Eq. 5.4–28, $\Psi(s)$ is identified with $W_m(s)$ as shown by Eq. 5.5–1. Thus, using the value of $\Delta^+(s)$ given by Eq. 5.5–12, the solution for the system function is

$$W_m(s) = e^{-2\nu\alpha} \quad \text{for } \alpha \geq 0 \qquad (5.5\text{-}26)$$

$$W_m(s) = e^{\alpha s} \quad \text{for } \alpha < 0 \qquad (5.5\text{-}27)$$

The reader will note that the system functions given by Eq. 5.5–26 and 5.5–27 agree with the weighting functions given by Eqs. 5.3–7 and 8 since the former are Fourier transforms of the latter. In view of the larger amount of work required to solve this problem by using the frequency domain, the reader may question the usefulness of the explicit solution formula. Before drawing any conclusions as to the ease or difficulty of solving problems in the frequency domain, the reader should solve more elaborate examples than the one chosen here for illustrative purposes. Usually time-domain solutions to integral equations are not as self-evident as the one for the example of Art. 5.3. It will be found that for most problems involving transformable functions the frequency domain is the preferred medium for solving the Wiener-Hopf equation provided the transforms are not extraordinarily complex.

5.6 CONCLUSION

In this chapter we develop the analytical design theory for free-configuration systems excited by stochastic input signals. An integral equation for the system weighting function that minimizes the mean-square error is derived using a method from the calculus of variations. This integral equation, known as the Wiener-Hopf equation, represents a time domain solution for the desired weighting function. Certain practical problems can be solved very effectively through its use either by formal methods or numerical analysis. However, if the correlation functions for the input and the desired output signals are Fourier transformable, solution for the system function is expedited through use of an explicit solution formula derived from the basic Wiener-Hopf equation by a technique known as spectrum factorization. This general solution formula for integral equations of the Wiener-Hopf type plays an extremely important role in the rest of this book.

The approach of this chapter has been first to solve in the time domain the minimization problem which leads to the system weighting function and then to transfer this solution into the frequency domain by the spectrum factorization procedure. Another approach is to solve the problem entirely within the frequency domain as is done by Bode and Shannon in Reference B.5. We do not use this approach here since the time domain solution is frequently useful in its own right and would be entirely omitted if only the frequency domain were used.

The results of this chapter are somewhat academic as far as the control system designer is concerned since he seldom has a completely free choice for the system. Usually he is faced with a system that is partially specified. This leaves him freedom only with respect to the choice of the compensation to be used with the fixed elements of the system. Such problems of partially free choice are called semi-free-configuration problems. The next chapter extends the techniques introduced here to the problem of a semi-free configuration.

6

MINIMIZATION OF MEAN-SQUARE

AND INTEGRAL-SQUARE ERROR,

SEMI-FREE CONFIGURATION

6.1 COMPENSATION FOR MINIMUM MEAN-SQUARE ERROR

In the preceding chapter we discussed the variational procedure for minimizing the mean-square error of a control system when the configuration is completely free.   The solution for the weighting function of the control system was found to be determined by an integral equation of the Wiener-Hopf type.   A general formula for solving integral equations of this type was developed using the Wiener method of spectrum factorization.   This general solution formula applies when the correlation functions are Fourier transformable.   As mentioned in Chapter 1, the control system designer seldom has complete freedom in his choice of the system function.   He is usually restricted by specifications for the output elements; therefore, a more realistic problem is the determination of the compensation for a control system that minimizes the mean-square error to the extent possible in the presence of fixed elements.   This type of problem we call minimization of the mean-square error when the configuration is semi-free.

As discussed in Chapter 1, it is possible to replace the normal feedback configuration of a control system such as is shown in Fig. 1.7–1 by an equivalent cascade configuration.   After solving for the cascade compensation, the closed-loop compensation $G_c(s)$ is found as indicated in Art. 1.7, Eq. 1.7–4. Therefore, this chapter is concerned primarily with the determination of the equivalent cascade compensation for a feedback control system. For stochastic signals we shall find that the minimization of the mean-square error will lead to a modified Wiener-Hopf equation such that the solution for the cascade compensation will be a function of the fixed elements. After the discussion of mean-square error and an example illustrating the use of the general formulae, we shall make similar derivations for the minimization of the integral-square error when the signals acting on the control system are of a transient nature.

Figure 6.1–1 shows an equivalent cascade configuration for a control system. Time domain notation is used in this block diagram. The object of the following derivation is to determine the shape of the

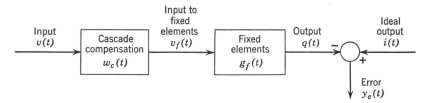

Fig. 6.1–1. Equivalent cascade configuration of control system.

weighting function $w_c(t)$ for the cascade compensation that minimizes the mean-square value of the error $y_e(t)$ between the ideal output $i(t)$ and the actual output $q(t)$. The square of the error is given by Eq. 5.2–2 which is repeated here for convenience.

$$y_e^2(t) = i^2(t) - 2q(t)i(t) + q^2(t) \qquad (5.2\text{–}2)$$

The input $v_f(t)$ to the fixed elements is given by the convolution of the compensation weighting function and the input signal. Symbolically this relationship is expressed as

$$v_f(t) = \int_{-\infty}^{\infty} dt_1 \, w_c(t_1)v(t - t_1) \qquad (6.1\text{–}1)$$

Likewise the output of the fixed elements $q(t)$ is determined by the convolution of their weighting function and input signal. This leads to

$$q(t) = \int_{-\infty}^{\infty} dt_2 \, g_f(t_2)v_f(t - t_2) \qquad (6.1\text{–}2)$$

Substituting the expression for $v_f(t)$ given by Eq. 6.1–1 into Eq. 6.1–2 and interchanging the order of integration yield as an expression for the output signal

$$q(t) = \int_{-\infty}^{\infty} dt_1 \, w_c(t_1) \int_{-\infty}^{\infty} dt_2 \, g_f(t_2) v(t - t_1 - t_2) \qquad (6.1\text{--}3)$$

From this result we conclude that the square of the output signal can be expressed as

$$q^2(t) = \left[\int_{-\infty}^{\infty} dt_1 \, w_c(t_1) \int_{-\infty}^{\infty} dt_2 \, g_f(t_2) v(t - t_1 - t_2) \right]$$

$$\times \left[\int_{-\infty}^{\infty} dt_3 \, w_c(t_3) \int_{-\infty}^{\infty} dt_4 \, g_f(t_4) v(t - t_3 - t_4) \right] \qquad (6.1\text{--}4)$$

where the integration variables t_3 and t_4 are introduced to avoid confusion with t_1 and t_2. These results for $q(t)$ and $q^2(t)$ are substituted into Eq. 5.2–2 to obtain an expression for the instantaneous square of the error. Integrating the square of the error and dividing by the range of integration give us, in the limit as the range of integration is made infinite, the mean-square error. Performing this operation and interchanging the orders of integration give us the following expression for the mean-square error in terms of the auto- and cross-correlation functions:

$$\overline{y_e^2(t)} = \varphi_{ii}(0) - 2 \int_{-\infty}^{\infty} dt_1 \, w_c(t_1) \int_{-\infty}^{\infty} dt_2 \, g_f(t_2) \varphi_{vi}(t_1 + t_2)$$

$$+ \int_{-\infty}^{\infty} dt_1 \, w_c(t_1) \int_{-\infty}^{\infty} dt_2 \, g_f(t_2) \int_{-\infty}^{\infty} dt_3 \, w_c(t_3)$$

$$\int_{-\infty}^{\infty} dt_4 \, g_f(t_4) \varphi_{vv}(t_1 + t_2 - t_3 - t_4) \qquad (6.1\text{--}5)$$

We now proceed to minimize the mean-square error by adjustment of the weighting function $w_c(t)$ that characterizes the equivalent cascade compensation. This is done by means of the same variational technique that was employed in Art. 5.2. We first assume that a solution for this weighting function exists; this solution we indicate by the symbol $w_{cm}(t)$ standing for the cascade-compensation weighting function that makes the mean-square error stationary with respect to small variations of the weighting function from this solution. The weighting function corresponding to a variation from the solution value is given by

$$w_c(t) = w_{cm}(t) + \epsilon w_\epsilon(t) \qquad (6.1\text{--}6)$$

Here the weighting function $w_\epsilon(t)$ is an arbitrary realizable weighting function, and ϵ is a parameter that can be varied in the process of finding the condition that $w_{cm}(t)$ must meet in order to be a solution. If $w_c(t)$ in Eq. 6.1–5 is replaced by the right member of Eq. 6.1–6, the mean-square error becomes a function of ϵ. If $w_{cm}(t)$ is to be a solution such that the mean-square error is stationary with respect to small variations in its neighborhood, then it follows that the derivative of the mean-square error with respect to ϵ at $\epsilon = 0$ must be equal to zero. Symbolically, this is expressed as

$$\frac{d[\overline{y_e{}^2(t)}]}{d\epsilon} = 0 \quad \text{at } \epsilon = 0 \tag{6.1-7}$$

This condition on the mean-square error is established by substituting the right member of Eq. 6.1–6 into Eq. 6.1–5, differentiating with respect to ϵ, and setting $\epsilon = 0$. The result is

$$-2 \int_{-\infty}^{\infty} dt_1\, w_\epsilon(t_1) \int_{-\infty}^{\infty} dt_2\, g_f(t_2)\varphi_{vi}(t_1 + t_2)$$

$$+ \int_{-\infty}^{\infty} dt_1\, w_\epsilon(t_1) \int_{-\infty}^{\infty} dt_2\, g_f(t_2) \int_{-\infty}^{\infty} dt_3\, w_{cm}(t_3)$$

$$\int_{-\infty}^{\infty} dt_4\, g_f(t_4)\varphi_{vv}(t_1 + t_2 - t_3 - t_4)$$

$$+ \int_{-\infty}^{\infty} dt_1\, w_{cm}(t_1) \int_{-\infty}^{\infty} dt_2\, g_f(t_2) \int_{-\infty}^{\infty} dt_3\, w_\epsilon(t_3)$$

$$\int_{-\infty}^{\infty} dt_4\, g_f(t_4)\varphi_{vv}(t_1 + t_2 - t_3 - t_4) = 0 \tag{6.1-8}$$

Because the autocorrelation function $\varphi_{vv}(\tau)$ is an even function, the second and third terms in Eq. 6.1–8 are equal to one another. This may be shown by interchanging orders of integration so that we integrate first with respect to t_4 and then t_2. The result of this double integration will be the autocorrelation function of the input signal filtered by the fixed elements. At this point, interchanging the order of integration of the third term so that we integrate with respect to t_1 first and t_3 second will show that the second and third terms are identical except for the labelling of integration variables and the sign of the argument of an autocorrelation function. Eliminating the third term on the left side of Eq. 6.1–8 and multiplying the second term by 2 in order to compensate for this yield an equation of the form

$$2 \int_{-\infty}^{\infty} dt_1\, w_\epsilon(t_1)f(t_1) = 0 \tag{6.1-9}$$

where $f(t_1)$ is the left member of Eq. 6.1–10 below. Since $w_\epsilon(t_1)$ is arbitrary and may be non-zero for positive values of time, it is evident that $f(t_1)$ must be zero except for t_1 less than zero. $w_\epsilon(t_1)$ is zero for negative time since by hypothesis it is a realizable weighting function. Thus the resulting condition on $w_{cm}(t)$ is given by

$$\int_{-\infty}^{\infty} dt_3\, w_{cm}(t_3) \int_{-\infty}^{\infty} dt_2\, g_f(t_2) \int_{-\infty}^{\infty} dt_4\, g_f(t_4)\varphi_{vv}(t_1 + t_2 - t_3 - t_4)$$

$$- \int_{-\infty}^{\infty} dt_2\, g_f(t_2)\varphi_{vi}(t_1 + t_2) = 0 \quad \text{for } t_1 \geq 0 \tag{6.1-10}$$

This expression is a modified form of the Wiener-Hopf equation. It expresses the solution for the cascade-compensation weighting function that minimizes the mean-square error in the form of an integral equation which, in general, must be solved by either numerical methods or, in the case of transformable weighting and correlation functions, by the solution formula derived in Art. 5.4.

In connection with Eq. 6.1–10 it was asserted without proof that the solution represents a weighting function that minimizes the mean-square error. Mathematically, we are justified in saying only that the solution makes the mean-square error stationary. By physical considerations, however, it is easy to see that the solution must correspond to a minimum (or at worst a saddle point) since there is, in general, no finite maximum value for the mean-square error. Mathematically, a consideration of the second derivative of the mean-square error with respect to ϵ similar to that in Art. 5.2 indicates that this is always positive and thereby shows that the solution to Eq. 6.1–10 corresponds to a true minimum.

When the correlation functions and the weighting functions appearing in Eq. 6.1–10 are Fourier transformable, it is usually convenient to make use of the explicit solution formula given in Art. 5.4. In Eq. 5.4–1 we make the following identifications with quantities which appear in Eq. 6.1–10

$$\tau = t_1$$

$$\psi(t_1) = w_{cm}(t_3)$$

$$\Delta(\tau - t_1) = \int_{-\infty}^{\infty} dt_2\, g_f(t_2) \int_{-\infty}^{\infty} dt_4\, g_f(t_4)\varphi_{vv}(t_1 + t_2 - t_3 - t_4)$$

$$\Gamma(\tau) = \int_{-\infty}^{\infty} dt_2\, g_f(t_2)\varphi_{vi}(t_1 + t_2)$$

(6.1–11)

In accordance with these identifications we observe that the transforms for $\Gamma(s)$ and $\Delta(s)$ are given by

$$\Gamma(s) = 2\pi G_f(-s)\Phi_{vi}(s)$$

$$\Delta(s) = 2\pi G_f(-s)G_f(s)\Phi_{vv}(s)$$

(6.1–12)

Substituting these transforms into the explicit solution formula given in Art. 5.4, namely,

$$\Psi(s) = \frac{\left[\dfrac{\Gamma(s)}{\Delta^-(s)}\right]_+}{\Delta^+(s)}$$

(5.4–28)

yields

$$W_{cm}(s) = \frac{\left\{\dfrac{G_f(-s)\Phi_{vi}(s)}{[G_f(-s)G_f(s)]^-\Phi_{vv}^-(s)}\right\}_+}{[G_f(-s)G_f(s)]^+\Phi_{vv}^+(s)} \qquad (6.1\text{--}13)$$

This solution for the cascade-compensation transfer function is particularly significant when the fixed elements have a non-minimum-phase transfer function. It is therefore desirable to discuss briefly the properties of minimum-phase and non-minimum-phase transfer functions before proceeding to a physical interpretation of Eq. 6.1–13.

6.2 MINIMUM- AND NON-MINIMUM-PHASE TRANSFER FUNCTIONS

Transfer functions are divided into two classes described by the terms *minimum phase* and *non-minimum phase*, respectively. A minimum-phase transfer function has the least possible phase shift at any real frequency that can be associated with the given gain characteristic. On the other hand, for a given gain-versus-frequency characteristic a non-minimum-phase transfer function has a greater negative phase shift at a given frequency than must necessarily exist. The intimate relationship that exists between gain and phase for minimum-phase transfer functions follows directly from the Fourier transform definition of a transfer function. This relationship has been discussed by previous writers (see References L.2 and B.4). Some of their important results are presented in Appendix F to which the reader should refer if he is unfamiliar with the relationship of phase to gain for minimum-phase transfer functions.

As a specific illustration of the concept of a non-minimum-phase network, consider the transfer function represented by

$$G(s) = \frac{(s+1)(s-1+j)(s-1-j)}{(s+0.5)(s+1.5)(s+2)(s+3)} \qquad (6.2\text{--}1)$$

The pole-zero configuration of this transfer function is indicated in Fig. 6.2–1. Writing this transfer function as the product of a minimum-phase factor and an all-pass factor yields

$$G(s) = \left[\frac{(s+1)(s+1+j)(s+1-j)}{(s+0.5)(s+1.5)(s+2)(s+3)}\right]$$
$$\left[\frac{(s-1+j)(s-1-j)}{(s+1+j)(s+1-j)}\right] \qquad (6.2\text{--}2)$$

The pole-zero configuration of the minimum-phase factor is shown in

Fig. 6.2–2(A) and that of the all-pass factor in Fig. 6.2–2(B). By observing how the phasors corresponding to the poles and zeros of the all-pass factor change in angle as the frequency ω is increased, it is easy to see that a negative phase shift is contributed by this factor at all finite frequencies. Obviously, a transfer function containing an all-pass factor must therefore have more negative phase shift than it would have if this factor were not present. This explains the term

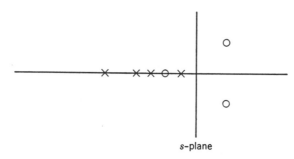

Fig. 6.2–1.   Poles and zeros of $G(s)$ example.

non-minimum phase used to describe transfer functions that have zeros that lie in the right half-plane.

The foregoing discussion clarifies the meaning of the terms *minimum phase* and *non-minimum phase* as applied to transfer functions. The significance of a non-minimum-phase transfer function lies in the fact

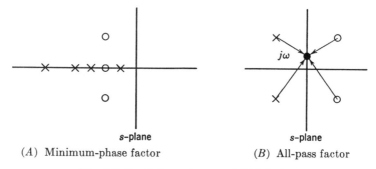

(A) Minimum-phase factor   (B) All-pass factor

Fig. 6.2–2.   Poles and zeros of $G(s)$ factors.

that no rigid tie between phase and gain exists and also in the fact that such a transfer function in the fixed elements of a system imposes a definite limitation upon the performance that can be achieved. The next article will be devoted to this second point.

6.3 LIMITATION IMPOSED BY FIXED ELEMENTS; EXAMPLE

In this article we shall see that the fixed elements of a control system impose no limitation on its performance provided they are minimum phase. A performance limitation associated with the fixed elements can only arise when they are non-minimum phase. When a control system has minimum-phase fixed elements, the transfer function for the equivalent cascade compensation that minimizes the mean-square error can be found by solving for the over-all system function without regard to the fixed elements. Division of the over-all system function thus found by the transfer function of the fixed elements will then yield the transfer function of the equivalent cascade compensation. The validity of this procedure will be demonstrated in the next paragraph. When the fixed elements are non-minimum phase, the equivalent cascade compensation cannot be computed as a ratio of the over-all system function to the transfer function of the fixed elements since such a ratio would contain poles in the right half-plane, thereby violating the requirement of stability. For non-minimum-phase fixed elements it is necessary to use the solution formulas represented by Eq. 6.1–10 or 6.1–13. Specific examples of the performance limitations imposed by non-minimum-phase fixed elements will be presented in later paragraphs.

Let us now consider the solution of Eq. 6.1–13 for the transfer function $W_{cm}(s)$ of the equivalent cascade compensation when the fixed elements are minimum phase. If the fixed elements have a transfer function $G_f(s)$ which is minimum phase, we see that

$$[G_f(-s)G_f(s)]^- = G_f(-s) \qquad (6.3\text{–}1)$$

and that

$$[G_f(-s)G_f(s)]^+ = G_f(s) \qquad (6.3\text{–}2)$$

For rational minimum-phase functions these relations follow immediately from the fact that $G_f(s)$ has all its poles and zeros in the left half-plane and $G_f(-s)$ has all its poles and zeros in the right half-plane. Making use of these relations in Eq. 6.1–13 yields

$$W_{cm}(s) = \frac{\left\{ \dfrac{\Phi_{vi}(s)}{\Phi_{vv}^-(s)} \right\}_+}{G_f(s)\Phi_{vv}^+(s)} \qquad (6.3\text{–}3)$$

In other words, we can write for the transfer function of the equivalent cascade compensation

$$W_{cm}(s) = \left[\frac{1}{G_f(s)}\right] W_m(s) \qquad (6.3\text{–}4)$$

where

$$W_m(s) = \frac{\left\{\dfrac{\Phi_{vi}(s)}{\Phi_{vv}^-(s)}\right\}_+}{\Phi_{vv}^+(s)} \qquad (6.3\text{–}5)$$

Note that $W_m(s)$ is the solution for the over-all system function that minimizes the mean-square error that is obtained when there are no fixed elements. Thus the over-all system function is independent of the transfer function of the fixed elements when it is minimum phase. Consequently, minimum-phase fixed elements impose no limitation upon the performance of the system measured in terms of mean-square error. When the fixed elements are minimum phase, it is simplest to compute the transfer function of the equivalent cascade compensation by first computing the over-all system function by Eq. 6.3–5 and then dividing this result by the transfer function of the fixed elements as indicated by Eq. 6.3–4.

Having completed our discussion of the effect of minimum-phase fixed elements on system performance, we now consider the effect of non-minimum-phase fixed elements. Equations 6.3–1 and 6.3–2 do not hold when $G_f(s)$ is non-minimum phase. Consequently, the over-all system function cannot be found as indicated in Eq. 6.3–5, and we must employ Eq. 6.1–13 in order to find the transfer function of the equivalent cascade compensation. The over-all system function is then given by the product of $W_{cm}(s)$ and $G_f(s)$. A very definite limitation on system performance is imposed by the non-minimum-phase nature of the fixed elements. This limitation is revealed very clearly in the following examples.

In our first example, the fixed elements will be represented by a first-order all-pass transfer function having a single pole on the negative real axis and a single zero on the positive real axis. Such a transfer function could arise from a resistance-capacitance lattice or as an approximation to a pure time delay or transportation lag. The transfer function of the feedback elements is unity. The input is a stochastic signal described as a rectangular wave of amplitude plus or minus β and with zero crossings Poisson distributed with average frequency ν. The desired output signal is exactly equal to the input signal. We desire to know the minimum mean-square error and the transfer function for the compensation that yields this minimum. The given data for this example are summarized as follows:

Given.   The transfer functions of the fixed elements and the feedback elements are

$$G_f(s) = \frac{-(T/2)s + 1}{+(T/2)s + 1} \tag{6.3-6}$$

and

$$H_f(s) = 1 \tag{6.3-7}$$

The power-density spectrum of the input signal has been discussed in Art. 4.5 and 5.5.   The result obtained by transforming the autocorrelation function is

$$\Phi_{vv}(s) = \frac{\beta^2}{\pi} \frac{2\nu}{(-s^2 + 4\nu^2)} \tag{6.3-8}$$

Since the desired output is equal to the input, the cross-power-density spectrum is given by the same function; that is,

$$\Phi_{vi}(s) = \frac{\beta^2}{\pi} \frac{2\nu}{(-s^2 + 4\nu^2)} \tag{6.3-9}$$

Equations 6.3–6 through 6.3–9 compactly state the given data for this example.

That the transfer function for the fixed elements can be regarded as an approximation to the transfer function for a pure delay e^{-Ts} becomes evident upon comparing their two MacLaurin's series. Specifically,

$$G_f(s) = 1 - Ts + \frac{T^2}{2} s^2 - \frac{T^3}{4} s^3 + \frac{T^4}{8} s^4 + \cdots \tag{6.3-10}$$

and

$$e^{-Ts} = 1 - Ts + \frac{T^2}{2} s^2 - \frac{T^3}{6} s^3 + \frac{T^4}{24} s^4 + \cdots \tag{6.3-11}$$

We observe that the two series agree through the second-order terms and differ only by 50 percent in the third-order terms.   Thus we are justified in regarding the fixed elements of this example as a low-frequency approximation to a pure delay.

Find.   We wish to find for the above data the equivalent cascade compensation $W_{cm}(s)$ that minimizes the mean-square error.   In addition, we should like to know the compensation $G_{cm}(s)$ that should be used inside the feedback loop.   We also ask for the value of the minimum mean-square error.   We desire all three of the foregoing quantities as functions of the parameters β, ν, and T.

Solution. Since the fixed elements are non-minimum phase and since all the given data are expressed in terms of Fourier transforms, we shall employ Eq. 6.1–13. The product of $G_f(-s)$ and $G_f(s)$ is given by

$$[G_f(-s)G_f(s)] = 1 \tag{6.3-12}$$

Thus the factor of this product containing all the poles and zeros lying in the right half-plane is 1 and likewise the factor containing all the poles and zeros lying in the left half-plane is 1.   The factor of the input power-density spectrum containing all the poles and zeros in the right half-plane is taken as

$$\Phi_{vv}^-(s) = \frac{\beta^2}{\pi}\left(\frac{2v}{-s+2v}\right) \tag{6.3-13}$$

Consequently, the factor containing all the poles and zeros lying in the left half-plane is given by

$$\Phi_{vv}^+(s) = \frac{1}{s+2v} \tag{6.3-14}$$

Substituting these results into Eq. 6.1–13 yields

$$W_{cm}(s) = \frac{\left[\left(\dfrac{\dfrac{T}{2}s+1}{-\dfrac{T}{2}s+1}\right)\left(\dfrac{1}{s+2v}\right)\right]_+}{\left(\dfrac{1}{s+2v}\right)} \tag{6.3-15}$$

By making a partial fraction expansion of the quantity enclosed in brackets in the numerator of the right member of this equation and retaining only terms corresponding to poles in the left half-plane, we find

$$\left[\left(\frac{\dfrac{T}{2}s+1}{-\dfrac{T}{2}s+1}\right)\left(\frac{1}{s+2v}\right)\right]_+ = \frac{k}{s+2v} \tag{6.3-16}$$

where

$$k = \frac{-Tv+1}{Tv+1} \tag{6.3-17}$$

Thus

$$W_{cm}(s) = k \tag{6.3-18}$$

and we have the rather interesting result that the equivalent cascade compensation that minimizes the mean-square error is merely a constant.

In order to find the compensation that would be used inside the closed loop, we make use of Eq. 1.7–4. Using $W_{cm}(s)$ for $W_c(s)$ in this equation, we find

$$G_{cm}(s) = \frac{W_{cm}(s)}{1 - W_{cm}(s)G_f(s)H_f(s)} \qquad (6.3\text{–}19)$$

Substituting the values of the transfer functions yields

$$G_{cm}(s) = \frac{\left(\dfrac{1}{2T\nu} - \dfrac{1}{2}\right)\left(\dfrac{T}{2}s + 1\right)}{\left(\dfrac{1}{2\nu}s + 1\right)} \qquad (6.3\text{–}20)$$

For values of the average frequency ν small compared to the reciprocal of the time constant T of the fixed elements, this compensation corresponds to a simple lag (undercompensated integral) network.

We now compute the mean-square error. The mean-square error is equal to the autocorrelation function of the error evaluated at $\tau = 0$. This value of the autocorrelation function is given by Eq. 4.4–2 which is repeated here for convenience.

$$\varphi_{yy}(0) = \frac{1}{j}\int_{-j\infty}^{j\infty} ds\, \Phi_{yy}(s) \qquad (4.4\text{–}2)$$

Since there is no input noise, the power-density spectrum of the error is given by

$$\Phi_{yy}(s) = W_y(-s)W_y(s)\Phi_{vv}(s) \qquad (6.3\text{–}21)$$

In view of the equivalence of the desired output and the input, the error transfer function is given by

$$W_y(s) = 1 - W(s) \qquad (6.3\text{–}22)$$

Upon substituting the product of $G_f(s)$ and $W_{cm}(s)$ for $W(s)$ in this equation, there results

$$W_y(s) = \frac{(1 + k)\dfrac{T}{2}s + (1 - k)}{\dfrac{T}{2}s + 1} \qquad (6.3\text{–}23)$$

Thus the power-density spectrum for the error can be written as

$$\Phi_{yy}(s) = \frac{2\nu\beta^2}{\pi} \frac{c(s)c(-s)}{d(s)d(-s)}$$

where

$$\frac{c(s)}{d(s)} = \frac{(1 + k)\dfrac{T}{2}s + (1 - k)}{\dfrac{T}{2}s^2 + (T\nu + 1)s + 2\nu} \tag{6.3–24}$$

The integral of Eq. 4.4–2 may be evaluated using the formula for I_2 given in the table of integrals of Appendix E. In this manner the minimum value of the mean-square error is found to be

$$\overline{y_e^2(t)} = 4\beta^2 \frac{T\nu}{(T\nu + 1)^2} \tag{6.3–25}$$

The behavior of the mean-square error as a function of the average signal frequency ν is interesting. For low frequencies the mean-square error is simply equal to the mean-square value of the input signal multiplied by $4T\nu$. As the frequency increases the mean-square error approaches a maximum value at $T\nu = 1$; this maximum value is equal to the mean-square value of the input signal and corresponds to the condition in which the equivalent cascade compensation, given by Eq. 6.3–18, is equal to zero. As the signal frequency increases further the mean-square error diminishes and becomes zero for larger frequencies. This behavior of the mean-square error seems reasonable in view of the frequency characteristic of the fixed elements. At all frequencies, the fixed elements transmit with neither gain nor loss. The phase shift of the output of the fixed elements relative to the input increases from zero to minus 180 degrees as the frequency varies from zero to infinity. Thus at high frequencies the fixed elements correspond to a reversal of polarity. At high frequencies the equivalent cascade compensation acquires negative values to compensate for the reversal of polarity caused by the fixed elements. Only for intermediate signal frequencies is the mean-square error large. The large mean-square errors in this frequency range are caused by the rapidly changing negative phase shift of the fixed elements.

In concluding this example, we should carefully observe that the only reason for a mean-square error different from zero lies in the nature of the fixed elements. These fixed elements are non-minimum phase. If they had been minimum phase, the over-all system function would have turned out to be unity since the desired output is equal to the input and the mean-square error would be zero.   Thus the non-minimum-phase property of the fixed elements in this example is solely responsible for the mean-square error that does exist even with the best possible compensation.

As the second example, let us repeat the foregoing problem with the fixed elements changed to a pure time delay of T seconds.   All the specifications will be unchanged except that $G_f(s)$ will be represented by

$$G_f(s) = e^{-Ts} \qquad (6.3\text{--}26)$$

Although this transfer function for the fixed elements is transcendental it is possible to carry out the solution for the equivalent cascade compensation in essentially the same manner as before.

Solution.   Using the solution formula represented by Eq. 6.1–13 we again note that

$$G_f(-s)G_f(s) = 1 \qquad (6.3\text{--}27)$$

Equation 6.1–13 yields

$$W_{cm}(s) = \frac{\left(\dfrac{e^{Ts}}{s + 2\nu}\right)_+}{\left(\dfrac{1}{s + 2\nu}\right)} \qquad (6.3\text{--}28)$$

As discussed in Art. 5.4, we shall use the notation

$$\gamma(s) = \left(\frac{e^{Ts}}{s + 2\nu}\right) \qquad (6.3\text{--}29)$$

Making use of the same reasoning that was employed in Art. 5.5, we observe that

$$\gamma(t) = \delta_{-1}(t + T)e^{-2\nu(T+t)} \qquad (6.3\text{--}30)$$

Because T is always positive for a time delay, $\gamma(t)$ is always an exponential pulse which begins before $T = 0$.   Thus $\gamma_+(t)$, the part of $\gamma(t)$ that is non-zero for positive time and is zero for negative time, is the tail of the exponential pulse and is given by

$$\gamma_+(t) = \delta_{-1}(t)e^{-2\nu T}e^{-2\nu t} \qquad (6.3\text{--}31)$$

Transforming both sides of this equation and making use of the identity

$$\gamma_+(s) = \left(\frac{e^{Ts}}{s + 2\nu}\right)_+ \qquad (6.3\text{--}32)$$

yield

$$\left(\frac{e^{Ts}}{s+2\nu}\right)_+ = \frac{k}{s+2\nu} \qquad (6.3\text{–}33)$$

where

$$k = e^{-2T\nu} \qquad (6.3\text{–}34)$$

Thus, by substituting the right member of Eq. 6.3–33 in Eq. 6.3–28, we find the transfer function for the equivalent cascade compensation to be given by

$$W_{cm}(s) = k \qquad (6.3\text{–}35)$$

Again this transfer function turns out to be a simple constant.

The compensation to be placed within the feedback loop in order to realize the equivalent cascade compensation of Eq. 6.3–35 is determined by Eq. 6.3–19. The result is

$$G_{cm}(s) = \frac{1}{e^{2T\nu} - e^{-Ts}} \qquad (6.3\text{–}36)$$

Note the periodic behavior of this compensation as a function of the real frequency ω.

We now wish to compute the value of the mean-square error that results when the compensation of Eq. 6.3–35 is employed. This compensation, of course, minimizes the mean-square error. If we attempt to evaluate the mean-square error by means of Eq. 4.4–2, we encounter transcendental functions in the power-density spectrum of the error. The available integral tables are worked out for rational functions only; this means that we would have to evaluate the right member of Eq. 4.4–2 by contour integration. In this particular instance, it is simpler to employ Eq. 6.1–5 and work entirely in the time domain. The autocorrelation function of the input signal is derived in Art. 3.6 and is given by Eq. 3.6–8. Since the ideal output is equal to the input, the cross-correlation function between the input and the ideal output is the same as the autocorrelation function of the input. Likewise, the autocorrelation function of the ideal output is the same as the autocorrelation function of the input. These facts are summarized by

$$\varphi_{vv}(\tau) = \varphi_{vi}(\tau) = \varphi_{ii}(\tau) = \beta^2 e^{-2\nu|\tau|} \qquad (6.3\text{–}37)$$

The weighting function of the equivalent cascade compensation is given by

$$W_{cm}(t) = k\delta(t) \qquad (6.3\text{–}38)$$

The weighting function of the fixed elements is simply a delayed impulse

$$g_f(t) = \delta(t - T) \tag{6.3-39}$$

Substituting these functions in Eq. 6.1–5 yields the following formula for the mean-square error

$$\overline{y_e{}^2(t)} = \varphi_{ii}(0) - 2k \int_{-\infty}^{\infty} dt_1\, \delta(t_1) \int_{-\infty}^{\infty} dt_2\, \delta(t_2 - T)\varphi_{vi}(t_1 + t_2)$$
$$+ k^2 \int_{-\infty}^{\infty} dt_1\, \delta(t_1) \int_{-\infty}^{\infty} dt_2\, \delta(t_2 - T) \int_{-\infty}^{\infty} dt_3\, \delta(t_3)$$
$$\int_{-\infty}^{\infty} dt_4\, \delta(t_4 - T)\varphi_{vv}(t_1 + t_2 - t_3 - t_4) \tag{6.3-40}$$

In view of the fact that the weighting functions are simple delta functions, the integrals are very easy to evaluate. The result is

$$\overline{y_e{}^2(t)} = \beta^2 - 2k\beta^2 e^{-2T\nu} + k^2\beta^2 \tag{6.3-41}$$

Substituting the value of k given by Eq. 6.3–34 permits us to write the mean-square error as

$$\overline{y_e{}^2(t)} = \beta^2(1 - e^{-4T\nu}) \tag{6.3-42}$$

In concluding this example, a few remarks on the physical interpretation of our results are in order. First, it should be observed that for small average signal frequencies the mean-square error given by Eq. 6.3–42 is approximated by $4\beta^2 T\nu$, which is exactly the same as the result that we obtained by means of the first-order, all-pass approximation to the transfer function of the fixed elements. This would seem to justify the rational function approximation for the pure time delay for low signal frequencies. In fact, for average signal frequencies up to $T\nu = \frac{1}{2}$ the mean-square error for the first-order rational approximation to the time delay is within 3 percent of the value given by the exact solution.

As our second observation, we notice that the mean-square error given by Eq. 6.3–42 continually increases up to a maximum value of β^2 as the average signal frequency increases. This is in distinct contrast to the result represented by the Eq. 6.3–25 for the rational function approximation to the time delay. A pure time delay in the fixed elements places a very stringent limitation upon the system's performance. Even the best possible compensation from the viewpoint of minimizing the mean-square error cannot overcome the effect of a time delay in the fixed elements. Thus a time delay must be regarded as a very fundamental factor in limiting the performance that may be achieved with a linear system.

Finally, we observe that the transfer function for the equivalent cascade compensation for a pure time delay is identical with the system function derived in Art. 5.5 for pure prediction. This is entirely reasonable. The problem of reproducing the input in the presence of a pure time delay is identical with the problem of producing the input advanced in time when there is no time delay.

6.4 COMPENSATION FOR MINIMUM INTEGRAL-SQUARE ERROR; EXAMPLE

So far in this chapter we have discussed compensation of systems that are subjected to stochastic input signals. We have found solutions for the equivalent cascade compensation that is to be used with arbitrarily specified fixed elements in order to minimize the mean-square error. However, many problems involve transient signals rather than stochastic signals. To handle these problems we need solutions for the equivalent cascade compensation analogous to those already derived. Instead of minimizing the mean-square error, these solutions are found by minimizing the integral-square error through the adjustment of the weighting function of the compensation. In this article, we shall present formulas for the compensation of systems that are subject to transient input signals; in addition, we shall give an example to illustrate these results.

In Art. 2.4 the concept of a translation function for a transient signal was introduced. For example, the cross-translation function between signals $x_1(t)$ and $x_2(t)$ is defined as

$$I_{12}(\tau) \triangleq \int_{-\infty}^{\infty} dt\, x_1(t) x_2(t + \tau) \tag{2.4-2}$$

In terms of the translation functions, the integral-square error for a control system can be written as

$$
\begin{aligned}
I_y = I_{ii}(0) &- 2 \int_{-\infty}^{\infty} dt_1\, w_c(t_1) \int_{-\infty}^{\infty} dt_2\, g_f(t_2) I_{vi}(t_1 + t_2) \\
&+ \int_{-\infty}^{\infty} dt_1\, w_c(t_1) \int_{-\infty}^{\infty} dt_2\, g_f(t_2) \int_{-\infty}^{\infty} dt_3\, w_c(t_3) \\
&\qquad \int_{-\infty}^{\infty} dt_4\, g_f(t_4) I_{vv}(t_1 + t_2 - t_3 - t_4) \tag{6.4-1}
\end{aligned}
$$

This equation is written in terms of the weighting functions for the equivalent cascade compensation $w_c(t)$ and the fixed elements $g_f(t)$. The translation functions that are involved are the autotranslation function of the ideal output $I_{ii}(\tau)$, the cross-translation function between the input and the ideal output $I_{vi}(\tau)$ and the autotranslation function of the input $I_{vv}(\tau)$. Equation 6.4–1 is analogous to Eq. 6.1–5 for the mean-square error in terms of the correlation functions.

The derivation for the above expression for the integral-square error is identical with the derivation of the mean-square error except that averaging with respect to time is omitted.

In order to derive the condition that the compensation must meet in order to minimize the integral-square error, we employ the standard variational procedure; that is, we let the compensation be represented by

$$w_c(t) = w_{cm}(t) + \epsilon w_\epsilon(t) \qquad (6.1\text{--}6)$$

where $w_{cm}(t)$ is the weighting function that minimizes the integral-square error, $w_\epsilon(t)$ is an arbitrary realizable weighting function, and ϵ is an adjustable constant. Using the same reasoning as in Art. 6.1, we substitute for the compensation in Eq. 6.4–1 the right member of the above equation. This makes the integral-square error a function of ϵ. By hypothesis the derivative of the integral-square error with respect to ϵ must be equal to zero at $\epsilon = 0$ if $w_{cm}(t)$ is the compensation that minimizes the integral-square error. Setting the derivative of the integral-square error with respect to ϵ equal to zero at $\epsilon = 0$ yields the following condition

$$\int_{-\infty}^{\infty} dt_3 \, w_{cm}(t_3) \int_{-\infty}^{\infty} dt_2 \, g_f(t_2) \int_{-\infty}^{\infty} dt_4 \, g_f(t_4) I_{vv}(t_1 + t_2 - t_3 - t_4)$$
$$- \int_{-\infty}^{\infty} dt_2 \, g_f(t_2) I_{vi}(t_1 + t_2) = 0 \quad \text{for } t_1 \geq 0 \qquad (6.4\text{--}2)$$

This is the time domain solution for the compensation that minimizes the integral-square error.

Since the above solution for the weighting function of the equivalent cascade compensation is in the form of the generalized Wiener-Hopf integral equation (given as Eq. 5.4–1), the explicit solution formula of Eq. 5.4–28 applies provided the translation functions and the weighting function of the fixed elements are Fourier transformable. In this instance we find for the transfer function of the compensation the following expression:

$$W_{cm}(s) = \frac{\left\{ \dfrac{G_f(-s) I_{vi}(s)}{[G_f(-s)G_f(s)]^- I_{vv}^-(s)} \right\}_+}{[G_f(-s)G_f(s)]^+ I_{vv}^+(s)} \qquad (6.4\text{--}3)$$

This result, of course, is identical in form with Eq. 6.1–13; the only difference is the replacement of power-density spectra by the corresponding transforms of translation functions.

Equations 6.4–1, 6.4–2, and 6.4–3 are the basic results for transient input signals impressed upon a system with a semi-free configuration. Just as for stochastic signals, the presence of fixed elements has no effect on the solution provided they are minimum phase. The over-all system function depends upon the fixed elements only when they are non-minimum phase.

Let us now illustrate by means of an example our general solution formula for the equivalent cascade compensation that minimizes the integral square-error for transient input signals. For this example let the fixed elements be a pure time delay. As the input signal we shall use a simple ramp, and we shall consider the ideal output to be identical with the input. For this situation let us find the cascade compensation that minimizes the integral-square error and also the value of the integral-square error, using this compensation. We now summarize this problem statement in terms of symbols.

Given. The transfer function for the fixed elements is

$$G_f(s) = e^{-Ts} \tag{6.4-4}$$

For the input signal we have

$$v(t) = \Omega\delta_{-2}(t) \tag{6.4-5}$$

where Ω is the slope of this ramp function. The given data for this example are completed by the specification of the ideal output as

$$i(t) = v(t) \tag{6.4-6}$$

In practice the designer of positional control systems or servomechan-isms often attempts to achieve equality between the output and the input.

Find. In this example we seek the transfer function $W_{cm}(s)$ of the equivalent cascade compensation that minimizes the integral-square error I_y. In addition, we desire the value of the integral-square error when the system has this compensation.

Solution. The solution for the compensation is found by substi-tuting in the general solution formula of Eq. 6.4–3. From the given data we note that

$$G_f(-s)G_f(s) = 1 \tag{6.4-7}$$

By means of Eq. 2.4–30 the transform of the autotranslation function of the input signal is found in terms of the transform of the signal itself. Specifically we have

$$I_{vv}(s) = v(-s)v(s) \tag{6.4-8}$$

The Fourier transform of the input signal can be found provided a convergence factor is used.   (See Appendix A.)   The result is

$$v(s) = \frac{\Omega}{s^2} \qquad (6.4\text{--}9)$$

Thus we find the transform of the autotranslation function of the input signal to be given by

$$I_{vv}(s) = \frac{\Omega^2}{s^4} \qquad (6.4\text{--}10)$$

Since the ideal output is equal to the input, the transform of the cross-translation function between the input and the ideal output is given by

$$I_{vi}(s) = I_{vv}(s) \qquad (6.4\text{--}11)$$

The transform of the autotranslation function of the input signal is factored as follows:

$$I_{vv}^{-}(s) = \frac{\Omega^2}{(-s)(-s)} \qquad (6.4\text{--}12)$$

$$I_{vv}^{+}(s) = \frac{1}{(s)(s)} \qquad (6.4\text{--}13)$$

The signs associated with the s's in the above factors can be justified by regarding the double-order pole of the transform of the input signal to be located slightly to the left of the imaginary axis in the s-plane. That is, formally the transform of the input signal is given by

$$v(s) = \lim_{\epsilon \to 0} \frac{\Omega}{(s + \epsilon)^2} \qquad (6.4\text{--}14)$$

Starting with this expression for $v(s)$ it is easy to see that the minus s factors in Eq. 6.4–12 represent the limit of $(-s + \epsilon)$ factors when $\epsilon = 0$.   A similar argument holds for Eq. 6.4–13.

By substituting the above results into Eq. 6.4–3, we arrive at the following expression for the transfer function of the equivalent cascade compensation.

$$W_{cm}(s) = \frac{(e^{Ts}/s^2)_+}{(1/s^2)} \qquad (6.4\text{--}15)$$

The numerator of this expression can be written as

$$\left(\frac{e^{Ts}}{s^2}\right)_+ = \frac{k_2}{s^2} + \frac{k_1}{s} \qquad (6.4\text{--}16)$$

Here the constants k_1 and k_2 are evaluated in the standard manner for partial fraction expansions. Adding to both sides of Eq. 6.4–16 $(e^{Ts}/s^2)_-$, multiplying through by s^2, and setting $s = 0$ yield

$$k_2 = 1 \qquad (6.4\text{–}17)$$

Repeating the above operation but differentiating with respect to s before setting $s = 0$ gives

$$k_1 = T \qquad (6.4\text{–}18)$$

Thus the equivalent cascade compensation that minimizes the integral-square error is found to be

$$W_{cm}(s) = Ts + 1 \qquad (6.4\text{–}19)$$

It is interesting that this compensation has such a simple form.

In order to compute the integral-square error corresponding to the above compensation, we shall first evaluate the error as a function of time and then employ the definition of the integral-square error, namely,

$$I_y = \int_{-\infty}^{\infty} dt \, y_e{}^2(t) \qquad (6.4\text{–}20)$$

The error as a function of time is given by the convolution integral

$$y_e(t) = \int_{-\infty}^{\infty} dt_1 \, w_y(t_1) v(t - t_1) \qquad (6.4\text{–}21)$$

where $w_y(t)$ is the weighting function relating the error to the input signal. In this instance this weighting function is given by

$$w_y(t) = \delta(t) - w(t) \qquad (6.4\text{–}22)$$

The over-all weighting function $w(t)$ is given by the convolution of the weighting function of the compensation and that of the fixed elements. That is,

$$w(t) = \int_{-\infty}^{\infty} dt_1 \, g_f(t_1) w_{cm}(t - t_1) \qquad (6.4\text{–}23)$$

The weighting function for the compensation, obtained by inverse transforming Eq. 6.4–19, is

$$w_{cm}(t) = T\delta_1(t) + \delta(t) \qquad (6.4\text{–}24)$$

The weighting function of the fixed elements is simply that of pure time delay

$$g_f(t_1) = \delta(t_1 - T) \qquad (6.4\text{–}25)$$

By Eqs. 6.4–22 through 25 the weighting function relating the error

to the input is found to be

$$w_y(t) = \delta(t) - \delta(t - T) - T\delta_1(t - T) \qquad (6.4\text{--}26)$$

Using the relation that

$$\int_{-\infty}^{\infty} dt_1\, \delta_1(t_1 - T)f(t - t_1) = \frac{df(t - T)}{dt} \qquad (6.4\text{--}27)$$

We find by Eq. 6.4–21 that the error is given by

$$y_e(t) = v(t) - v(t - T)$$
$$- T\,\frac{dv(t - T)}{dt} \qquad (6.4\text{--}28)$$

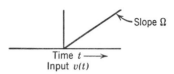

Slope Ω

Time $t \longrightarrow$
Input $v(t)$

Substituting in this equation the right member of Eq. 6.4–5 for $v(t)$ yields

$$y_e(t) = \Omega[\delta_{-2}(t) - \delta_{-2}(t - T)]$$
$$- \Omega T\delta_{-1}(t - T) \qquad (6.4\text{--}29)$$

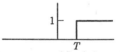

1

T

Step response of fixed elements

This result can be re-expressed as

$$y_e(t) = \Omega t[\delta_{-1}(t) - \delta_{-1}(t - T)]$$
$$\qquad (6.4\text{--}30)$$

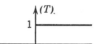

(T)

1

Step response of cascade compensation

By substituting this expression for the error as a function of time in Eq. 6.4–20 we find the integral-square error to be given by

$$I_y = \frac{\Omega^2 T^3}{3} \qquad (6.4\text{--}31)$$

ΩT

Input to fixed elements $m(t)$

This shows that the minimum integral-square error for this example is directly proportional to the cube of the time delay of the fixed elements.

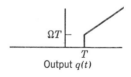

ΩT

T

Output $q(t)$

Figure 6.4–1 illustrates some of the important wave forms for this example. The compensation has the effect of making the output

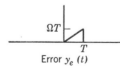

ΩT

T

Error $y_e(t)$

Fig. 6.4–1. Wave forms for system with delay compensated for ramp input.

equal to the input after the time delay of the fixed elements has elapsed. For times between zero and the value of the time delay T, it is evident that the output must be zero in view of the delay of the fixed elements. Thus the error must build up at the same rate as the input during this interval. This explains the error wave form shown in Fig. 6.4–1. It is interesting to observe that the compensation found by minimizing the integral-square error in this particular instance appears to minimize the peak of the absolute value of the error, the integral of the absolute value of the error, or almost any other reasonable performance index. This, of course, is a result that normally does not hold. Usually, minimizing the integral-square error does not minimize other error indices.

With this example we have completed our discussion of the minimization of integral-square error in the presence of fixed elements. Throughout this discussion we have had to assume that the fixed elements are stable. This has been necessary in order to permit an equivalent cascade compensation to be used for design purposes instead of the actual compensation located inside the closed loop. By using an equivalent cascade compensation the design problem is considerably simplified. However, the resultant requirement that the fixed elements be stable may seem unduly restrictive. Therefore the next article discusses a method for treating unstable fixed elements.

6.5 METHOD FOR TREATING UNSTABLE FIXED ELEMENTS

The method for treating unstable fixed elements was outlined briefly in Art. 1.7. In this article we shall review the technique mentioned there and illustrate it with an example.

The method for treating unstable fixed elements is almost self-evident provided the source of instability is understood. Fixed elements can be unstable only when they contain positive feedback around a transfer function that includes one or more active elements. The technique for handling unstable fixed elements is simply to modify the fixed elements so as to make them stable. It matters little how they are modified provided they are made stable and provided they are not made more non-minimum phase than they were initially. The standard ways for stabilizing fixed elements that are initially unstable are:

1. Reduction of gain around one or more internal feedback paths.

2. Insertion of compensation into one or more of the internal feedback paths.

3. Introduction of additional negative feedback paths around all or a portion of the fixed elements.

Once the fixed elements have been stabilized the design can proceed in terms of an equivalent cascade compensation. After the equivalent cascade compensation has been determined and the over-all transfer function for the system is established, it may be desirable to rearrange the auxiliary feedback paths in order to simplify the system. Frequently the need for an auxiliary feedback path inside the fixed elements can be completely eliminated by suitable adjustment of the compensation in the main loop. It is therefore evident that the main purpose of initially stabilizing the fixed elements (on paper, at least) is simply to facilitate the design by making the use of an equivalent cascade compensation possible. After the design is completed by going back to the feedback configuration, the need for stable fixed elements frequently may be eliminated by suitable adjustment of the compensation within the closed loop. The presence of unstable fixed elements in the specifications for a design does not of itself in any way imply an additional performance limitation.

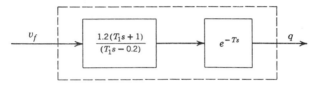

Fig. 6.5–1.   Unstable fixed elements.

In order to illustrate the foregoing ideas for handling unstable fixed elements let us reconsider the example of the preceding article. Let all the specifications be unchanged except that for the fixed elements. Instead of a pure time delay T, let us suppose that the fixed elements are as illustrated in Fig. 6.5–1. That is, the transfer function for the new fixed elements is given by

$$G_{fu}(s) = \frac{1.2(T_1 s + 1)}{(T_1 s - 0.2)} e^{-Ts} \qquad (6.5-1)$$

where the subscript u indicates unstable. This transfer function is unstable because of the pole located in the right half-plane. Physically, the transfer function of the block preceding the time delay in Fig. 6.5–1 could represent an overcompensated lag network formed by positive feedback through a low-pass filter around a pure gain.

It is possible to stabilize the fixed elements by placing a negative feedback loop around the first block. Figure 6.5–2 shows such a loop. By using a gain factor of 0.5 in the negative feedback loop, we arrive at the resultant stabilized fixed elements shown in Fig. 6.5–3. With the aid of the negative feedback loop the transfer function for the fixed elements has been modified from that of Eq. 6.5–1 to

$$G_{fs}(s) = \frac{0.75(T_1 s + 1)}{(T_1 s + 0.25)} e^{-Ts} \qquad (6.5\text{–}2)$$

Here the subscript s indicates stable.   The principal effect of the negative feedback loop has been to move the pole from the right half-plane into the left half-plane.   It has also changed the zero-frequency gain of the fixed elements from -6 to $+3$, but this is of minor significance.

Now that the fixed elements have been modified to provide stability, the designer may proceed exactly as before.   Since the modified fixed

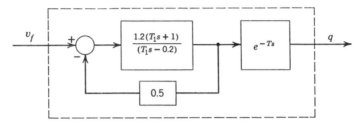

Fig. 6.5–2.   Internal feedback loop used to stabilize fixed elements.

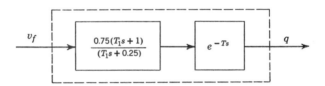

Fig. 6.5–3.   Resultant stabilized fixed elements.

elements represented by Eq. 6.5–2 are minimum phase except for the same time delay as in the previous example, where the fixed elements were represented by a pure time delay, the solution for the equivalent cascade compensation that minimizes the integral-square error is found by multiplying the compensation for the pure delay case by the reciprocal of the minimum-phase portion of the transfer function for the new fixed elements.   This follows from our discussion in Art. 6.3.   There we noted that to the extent to which the fixed elements are minimum phase they have no effect on the over-all transfer function for the system.   This means that minimum-phase factors can be omitted from the fixed elements in determining the compensation provided the compensation so determined is multiplied by the reciprocal of these factors before solving for the compensation to be used in the feedback configuration.   Using this method we find that the compensation to be used with the stable version of the fixed elements given by Eq. 6.5–2 is

$$W_{cms}(s) = \frac{4(T_1 s + 0.25)}{3(T_1 s + 1)} (Ts + 1) \qquad (6.5-3)$$

When this compensation is used, the integral-square error is the same as in the example of Art. 6.4 and the signal wave forms are identical with those shown in Fig. 6.4–1. In other words, the addition of an instability in the fixed elements does not in any way modify the over-all system performance.

6.6   GENERAL CONCLUSIONS CONCERNING PERFORMANCE LIMITATIONS IN LINEAR SYSTEMS

As the result of the theory and examples presented in Chapter 5 and also in this chapter, we are in a position to draw a number of general conclusions concerning performance limitations in linear systems. In Chapter 5 we saw that an attempt to predict the future value of a stochastic signal by means of a linear system leads to a definite performance limitation in the sense that the mean-square error cannot be made indefinitely small. Even when the system is adjusted for minimum mean-square error, there is a lower limit below which this error cannot be reduced. In general, imposing a requirement for prediction on a linear system necessarily limits the performance that can be achieved since a linear system operates only on present and past information. Another situation in which the performance of a linear system is inherently limited exists when the ideal output differs from the input because of noise. A similar situation comes about even when the ideal output and input are identical if disturbance signals enter the system at other points than the input. In general, noise and disturbances make it impossible for a linear system to establish equality between the ideal output and the actual output. In other words, any requirement for noise or disturbance filtering implies a definite limitation on the performance of a linear system.

In this chapter we examined in some detail the effect of fixed elements on the performance that can be achieved by linear systems. We concluded that minimum-phase fixed elements have no effect on the performance level that can be achieved in a linear system. If the fixed elements are non-minimum phase, however, very stringent performance limitations may result.

In summary, there are three performance requirements that inherently contain definite performance limitations for linear systems.

These are:

1. Prediction.
2. Noise and disturbance filtering.
3. Non-minimum-phase fixed elements.

If the specifications for a control system contain none of the above requirements, is there any conceivable limitation on its performance? For example, a positional control system may be required merely to reproduce the input signal. We ask, "Is there any possible limitation on its performance?" If the system is truly linear and the fixed elements are minimum phase, then the answer to this question is "No."

In practice, however, we know that this answer for a theoretical linear system is not satisfactory. In reality the fixed elements of a linear system at best are linear only over finite signal ranges. If the fixed elements are minimum phase and the system is merely required to reproduce the input signal, the equivalent cascade compensation for the fixed elements turns out to be the reciprocal of their transfer function. If the fixed elements contain integrations and lags, the compensation will have the effect of differentiating the input signal a number of times. This will tend to make the input signal to the fixed elements and the signals within the fixed elements have such large excursions that saturation sets in at one or more points. This saturation, in effect, negates the advantages that otherwise would accrue from the compensation. From a practical viewpoint, it therefore appears that saturation tendencies in the fixed elements will definitely limit the performance that can be achieved by a control system. If linear design theory is to be valid, we must learn how to design the compensation for the fixed elements so that saturation is avoided. The next chapter will show how our design theory can be modified to cope with saturation tendencies in the fixed elements.

7

LIMITATION OF
SATURATION TENDENCIES
IN FIXED ELEMENTS

7.1 THE PROBLEM OF SATURATION

Previous chapters considered situations in which the mathematical models were linear. The results of the examples showed that the systems designed in accordance with the analytical design theory exhibited signal amplitudes that were extremely large and in practice would exceed the range of linear operation of the system components. In order to account for the physical limitations due to saturation, Arts. 2.6, 2.7, and 4.7 discussed the use of constraints for keeping signals from exceeding their linear ranges. The advantage of attempting to limit signal amplitudes shows up more strongly when the implications of linearity are considered. If the fixed components are minimum phase, the compensation cancels the transfer function of the fixed components and substitutes another one appropriate for the system specifications. If this occurs and if the system is required to respond to an input signal containing a wide band of frequencies, the signals driving the fixed elements will have high-frequency components. Since physical devices often cannot respond linearly to high-frequency signals unless the amplitudes associated with these signals are exceedingly small, saturation may occur and the system will no longer behave according to the basic assumption of linearity. Thus, even though the compensation may minimize the performance index for the linear model, the physical system will not exhibit a minimum value for the performance index in view of its departure from linear operation. Furthermore the tendency of the physical system to saturate is often aggravated by the compensation obtained from linear theory.

Two approaches to the problem of saturation in free-configuration design are possible. In the first approach the combination of linear and non-linear elements can be described by a non-linear mathematical model and the effects of the non-linearities can be included in the analysis. The system is allowed to saturate and the effect of saturation on performance is analyzed by non-linear techniques. A general analytical method for minimizing a performance index under these conditions has not been developed; therefore trial-and-error design procedures usually must be employed.

The second approach is to replace the saturating elements by a linear model which represents the behavior of the saturating elements as long as the saturating signal is within its linear range.* The linear compensation to be designed is required to minimize the performance index under the constraint that the probability of the saturating signal exceeding its linear range be kept small. Under these conditions the saturating element will behave linearly for a large fraction of the time. The degree to which the linear model used for design is not valid is measured by the fraction of the time that the saturating signal exceeds its linear range. The validity of the linear model can be increased by reducing the probability of saturation. This second technique for accounting for saturation will be the method considered here. Limiting saturation by means of constraints on saturating signal amplitudes was proposed by Newton (Reference N.1). In our context the signals considered are stochastic variables, and the constraint on saturating signal amplitude will involve limiting the rms amplitude of the saturating signal to some specified fraction of the linear range of the saturating element. The configurations to be considered will be semi-free and the constraint on the saturating signal will be introduced by the Lagrangian multiplier technique (Art. 2.6).

The general problem of compensation for a semi-free configuration in the presence of saturation can be stated as follows:

Given. Information describing the statistical properties of the input and the ideal output, the properties of the fixed elements, and the maximum allowable rms value of the saturating signal.

---

* A saturating signal is any signal within the fixed elements whose response exhibits saturation when the value of the signal falls outside a certain range known as the linear range. As an example, consider the field flux of a d-c generator. The field current is a saturating signal since the flux fails to be proportional to the current when the magnitude of the current is large.

Find. The compensating network which minimizes the mean-square error subject to the constraint that the rms value of the saturating signal is less than or equal to its maximum allowable value.

The design problem is illustrated in Fig. 7.1–1 where the function $g_s(t)$ represents the impulse response relating the input $m(t)$ of the fixed elements to the saturating signal $q_s(t)$. In terms of the symbols of Fig. 7.1–1, the problem can be stated as follows:

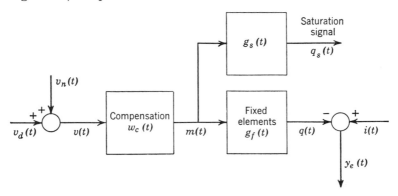

Fig. 7.1–1. Block diagram of semi-free-configuration compensation in the presence of saturation.

Given. $v_d(t)$, $v_n(t)$, $g_f(t)$, $g_s(t)$, and $i(t)$.

Find. $w_c(t)$ such that $\overline{y_e^2(t)}$ is minimized subject to the constraint that $\overline{q_s^2(t)} \leq \sigma_{sm}^2$, where σ_{sm} is the maximum allowable rms value of $q_s(t)$.

7.2 RELATION BETWEEN PROBABILITY OF SATURATION AND RMS AMPLITUDE LIMITATION

The basic assumption of the preceding section was that the probability of saturation can be limited by limiting the rms value of the saturating signal. The reasonableness of this assumption can be seen more readily through an examination of probability distributions and their relation to mean-square values in linear systems. Figure 7.2–1 shows the excitation-response characteristic of a saturating element. We see that the saturating element and its equivalent linear model are identical as long as the response does not exceed the linear response range. If we could hold the peak value of the response within the linear response range, then the linear model and the saturating element would be identical at all times for all practical purposes. Since it is extremely difficult to handle a peak value constraint by analytical techniques, we shall focus our attention on rms response, with the implicit assumption that controlling the maximum value of the rms response effectively limits the tendency of the response to exceed its linear range.

The relation between rms response and probability of saturation can be seen from the following considerations. Consider a linear system

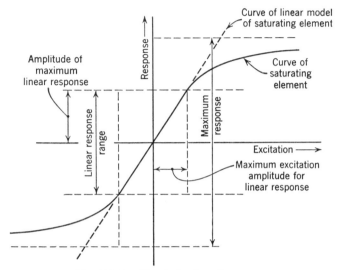

Fig. 7.2–1.   Typical saturation curve.

whose impulse response is $w(t)$ and whose input is a stationary stochastic signal with a *normal* (Gaussian) amplitude distribution given by

$$p(v)dv = \frac{dv}{\sigma\sqrt{2\pi}} \exp -\frac{1}{2}\left(\frac{v-\bar{v}}{\sigma}\right)^2 \tag{7.2–1}$$

where $p(v)dv$ = probability of finding v between v and $v + dv$

$$\bar{v} = \text{mean value of } v = \int_{-\infty}^{+\infty} v\, p(v)dv$$

$$\sigma^2 = \text{variance of } v = \int_{-\infty}^{+\infty} (v-\bar{v})^2 p(v)dv$$

In the normal distribution σ is called the standard deviation of the variable with respect to its mean value.

For the system we are describing we want to find the amplitude probability distribution of the output signal. The input signal $v(t)$ can be considered the sum of elementary impulses of intensity $v(t - t_1)dt_1$ where t_1 is the time of occurrence of the impulse and t is the time of observation of the output (see Fig. 1.3–2B). The output at time t due to one of these elementary impulses is $w(t_1)v(t - t_1)dt_1$.

By hypothesis $v(t - t_1)$ is normally distributed. Therefore the quantity $w(t_1)v(t - t_1) \, dt$ is also normally distributed since $w(t_1)$ is a weighting factor depending on t_1 only and independent of $v(t - t_1)$. The total output at the observation time t is given by the sum of the elementary contributions to the output from each of the impulse components of the input as given by the convolution integral (Eq. 1.3–3). But the sum of the elementary output components is the sum of a set of normally distributed variables, and statistical theory (Reference C.7, p. 212) states that the sum of a set of normal variables is also normal. Therefore if the input to a linear system is normally distributed its output is also normally distributed.

A more general result can be derived for inputs whose amplitude distributions are not normal by application of the Central Limit theorem (Reference C.7, pp. 213–220), which states, under rather general restrictions, that, whatever the distributions of a set of independent variables, the distribution of their sum asymptotically approaches a normal distribution as the number of variables increases. The asymptotic approach to normality of the output of a linear system whose input is not normal is most pronounced if the system function has low-pass characteristics. In practice we find that many actual signal amplitude distributions can be approximated by normal amplitude distributions. Thus for our purposes we can limit discussion to normal distributions and extend our result approximately to non-normal distributions when necessary.

We note that for normally distributed signals the first amplitude probability distribution function is determined by the average value and rms value of the signal. This follows from the definition of the variance of a variable. The variance of a stochastic variable is given by

$$\sigma^2 = \overline{(v - \bar{v})^2} \tag{7.2-2}$$

or

$$\sigma^2 = \overline{v^2} - (\bar{v})^2 \tag{7.2-3}$$

From Eq. 7.2–3 we see that the variance of v is uniquely related to $\overline{v^2}$, which is the mean-square value of v, and $\bar{v}$, which is the mean value of v. Since the properties of a normal distribution are determined by its variance σ^2 and its mean value $\bar{v}$ the rms value and mean value of a signal that is known to be normally distributed completely determine its first amplitude probability distribution function.

Returning to Fig. 7.2–1 let us assume that the excitation of the saturating element has a normal amplitude distribution with zero mean. In this case the probability of finding the saturating signal outside the range of maximum linear response is given exactly by:

$$P_s = 1 - \frac{1}{\sqrt{2\pi}} \int_{-\sigma_{sL}/\sigma_s}^{+\sigma_{sL}/\sigma_s} d(y/\sigma_s) \exp - \frac{y^2}{2\sigma_s{}^2} \qquad (7.2\text{–}4)$$

where

$P_s \triangleq$ probability of finding the actual response outside the linear range

$\sigma_{sL} \triangleq$ maximum linear response of the saturating element

$\sigma_s \triangleq$ rms response of the equivalent linear model (standard deviation of the distribution of the response of the equivalent linear model)

A plot of Eq. 7.2–4 appears in Fig. 7.2–2. From this curve we see, for example, that holding the rms response of the equivalent linear model

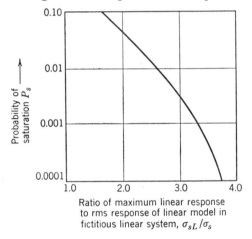

Fig. 7.2–2. Probability of saturation for a saturating element whose excitation is normally distributed with zero mean.

to 40 per cent of the maximum linear response will insure that the actual response will be within the maximum linear response range 99 per cent of the time. This supports the basic assumption that limiting the rms response in the equivalent linear model limits the probability of saturation in the actual saturating element. We conclude that the approach to the problem of saturation to be used here will become more accurate as the rms saturating signal is made small relative to its maximum linear range.

The foregoing discussion applies to the cascade configuration of Fig. 7.1–1 when the input to the system is normally distributed. The exact calculation of the probability of saturation by means of Eq. 7.2–4 is then possible since the input to the saturating element will be

normal.   Let us consider a feedback control system with a saturating
element (Fig. 7.2–3).   If the input to the system is normal the input
to the saturating element is not normal since the actuating signal
$e(t)$ will be the sum of the normally distributed input $v(t)$ and the non-
normally distributed output $q(t)$.   Under these conditions Eq. 7.2–4
cannot be used to calculate the probability of saturation.   However it
seems reasonable that the actuating signal will be a closer approxima-

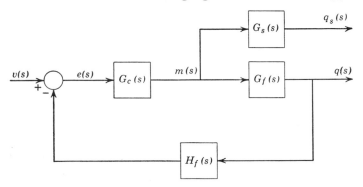

Fig. 7.2–3.   Equivalent linear model of a saturating feedback control system.

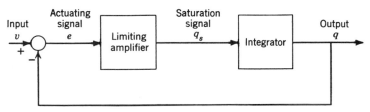

Fig. 7.2–4.   Experimental system used to study saturation in a feedback control
system.

tion to a normal distribution than the output $q_s(t)$ of the saturating
element since in most systems the saturating element is followed by
integrations and lags.   These low-pass elements tend to make the
output $q(t)$ of the system approach a normal distribution (as indicated
by application of the Central Limit theorem).   Thus even though the
exact functional relationship between the probability of saturation and
the rms value of the input to the saturating element is not known for a
saturating feedback control system, we are still justified in assuming
that the probability of saturation in this case is controlled by limiting
the rms saturation signal $q_s(t)$.

The ideas and assumptions of this article have been verified for one
case in an experiment carried out by Newton (Reference N.1).   The
system studied in this experiment is shown in Fig. 7.2–4.   The system

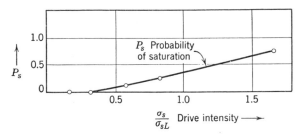

Fig. 7.2–5.   Probability of saturation as a function of drive intensity in experimental feedback control system.

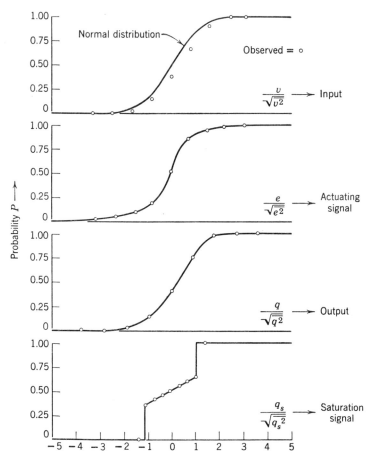

Fig. 7.2–6.   Probability distribution functions in experimental feedback control system, $\dfrac{\sigma_s}{\sigma_{sL}} = 1.65.$

represents a simple positional servomechanism subject to velocity saturation. The input to the system is approximately normally distributed. Results of the experiment that are of interest here are shown in Figs. 7.2–5 and 7.2–6. Figure 7.2–5 shows the relation between probability of saturation and drive intensity (ratio of rms saturation signal in the equivalent linear model to the maximum linear range of the actual saturating element) and demonstrates that the probability of saturation is controlled by the rms value of the saturating signal. Figure 7.2–6 shows the probability distribution functions of the input, the actuating signal, the output, and the saturation signal for a severe intensity ($\sigma_s/\sigma_{sL} = 1.65$). Even though the output of the saturating element departs radically from a normal distribution, we see that the other signals in the system are good approximations of a normal distribution. These results tend to support the general conclusions of this article.

7.3 SEMI-FREE-CONFIGURATION MINIMIZATION WITH SATURATION-SIGNAL CONSTRAINT

The problem of minimizing the mean-square error with a constraint on the rms value of the saturating signal is stated in Art. 7.1 and illustrated in Fig. 7.1–1. Referring to Fig. 7.1–1 the quantity to be minimized is $\overline{y_e^2(t)}$ and the constraint is

$$\overline{q_s^2(t)} \leq \sigma_{sm}^2 \qquad (7.3\text{–}1)$$

where $\sigma_{sm} \triangleq$ maximum allowable rms value of the saturating signal. The procedure for solving this problem involves establishing an expression for $\overline{y_e^2(t)}$ in terms of $g_f(t)$, $w_c(t)$, $v(t)$, and $i(t)$. $\overline{q_s^2(t)}$ is found in terms of $g_s(t)$, $w_c(t)$, and $v(t)$. Since the form of $w_c(t)$ is unknown we construct a functional by means of the Lagrangian multiplier technique. This functional is

$$F = \overline{y_e^2(t)} + \rho\overline{q_s^2(t)} \qquad (7.3\text{–}2)$$

where $\rho \triangleq$ Lagrangian multiplier. Since $\overline{y_e^2(t)}$ and $\overline{q_s^2(t)}$ are functionals of the unknown $w_c(t)$, application of the calculus of variations to the minimization of F yields an integral equation for $w_c(t)$ as a function of the Lagrangian multiplier ρ. After solving this integral equation we substitute $w_c(t)$ into the expression for $\overline{q_s^2(t)}$. The Lagrangian multiplier ρ is then adjusted so that the constraint (Eq. 7.3–1) is satisfied. Next the value of ρ thus found is substituted back into the expression for $w_c(t)$ thereby yielding a solution for the compensation. Determination of $\overline{y_e^2(t)}$, which is a function of $w_c(t)$ and therefore ρ, completes the solution by indicating the minimum value of $\overline{y_e^2(t)}$.

We shall now develop the above steps in detail. We can find expressions for $\overline{y_e^2(t)}$ and $\overline{q_s^2(t)}$ by repeated application of the convolution integral. In Fig. 7.1–1

$$y_e(t) = i(t) - q(t) \tag{7.3–3}$$

In terms of $g_f(t)$, $w_c(t)$ and $v(t)$

$$q(t) = \int_{-\infty}^{\infty} dt_1 \, w_c(t_1) \int_{-\infty}^{\infty} dt_2 \, g_f(t_2) v(t - t_1 - t_2) \tag{7.3–4}$$

In terms of $g_s(t)$, $w_c(t)$, and $v(t)$

$$q_s(t) = \int_{-\infty}^{\infty} dt_1 \, w_c(t_1) \int_{-\infty}^{\infty} dt_2 \, g_s(t_2) v(t - t_1 - t_2) \tag{7.3–5}$$

Squaring both sides of Eq. 7.3–3 and substituting Eq. 7.3–4 into the result give an expression for the square of the error

$$y_e^2(t) = i^2(t) - 2 \left[\int_{-\infty}^{\infty} dt_1 \, w_c(t_1) \int_{-\infty}^{\infty} dt_2 \, g_f(t_2) v(t - t_1 - t_2) \right] i(t)$$
$$+ \left[\int_{-\infty}^{\infty} dt_1 \, w_c(t_1) \int_{-\infty}^{\infty} dt_2 \, g_f(t_2) v(t - t_1 - t_2) \right]$$
$$\left[\int_{-\infty}^{\infty} dt_3 \, w_c(t_3) \int_{-\infty}^{\infty} dt_4 \, g_f(t_4) v(t - t_3 - t_4) \right] \tag{7.3–6}$$

New dummy variables t_3 and t_4 are introduced in the last term of Eq. 7.3–6 to avoid confusion in the multiple integration. Similarly the square of the saturation signal $q_s(t)$ is found

$$q_s^2(t) = \int_{-\infty}^{\infty} dt_1 \, w_c(t_1) \int_{-\infty}^{\infty} dt_2 \, g_s(t_2) v(t - t_1 - t_2)$$
$$\int_{-\infty}^{\infty} dt_3 \, w_c(t_3) \int_{-\infty}^{\infty} dt_4 \, g_s(t_4) v(t - t_3 - t_4) \tag{7.3–7}$$

We take averages with respect to time on both sides of Eq. 7.3–6 and Eq. 7.3–7. Substituting correlation functions for averages of the products of given time functions simplifies the expression for the mean-square error $\overline{y_e^2(t)}$ to

$$\overline{y_e^2(t)} = \varphi_{ii}(0) - 2 \int_{-\infty}^{\infty} dt_1 \, w_c(t_1) \int_{-\infty}^{\infty} dt_2 \, g_f(t_2) \varphi_{vi}(t_1 + t_2)$$
$$+ \int_{-\infty}^{\infty} dt_1 \, w_c(t_1) \int_{-\infty}^{\infty} dt_2 \, g_f(t_2) \int_{-\infty}^{\infty} dt_3 \, w_c(t_3)$$
$$\int_{-\infty}^{\infty} dt_4 \, g_f(t_4) \varphi_{vv}(t_1 + t_2 - t_3 - t_4) \tag{7.3–8}$$

The mean-square value of the saturating signal $\overline{q_s^2(t)}$ becomes

$$\overline{q_s^2(t)} = \int_{-\infty}^{\infty} dt_1\, w_c(t_1) \int_{-\infty}^{\infty} dt_2\, g_s(t_2) \int_{-\infty}^{\infty} dt_3\, w_c(t_3)$$
$$\int_{-\infty}^{\infty} dt_4\, g_s(t_4)\varphi_{vv}(t_1 + t_2 - t_3 - t_4) \quad (7.3\text{–}9)$$

Substituting Eqs. 7.3–8 and 7.3–9 in Eq. 7.3–2 yields the functional to be minimized:

$$F = \varphi_{ii}(0) - 2 \int_{-\infty}^{\infty} dt_1\, w_c(t_1) \int_{-\infty}^{\infty} dt_2\, g_f(t_2)\varphi_{vi}(t_1 + t_2)$$
$$+ \int_{-\infty}^{\infty} dt_1\, w_c(t_1) \int_{-\infty}^{\infty} dt_2\, g_f(t_2) \int_{-\infty}^{\infty} dt_3\, w_c(t_3)$$
$$\int_{-\infty}^{\infty} dt_4\, g_f(t_4)\varphi_{vv}(t_1 + t_2 - t_3 - t_4)$$
$$+ \rho \int_{-\infty}^{\infty} dt_1\, w_c(t_1) \int_{-\infty}^{\infty} dt_2\, g_s(t_2) \int_{-\infty}^{\infty} dt_3\, w_c(t_3)$$
$$\int_{-\infty}^{\infty} dt_4\, g_s(t_4)\varphi_{vv}(t_1 + t_2 - t_3 - t_4) \quad (7.3\text{–}10)$$

Applying the calculus of variations we let

$$w_c(t) = w_{cm}(t) + \epsilon w_\epsilon(t) \quad (7.3\text{–}11)$$

where $\epsilon w_\epsilon(t) \triangleq$ the variation of $w_c(t)$.

$w_{cm}(t) \triangleq$ the value of $w_c(t)$ which makes F stationary.

Substitution of the right member of Eq. 7.3–11 in Eq. 7.3–10 yields F as a function of ϵ. The stationary value of $w_c(t)$ is then found by setting the derivative of F with respect to ϵ equal to zero at $\epsilon = 0$, i.e., $w_{cm}(t)$ is the solution of

$$\left. \frac{dF}{d\epsilon} \right|_{\epsilon=0} = 0 \quad (7.3\text{–}12)$$

The details of the differentiation of F with respect to ϵ are similar to those leading to Eqs. 5.2–18 and 6.1–10. They will therefore be omitted here. Upon carrying out the operations indicated by Eq. 7.3–12 and after making use of the fact that $\varphi_{vv}(\tau)$ is even, we find

$$2 \int_{-\infty}^{\infty} dt_1\, w_\epsilon(t_1)$$
$$\left\{ \begin{array}{l} \int_{-\infty}^{\infty} dt_3\, w_{cm}(t_3) \left[\int_{-\infty}^{\infty} dt_2\, g_f(t_2) \int_{-\infty}^{\infty} dt_4\, g_f(t_4) \right. \\ \left. + \rho \int_{-\infty}^{\infty} dt_2\, g_s(t_2) \int_{-\infty}^{\infty} dt_4\, g_s(t_4) \right] \varphi_{vv}(t_1 + t_2 - t_3 - t_4) \\ - \int_{-\infty}^{\infty} dt_2\, g_f(t_2)\varphi_{vi}(t_1 + t_2) \end{array} \right\}$$
$$= 0 \quad (7.3\text{–}13)$$

Since $w_e(t_1)$ is realizable, it is zero for $t_1 < 0$ and arbitrary for $t_1 \geq 0$. Therefore the expression enclosed in braces in Eq. 7.3–13 must be zero for $t_1 \geq 0$. This yields the following integral equation whose solution gives the desired value of $w_c(t)$:

$$\int_{-\infty}^{\infty} dt_3 \, w_{cm}(t_3) \left[\left[\int_{-\infty}^{\infty} dt_2 \, g_f(t_2) \int_{-\infty}^{\infty} dt_4 \, g_f(t_4) \right. \right.$$

$$+ \rho \int_{-\infty}^{\infty} dt_2 \, g_s(t_2) \int_{-\infty}^{\infty} dt_4 \, g_s(t_4) \left. \right] \varphi_{vv}(t_1 + t_2 - t_3 - t_4)$$

$$- \int_{-\infty}^{\infty} dt_2 \, g_f(t_2) \varphi_{vi}(t_1 + t_2) = 0 \quad \text{for } t_1 \geq 0 \quad (7.3\text{–}14)$$

Comparing our solution with Eq. 5.4–1 we see that Eq. 7.3–14 is of the Wiener-Hopf type if we make the following identifications:

$$\Gamma(t_1) = \int_{-\infty}^{\infty} dt_2 \, g_f(t_2) \varphi_{vi}(t_1 + t_2) \qquad (7.3\text{–}15)$$

$$\Delta(t_1 - t_3) = \left[\int_{-\infty}^{\infty} dt_2 \, g_f(t_2) \int_{-\infty}^{\infty} dt_4 \, g_f(t_4) \right.$$

$$+ \rho \int_{-\infty}^{\infty} dt_2 \, g_s(t_2) \int_{-\infty}^{\infty} dt_4 \, g_s(t_4) \left. \right] \varphi_{vv}(t_1 + t_2 - t_3 - t_4) \quad (7.3\text{–}16)$$

$$\psi(t_3) = w_{cm}(t_3) \qquad (7.3\text{–}17)$$

Article 5.4 presents Eq. 5.4–28 as an explicit solution formula for equations of the Wiener-Hopf type. This equation is in terms of the Fourier transforms of $\Gamma(t)$ and $\Delta(t)$. We therefore transform both sides of Eq. 7.3–15 and 7.3–16. The results are

$$\Gamma(s) = 2\pi G_f(-s)\Phi_{vi}(s) \qquad (7.3\text{–}18)$$

$$\Delta(s) = 2\pi[G_f(s)G_f(-s) + \rho G_s(s)G_s(-s)]\Phi_{vv}(s) \qquad (7.3\text{–}19)$$

Substitution of these transforms into Eq. 5.4–28 yields the transfer function $W_{cm}(s)$ of the equivalent cascade compensation in terms of the transfer functions $G_f(s)$ and $G_s(s)$, the correlation functions $\Phi_{vi}(s)$ and $\Phi_{vv}(s)$, and the Lagrangian multiplier ρ.

To conclude the solution of the problem as described at the beginning of this article we must now evaluate $\overline{q_s^2(t)}$ in terms of $W_{cm}(s)$ (and therefore the multiplier ρ). Examining Fig. 7.1–1 the power spectrum of $q_s(t)$ is readily seen to be

$$\Phi_{ss}(s) = W_{cm}(s)W_{cm}(-s)G_s(s)G_s(-s)\Phi_{vv}(s) \qquad (7.3\text{–}20)$$

Knowing $\Phi_{ss}(s)$, $\overline{q_s^2(t)}$ can be evaluated from

$$\overline{q_s^2(t)} = \varphi_{ss}(0) = \frac{1}{j} \int_{-j\infty}^{j\infty} ds \, \Phi_{ss}(s) \qquad (7.3\text{–}21)$$

Evaluation of Eq. 7.3–21 yields $\overline{q_s^2(t)}$ as a function of ρ.

At this point ρ must be adjusted so that the constraint of Eq. 7.3–1 on $\overline{q_s{}^2(t)}$ is satisfied. In practice the adjustment of ρ usually involves graphical procedures since the constraint equation cannot ordinarily be solved explicitly for ρ. Once the Lagrangian multiplier ρ is determined the value of $W_{cm}(s)$ is fixed and the mean-square error can be calculated according to the methods of Art. 4.4, Eq. 4.4–4, or Eq. 4.4–12.

The preceding development has shown how we carry out the minimization of the mean-square error for a semi-free configuration with a constraint on the rms value of a saturating signal. We have considered the case involving only one saturating element. The extension of the method to situations involving more than one saturating element is self-evident. In practice the solution of this problem for more than one saturating element becomes laborious since the adjustment of the Lagrangian multipliers to satisfy the constraints will almost always have to be done graphically.

7.4 EXAMPLES

In order to demonstrate the procedures discussed in this chapter we shall consider two examples of mean-square error minimization in the presence of a saturation constraint.

The first example is a feedback control system whose input consists of data plus noise. The data component of the input has a derivative that is "white" noise with zero mean. The noise component of the input is "white" noise with zero mean. The data and the noise are uncorrelated, and the ideal output is the input data. The output velocity of the system saturates, and the requirement of the problem is to minimize the mean-square error while constraining the output rms velocity to a value less than or equal to a specified upper limit σ_{sm}. The feedback elements have a unity transfer function, and the fixed elements are minimum phase.

The problem statement is symbolized as follows (see Fig. 7.4–1):

Given.

$$v(t) = v_d(t) + v_n(t) \tag{7.4-1}$$

$$\Phi_{dd}(s) = -\frac{\gamma_d}{\pi s^2} \tag{7.4-2}$$

$$\Phi_{nn}(s) = \frac{\gamma_n}{\pi} \tag{7.4-3}$$

$$\overline{q_s^2} \le \sigma_{sm}^2 \quad \text{where } q_s = \frac{dq}{dt} \tag{7.4-4}$$

$$i(t) = v_d(t) \tag{7.4-5}$$

$$H_f(s) = 1 \tag{7.4-6}$$

Find. We wish to find the compensation $W_{cm}(s)$ which minimizes $\overline{y_e^2}$ while maintaining $\overline{q_s^2} \le \sigma_{sm}^2$

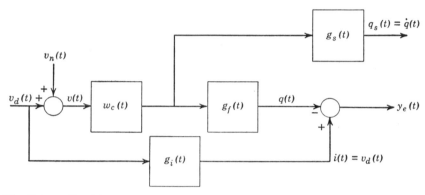

Fig. 7.4–1. Semi-free-configuration compensation with output-velocity saturation.

Solution. As explained in Art. 6.3, we need no information regarding the fixed components since they are minimum phase. Therefore for purposes of calculation we can assume that $G_f(s) = 1$. Then from the given data and Fig. 7.4–1 it is obvious that

$$G_i(s) = 1 \tag{7.4-7}$$

$$G_s(s) = s \tag{7.4-8}$$

Substituting the problem specifications into Eqs. 7.3–18 and 7.3–19

$$\Gamma(s) = 2\pi \Phi_{vi}(s) \tag{7.4-9}$$

$$\Delta(s) = 2\pi[1 - \rho s^2]\Phi_{vv}(s) \tag{7.4-10}$$

Since v_d and v_n are uncorrelated

$$\Phi_{vi}(s) = \Phi_{dd}(s) \tag{7.4-11}$$

$$\Phi_{vv}(s) = \Phi_{dd}(s) + \Phi_{nn}(s) \tag{7.4-12}$$

Therefore Eqs. 7.4–9 and 7.4–10 become

$$\Gamma(s) = \frac{2\gamma_d}{-s^2} \tag{7.4–13}$$

$$\Delta(s) = 2\gamma_n \frac{[1 - \rho s^2]\left[\dfrac{\gamma_d}{\gamma_n} - s^2\right]}{-s^2} \tag{7.4–14}$$

Letting $\dfrac{\gamma_d}{\gamma_n} = \beta^2$ for convenience we factor $\Delta(s)$ according to the method of Art. 5.4 yielding the factor of $\Delta(s)$ containing all poles and zeros of $\Delta(s)$ that lie in the right half-plane

$$\Delta^-(s) = 2\gamma_n \frac{[1 - \rho^{1/2}s][\beta - s]}{-s} \tag{7.4–15}$$

Then $\Gamma(s)/\Delta^-(s)$ becomes

$$\frac{\Gamma(s)}{\Delta^-(s)} = \frac{\beta^2}{s[1 - \rho^{1/2}s][\beta - s]} \tag{7.4–16}$$

After a partial fraction expansion of the right member of Eq. 7.4–16 we retain that part of the expansion associated with the poles of $\Gamma(s)/\Delta^-(s)$ in the left half-plane

$$\left[\frac{\Gamma(s)}{\Delta^-(s)}\right]_+ = \frac{\beta}{s} \tag{7.4–17}$$

Dividing Eq. 7.4–17 by $\Delta^+(s)$ yields the system function that minimizes $\overline{y_e^2}$ as a function of the Lagrangian multiplier ρ:

$$W_{cm}(s) = \frac{\beta}{[\beta + s][1 + \rho^{1/2}s]} \tag{7.4–18}$$

To complete the solution we must introduce the constraint on the output velocity. In terms of Fig. 7.4–1 the transform of the saturation signal is

$$q_s(s) = sW_{cm}(s)v(s) \tag{7.4–19}$$

Therefore the power-density spectrum of q_s is

$$\Phi_{ss}(s) = -s^2 W_{cm}(s)W_{cm}(-s)\Phi_{vv}(s) \tag{7.4–20}$$

Substituting the values for W_{cm} and Φ_{vv} (Eqs. 7.4–12 and 7.4–18)

$$\Phi_{ss}(s) = \frac{\gamma_d}{\pi(1 + \rho^{\frac{1}{2}}s)(1 - \rho^{\frac{1}{2}}s)} \qquad (7.4\text{–}21)$$

Now the mean-square output velocity is

$$\overline{\dot{q}^2} = \varphi_{ss}(0) = \frac{1}{j} \int_{-j\infty}^{j\infty} ds \, \Phi_{ss}(s) \qquad (7.4\text{–}22)$$

Therefore substituting the right member of Eq. 7.4–21 into Eq. 7.4–22

$$\overline{\dot{q}^2} = 2\gamma_d \frac{1}{2\pi j} \int_{-j\infty}^{j\infty} \frac{ds}{(1 + s\rho^{\frac{1}{2}})(1 - s\rho^{\frac{1}{2}})} \qquad (7.4\text{–}23)$$

Evaluating the right member of Eq. 7.4–23 we find the mean-square output velocity

$$\overline{\dot{q}^2} = \frac{\gamma_d}{\rho^{\frac{1}{2}}} \leq \sigma_{sm}{}^2 \qquad (7.4\text{–}24)$$

Next the mean-square error is evaluated, and then ρ is determined so as to satisfy the constraint on the output velocity while at the same time minimizing the mean-square error.

The power-density spectrum of y_e is given by (see Eq. 4.4–12)

$$\Phi_{yy}(s) = [1 - W_{cm}(s)][1 - W_{cm}(-s)]\Phi_{dd}(s)$$
$$+ W_{cm}(s)W_{cm}(-s)\Phi_{nn}(s) \qquad (7.4\text{–}25)$$

Substituting the values of W_{cm}, Φ_{dd}, and Φ_{nn}

$$\Phi_{yy}(s) = \frac{\gamma_d}{\pi} \frac{1 + (1 + \beta\rho^{\frac{1}{2}})^2 - \rho s^2}{d(s)d(-s)} \qquad (7.4\text{–}26)$$

where

$$d(s) = \rho^{\frac{1}{2}}(s)^2 + (1 + \beta\rho^{\frac{1}{2}})(s) + \beta \qquad (7.4\text{–}27)$$

Since the mean-square error is given by

$$\overline{y_e{}^2(t)} = \varphi_{yy}(0) = \frac{1}{j} \int_{-j\infty}^{j\infty} ds \, \Phi_{yy}(s) \qquad (7.4\text{–}28)$$

we use the integral tables in Appendix E to find the value of the mean-square error

$$\overline{y_e{}^2} = \gamma_d \left(\frac{2}{\beta} + \rho^{\frac{1}{2}} \right) \qquad (7.4\text{–}29)$$

From Eq. 7.4–29 we see that $\overline{y_e}^2$ is a minimum when ρ is as small as possible. From Eq. 7.4–24 ρ will be smallest when the equality holds for the constraint relation. Thus the Lagrangian multiplier will be adjusted such that

$$\rho^{1/2} = \frac{\gamma_d}{\sigma_{sm}^2} \tag{7.4-30}$$

The system function which minimizes the mean-square error becomes

$$W_{cm}(s) = \frac{1}{\left[1 + \left(\dfrac{\gamma_n}{\gamma_d}\right)^{1/2} s\right]\left[1 + \dfrac{\gamma_d}{\sigma_{sm}^2} s\right]} \tag{7.4-31}$$

The minimum mean-square error becomes

$$\overline{y_e}^2\bigg|_{\min} = \left[2(\gamma_d\gamma_n)^{1/2} + \left(\frac{\gamma_d}{\sigma_{sm}}\right)^2\right] \tag{7.4-32}$$

The behavior of the system we have just designed will depend on the "signal-to-noise" ratio $(\gamma_d/\gamma_n)^{1/2}$ and the "saturation" ratio $\sigma_{sm}/(\gamma_d)^{1/2}$. With no limit on the output velocity the minimum value of $\overline{y_e}^2$ is

$$\overline{y_e}^2\bigg|_{\min} = 2(\gamma_d\gamma_n)^{1/2} \tag{7.4-33}$$

Thus the absolute lower limit of the normalized rms error $(\overline{y_e}^2/\gamma_d)^{1/2}$ is determined by the "signal-to-noise" ratio. Increasing the signal-to-noise ratio reduces this lower limit. Since the lower limit of the normalized rms error is an absolute theoretical limit, it is of basic importance in describing the design limitations established by the problem specifications. We can express our results more succinctly by dividing rms errors by $(\gamma_d)^{1/2}$ to normalize them and by defining the following symbols:

y_n = normalized rms error in the presence of constraint.

y_{nm} = normalized rms error in the absence of constraint.

Then in terms of the signal-to-noise ratio $(\gamma_d/\gamma_n)^{1/2}$

$$y_{nm} = \sqrt{2}\left(\frac{\gamma_d}{\gamma_n}\right)^{-1/4} \tag{7.4-34}$$

The expression for the normalized minimum rms error in the presence of constraint (Eq. 7.4–32) can be written in terms of y_{nm} and the "saturation" ratio $\sigma_{sm}/\sqrt{\gamma_d}$ as

$$y_n = \left[y_{nm}{}^2 + \left(\frac{\sigma_{sm}}{\sqrt{\gamma_d}} \right)^{-2} \right]^{\frac{1}{2}} \qquad (7.4\text{–}35)$$

Equation 7.4–35 represents the normalized form of the "trading" curve of the problem since it indicates how we must trade error for linear range. Thus the larger the linear range (as measured by the ratio $\sigma_{sm}/\sqrt{\gamma_d}$), the closer we approach the absolute minimum error in the absence of constraint y_{nm}. The "amount" of trading to be done depends on the absolute minimum error y_{nm}.

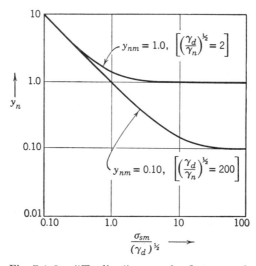

Fig. 7.4–2. "Trading" curves for first example.

The foregoing discussion is illustrated by the curves of Fig. 7.4–2 where values of 1 and 0.1 are used for y_{nm} to indicate the dependence of trading on the absolute minimum error (and therefore on the signal-to-noise ratio). Examining the trading curves we see that, as the signal-to-noise ratio $(\gamma_d/\gamma_n)^{\frac{1}{2}}$ increases, a wider linear range is needed for y_n to come within a given factor of the absolute minimum rms error y_{nm} associated with a given signal-to-noise ratio. In the absence of a constraint the rms value of the saturation signal is infinite regardless of the value of the signal-to-noise ratio. However when the saturating signal is constrained to a finite rms value the rms error increases relative to its absolute minimum for a given signal-to-noise ratio. Examining Eq. 7.4–32 we see that the error consists of two components—one arising from the presence of noise and the other arising from the saturation constraint. When the signal-to-noise ratio is high the error component due to the saturation constraint predominates and the total error is more sensitive to changes in the saturation constraint. Conversely, for a low signal-to-noise ratio, the error component due to noise predominates and a large reduction in linear range must take place before the error increases appreciably relative to the absolute minimum error associated with a given signal-to-noise ratio.

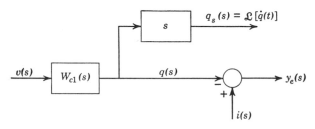

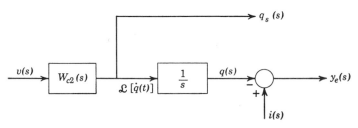

Fig. 7.4–3. Block diagrams of two equivalent minimization problems with saturation constraint.

It is of interest to note that the problem that we have just solved is also the solution to the problem where the transfer function of the fixed elements $G_f(s)$ is $1/s$ and the saturating signal is the input to the fixed elements. Of course in both cases the input properties are identical. The equivalence of the two problems is readily seen by examination of Fig. 7.4–3 where the block diagrams of the two problems are presented. It is evident from examination of Fig. 7.4–3 that

$$W_{c2}(s) = sW_{c1}(s) \tag{7.4–36}$$

As our second example we apply the concept of limitation of saturating signals to the design of a positional servomechanism which employs a field-controlled servomotor. Figure 7.4–4 shows the schematic diagram of this servomechanism. The shunt d-c servomotor has a constant current, supplied from a source not shown, flowing through its armature. The field flux established by the field current causes a torque to be developed on the armature in direct proportion to its value. It is assumed that the only load on the output member is its moment of inertia. Thus the acceleration of the output member is proportional to the field flux. The field flux is established by field current which in turn is controlled by an amplifier. The amplifier receives its signal from synchro devices used to measure the actuating signal or difference between the input and the output. The synchro signal is demodulated and operated upon by a compensating network in passing to the amplifier. This type of servomechanism is sometimes used in instrument applications. The field-controlled servomotor has the advantage that the main power required to drive it does not have

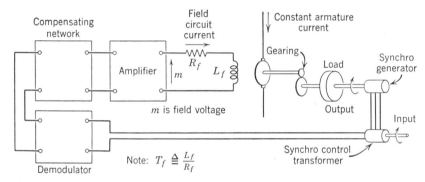

Fig. 7.4–4. Schematic diagram of servomechanism which uses field-controlled servomotor.

to be controlled because this power comes from the armature circuit. The amplifier merely has to control the power required for the field, and this is normally a small fraction of the output power.

The design problem is to find the compensation for the field-controlled servomotor that, for the input specified below, will make the rms error equal to or less than 1 percent of the rms input without causing appreciable saturation. The servomotor with its associated amplifier is subject to saturation in two ways: First, the amplifier is capable of supplying only a limited voltage to the field circuit. Second, the flux established by the field current ceases to be proportional to this current when its magnitude exceeds a certain value. Thus, the design problem that we face here can be represented by the block diagram of Fig. 7.4–5. We desire to find the equivalent cascade compensation $W_c(s)$ which will minimize the mean-square error between the desired output and the actual output subject to simultaneous limitations on the field voltage and field current. Determination of rms error for this compensation will then tell us if the error specification can be met.

The compensation $W_c(s)$ is taken to be the transfer function between the input $v(s)$ and the field voltage $m(s)$. There are two transfer functions relating field voltage to the saturating signals. These are $G_{s1}(s)$ and $G_{s2}(s)$. The first of these has the value unity, and the second is the admittance of the field circuit. The transfer function for the fixed elements $G_f(s)$ has the value indicated in Fig. 7.4–5 where k_f is the steady-state output acceleration developed per unit of field voltage. The time constant T_f is the field time constant and is equal to the inductance of the field divided by its resistance. The desired output will be assumed equal to the input because this is a positional servomechanism. The input signal will be taken to be a rectangular wave of amplitude plus or minus β and with zero crossings Poisson distributed with average frequency ν. The maximum output

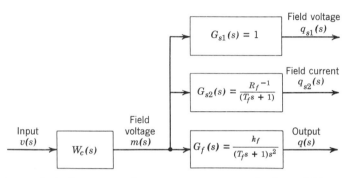

Fig. 7.4–5. Block diagram used to represent servomechanism which uses field-controlled servomotor.

voltage of the amplifier is plus or minus 100 volts. The field current produces flux proportional to its value up to 100 milliamperes and practically no increase in flux beyond this value. In order to have a probability of saturation of the order to 1 percent or less, the compensation for this system will be designed to maintain the rms value of the field voltage q_{s1} equal to or less than 30 volts and simultaneously to maintain the rms value of the field current q_{s2} equal to or less than 30 milliamperes. The numerical values of the parameters describing the motor are:

Field resistance $R_f = 1000$ ohms
Field time constant $T_f = 0.01$ sec
Motor gain constant $k_f = 40$ rad volt^{-1} sec^{-2}

The amplitude of the input signal β is 20 radians, and the average frequency ν of zero crossings is 0.1 second^{-1}. Thus a 1 percent allowable rms error corresponds to 0.2 radian.

We now restate the problem in terms of symbols:

Given.   The power-density spectrum of the input signal is

$$\Phi_{vv}(s) = \frac{\beta^2}{\pi} \frac{2\nu}{-s^2 + 4\nu^2} \qquad (\beta = 20 \text{ rad}, \ \nu = 0.1 \text{ sec}^{-1}) \quad (7.4\text{–}37)$$

This follows from the analysis of the input signal which was conducted in Chapters 3 and 4.

$$G_f(s) = \frac{k_f}{(T_f s + 1)s^2} \qquad (k_f = 40 \text{ rad volt}^{-1} \sec^{-2}, \ T_f = 0.01 \text{ sec})$$

$$(7.4\text{–}38)$$

$$G_{s1}(s) = 1 \qquad (7.4\text{–}39)$$

$$G_{s2}(s) = \frac{R_f^{-1}}{T_f s + 1} \qquad (R_f = 1000 \text{ ohms}) \qquad (7.4\text{–}40)$$

$$i(t) = v(t) \qquad (7.4\text{–}41)$$

$$\overline{y_e^2(t)} \leq \sigma_{em}^2 \qquad (\sigma_{em} = 0.2 \text{ rad}) \qquad (7.4\text{–}42)$$

$$\overline{q_{s1}^2(t)} \leq \sigma_{sm1}^2 \qquad (\sigma_{sm1} = 30 \text{ volts}) \qquad (7.4\text{–}43)$$

$$\overline{q_{s2}^2(t)} \leq \sigma_{sm2}^2 \qquad (\sigma_{sm2} = 0.030 \text{ amp} \qquad (7.4\text{–}44)$$

Find.   The compensation $W_c(s)$ that minimizes the mean-square value $\overline{y_e^2(t)}$ of the error subject to the constraints of Eqs. 7.4–43 and 7.4–44 above.

Solution.   This problem is solved by the general solution formula given as Eq. 5.4–28 in which we use

$$\Delta(s) = 2\pi[G_f(-s)G_f(s) + \rho_1 G_{s1}(-s)G_{s1}(s) + \rho_2 G_{s2}(-s)G_{s2}(s)]\Phi_{vv}(s)$$

$$(7.4\text{–}45)$$

This form for $\Delta(s)$ follows from the extension of the analysis of Article 7.3 needed to handle two simultaneous saturating signal constraints. The form for $\Gamma(s)$ is unchanged from Eq. 7.3–18.

In order to simplify the analysis to follow, an approximation will be used for the input power-density spectrum given by Eq. 7.4–37. We note that most of the mean-square error and mean-square value for the saturating signals is associated with the higher-frequency components of the input signal spectrum.   For frequencies appreciably above 2ν the power-density spectrum behaves as $1/-s^2$.   Thus the input-signal spectrum will be taken as

$$\Phi_{vv}(s) = -\frac{2\beta^2\nu}{\pi s^2} \qquad (7.4\text{–}46)$$

We next write expressions for $\Gamma(s)$ and $\Delta(s)$. These expressions are based on the transfer functions listed under the given data and on the approximation for the power-density spectrum for the input signal listed above. We also make use of the fact that the cross-power-density spectrum between the input and the desired output is equal to the spectrum of the input signal since the desired output is the same as the input. For this particular problem we find

$$\Gamma(s) = \frac{4\beta^2 \nu k_f}{(-T_f s + 1)(-s)^3 s} \qquad (7.4\text{--}47)$$

$$\Delta(s) = \left(\frac{4\beta^2 \nu k_f{}^2}{-s^2}\right)\left[\frac{1}{(-T_f{}^2 s^2 + 1)s^4} + \frac{\rho_2'}{(-T_f{}^2 s^2 + 1)} + \rho_1'\right] \qquad (7.4\text{--}48)$$

Here we have defined

$$\rho_1' = \rho_1 k_f{}^{-2} \qquad (7.4\text{--}49)$$

$$\rho_2' = \rho_2 R_f{}^{-2} k_f{}^{-2} \qquad (7.4\text{--}50)$$

Rearranging the expression for $\Delta(s)$, we find

$$\Delta(s) = \frac{4\beta^2 \nu k_f{}^2}{(-s^2)}\left[\frac{-\rho_1' T_f{}^2 s^6 + (\rho_1' + \rho_2')s^4 + 0s^2 + 1}{(-T_f s + 1)(-s)^2(T_f s + 1)s^2}\right]$$

$$(7.4\text{--}51)$$

$$\Delta^+(s) = \frac{a_3 s^3 + a_2 s^2 + a_1 s + 1}{(T_f s + 1)s^3} \qquad (7.4\text{--}52)$$

$$\Delta^-(s) = (4\beta^2 \nu k_f{}^2)\frac{a_3(-s)^3 + a_2(-s)^2 + a_1(-s) + 1}{(-T_f s + 1)(-s)^3}$$

$$(7.4\text{--}53)$$

where, by equating coefficients of $\Delta^+(s)\Delta^-(s)$ to those of $\Delta(s)$, we have

$$a_3{}^2 = \rho_1' T_f{}^2 \qquad (7.4\text{--}54)$$

$$a_2{}^2 - 2a_3 a_1 = \rho_1' + \rho_2' \qquad (7.4\text{--}55)$$

$$a_1{}^2 - 2a_2 = 0 \qquad (7.4\text{--}56)$$

Proceeding with the solution, we have

$$\frac{\Gamma(s)}{\Delta^-(s)} = \frac{k_f{}^{-1}}{[a_3(-s)^3 + a_2(-s)^2 + a_1(-s) + 1]s} \qquad (7.4\text{--}57)$$

Expanding in partial fractions and retaining poles in left half-plane only gives

$$\left[\frac{\Gamma(s)}{\Delta^-(s)}\right]_+ = \frac{k_f{}^{-1}}{s} \qquad (7.4\text{--}58)$$

Dividing by $\Delta^+(s)$ yields

$$W_{cm}(s) = \frac{k_f{}^{-1}(T_f s + 1)s^2}{a_3 s^3 + a_2 s^2 + a_1 s + 1} \tag{7.4--59}$$

This is the general form which the equivalent cascade compensation must have in order to satisfy the requirements of this problem. The coefficients of the denominator polynomial are functions of the Lagrangian multipliers. The next step is to express the mean-square values of the saturating signals in terms of these coefficients.

Reference to Fig. 7.4--5 shows that the power-density spectrum for the field voltage is given by

$$\Phi_{ss1}(s) = W_{cm}(-s)G_{s1}(-s)W_{cm}(s)G_{s1}(s)\Phi_{vv}(s) \tag{7.4--60}$$

Upon substituting into this expression the values for the transfer functions and the power-density spectrum of the input signal, we find

$$\Phi_{ss1}(s) = \frac{2\beta^2 \nu}{\pi k_f{}^2} \frac{c_1(-s)c_1(s)}{d(-s)d(s)} \tag{7.4--61}$$

where

$$c_1(s) = T_f s^2 + s \tag{7.4--62}$$

$$d(s) = a_3 s^3 + a_2 s^2 + a_1 s + 1 \tag{7.4--63}$$

The mean-square value of the field voltage is found by integrating the power-density spectrum along the imaginary axis. Thus

$$\overline{q_{s1}{}^2(t)} = \frac{1}{j} \int_{-j\infty}^{j\infty} ds\, \Phi_{ss1}(s) \tag{7.4--64}$$

Since the power-density spectrum is a rational function, it can be evaluated by reference to the table of integrals in Appendix E. Using the formula for I_3, we find

$$\overline{q_{s1}{}^2(t)} = \frac{2\beta^2 \nu}{k_f{}^2} \frac{\dfrac{T_f{}^2 a_1}{a_3} + 1}{a_2 a_1 - a_3} \tag{7.4--65}$$

Next, the mean-square value of the field current is found. The power-density spectrum for the field current is given by expressions analogous to Eq. 7.4--60 and Eq. 7.4--61, providing the subscript 1 is replaced by the subscript 2. Here the numerator polynomial is given by

$$c_2(s) = R_f{}^{-1}s \tag{7.4--66}$$

The denominator polynomial is given by Eq. 7.4--63 as before. Upon evaluating the integral for the mean-square value of the field current, we find

$$\overline{q_{s2}{}^2(t)} = \frac{2\beta^2\nu}{k_f{}^2R_f{}^2}\frac{1}{a_2a_1 - a_3} \tag{7.4-67}$$

Equations 7.4–65 and 7.4–67 give the mean-square values of the field voltage and the field current, respectively, as functions of the as yet undetermined denominator coefficients of the transfer function for the equivalent cascade compensation as given by Eq. 7.4–59. From Eqs. 7.4–54 through 7.4–56 it is seen that these coefficients are functions of the Lagrangian multipliers ρ_1' and ρ_2'. The next step is to adjust the Lagrangian multipliers so that the constraints on the field voltage and field current given by Eqs. 7.4–43 and 7.4–44 are satisfied. From Eq. 7.4–54 it is observed that a_3 is directly related to the first Lagrangian multiplier. If this multiplier is made equal to zero, a_3 will be equal to zero and the mean-square value of the field voltage will be infinite according to Eq. 7.4–65. Thus ρ_1' must have some value other than zero. On the other hand, setting the second Lagrangian multiplier equal to zero does not necessarily result in a violation of the constraint on the mean-square value of the field current. Therefore, our procedure in adjusting the Lagrangian multipliers is first to adjust ρ_1' so that the constraint on the field voltage is satisfied. Then the field current will be checked to see if the constraint on it is satisfied. If it is satisfied, the only additional analysis needed is a check to be sure not only that the mean-square error is stationary but also that it has the lowest minimum value in case more than one minimum exists. On the other hand, if the mean-square current constraint is violated, ρ_2' will be assigned non-zero values and a trial-and-error adjustment made so that both constraints are satisfied simultaneously.

In carrying out the above procedure of Lagrangian multiplier adjustment, it is convenient in Eqs. 7.4–54 through 7.4–56 to regard a_1 as a basic time constant and to solve for the other coefficients in terms of a_1. Of course, this basic time constant is a function of both Lagrangian multipliers. However, the first Lagrangian multiplier may be eliminated by combining Eqs. 7.4–54 and 7.4–55. Thus, with

$$a_2 = \frac{a_1{}^2}{2} \tag{7.4-68}$$

as determined from Eq. 7.4–56, we have

$$a_3 = T_f[(T_f{}^2a_1{}^2 + 0.25a_1{}^4 - \rho_2')^{\frac{1}{2}} - T_fa_1] \tag{7.4-69}$$

The procedure is first to consider ρ_2' equal to zero and to examine how the mean-square values of the field voltage, field current, and error vary as functions of a_1. To do this we need an expression for the mean-square error.

The mean-square error is found by integrating its power-density spectrum which in this case is given by

$$\Phi_{yy}(s) = W_y(-s)W_y(s)\Phi_{vv}(s) \tag{7.4-70}$$

where

$$W_y(s) = 1 - W_c(s)G_f(s) \tag{7.4-71}$$

Substituting in the values of the transfer functions and the input spectrum yields

$$\Phi_{yy}(s) = \frac{2\beta^2\nu}{\pi}\frac{c_y(-s)c_y(s)}{d(-s)d(s)} \tag{7.4-72}$$

where

$$c_y(s) = a_3s^2 + a_2s + a_1 \tag{7.4-73}$$

Upon evaluating the integral for the mean-square error, we find

$$\overline{y_e^2(t)} = 2\beta^2\nu\frac{a_2{}^2 + a_2a_1{}^2 - a_3a_1}{a_2a_1 - a_3} \tag{7.4-74}$$

The problem now becomes one of numerical analysis in which a_1 is regarded as the basic parameter. For selected values of a_1, corresponding values of a_2 and a_3 are found by Eqs. 7.4–68 and 7.4–69. Thus the mean-square field voltage, field current, and error are all determined as functions of a_1 through the use of Eqs. 7.4–65, 7.4–67, and 7.4–74. In general, the mean-square field voltage and field current are found to be monotonic decreasing functions of a_1 whereas the mean-square error is found to be a monotonic increasing function of a_1. By plotting these functions for ρ_2' equal to zero, a value of a_1 is found that satisfies the field voltage constraint. In particular, for

$$a_1 = 0.0575 \text{ sec} \tag{7.4-75}$$

$$a_2 = 1.650 \times 10^{-3} \text{ sec}^2 \tag{7.4-76}$$

$$a_3 = 1.175 \times 10^{-5} \text{ sec}^3 \tag{7.4-77}$$

we find that

$$[\overline{q_{s1}{}^2(t)}]^{1/2} = 30 \text{ volts} \tag{7.4-78}$$

$$[\overline{q_{s2}{}^2(t)}]^{1/2} = 0.0246 \text{ amp} \tag{7.4-79}$$

$$[\overline{y_e{}^2(t)}]^{1/2} = 2.69 \text{ rad} \tag{7.4-80}$$

Thus, with a_1 adjusted to satisfy the field-voltage constraint, the field-current constraint is automatically satisfied, and there is no need to consider values of ρ_2' different from zero in this particular instance. However, we observe that the rms error is over 13 percent of the rms value of the input signal. Since we desired an rms error of 1 percent, it is clear that the specifications for this problem can never be met and that they must be rejected as inconsistent within themselves.

If the constraint on the field current specified an rms value less than 0.0246 ampere, a value of ρ_2' different from zero would have to be used. From Eq. 7.4–69 it is seen that the effect of a positive value for ρ_2' is to decrease the value of a_3. This in turn tends to increase the value of the mean-square field voltage with the result that a_1 must be increased to satisfy the constraint. Since the mean-square error is a very strong function of a_1 (tending to increase approximately as the cube of this quantity), it is seen that the effect of requiring a value of the second Lagrangian multiplier different from zero is to increase the error.

In conclusion, this example has demonstrated the feasibility of considering more than one constraint on signal levels within the fixed elements of a control system. In addition, it has also demonstrated to us very clearly one of the great advantages of the analytical design procedure. This advantage is the ability to detect an inconsistent set of specifications. The trial-and-error design procedure could never determine with certainty the inconsistency in the specifications of this example.

7.5 CONCLUSION

This chapter deals with an extension of the semi-free-configuration problem to the very practical case of saturation. We show that a linear model can be constructed for a non-linear saturating system by limiting the probability of saturation in the model. Consideration of an elementary feedback control system indicates that the approximation involved in replacing a non-linear system by an equivalent linear system is a valid one. The saturation problem is then treated by minimizing the rms error with the constraint that the rms saturating signal be held below a specified upper limit. This is a problem that can be solved by the Lagrangian multiplier technique. The solution that results is an integral equation of the Wiener-Hopf type.

Two examples are considered to demonstrate the significance of the solution. The trading curve concept is used in the first of these examples to emphasize the dependence of error on linear range. The second example shows how multiple constraints on saturating signals can be handled.   The technique for multiple constraints is illustrated by the design of a positional servomechanism that has two signals which must be limited to avoid saturation.

The results of this chapter are of practical significance since the designer now is able to include physical limitations in an analytical design.   The next chapter deals with another practical situation that can be interpreted in terms of analytical design theory, namely, the problem of bandwidth minimization.

8

DESIGN OF
CONTROL SYSTEMS
FOR MINIMUM BANDWIDTH

8.1 IMPORTANCE OF MINIMIZING BANDWIDTH

In this chapter we shall discuss first the relationship between system bandwidth and system performance, design, and cost. After realizing the importance of minimizing bandwidth we then proceed to define bandwidth in such a way that we transpose our problem of minimizing bandwidth to that of minimizing the mean-square value of the filtered output of the system to a noise input. The performance specifications of the system for normal input signals are introduced into the problem as constraints in the minimization procedure. By application of the variational method an integral equation results whose solution is the optimum system weighting function having a minimum bandwidth and satisfying the other performance specifications. Three examples are given that illustrate the application of the method.

The approach to system design developed in the preceding chapters is based upon the performance indices of mean-square error for stochastic inputs and integral-square error for transient inputs. The designs so obtained by using these criteria, especially the integral-square error criterion, often have large bandwidths. Here bandwidth is used in a very general sense as the frequency range over which the system will have an output $q(t)$ approximately equal to the desired output $i(t)$.

215

Looking at the question of bandwidth from a different viewpoint we consider, for example, a positional servomechanism in which the desired output is simply the input. If we represent the input signal by its power-density spectrum when the signal is stochastic in nature or by its energy-density spectrum when the signal is transient in form then, in order for the error to be small, the system must be capable of transmitting with negligible amplitude and phase change all those frequencies present in the input. If the input signal is periodic, the spectrum is composed of discrete frequencies all of which are integer multiples of some fundamental frequency. If the input signal is aperiodic, the spectrum is continuous and includes all frequencies. Hence for zero error our system must have infinite bandwidth. Usually a compromise is made that accepts a finite value of integral-square error or mean-square error in return for easing the bandwidth requirement from infinity to a finite value. Even with this relaxation of error specification the actual realization of the compromise system may be very difficult with the hardware or components that are available. The difficulties that arise in a practical problem are directly dependent upon the bandwidth demanded of the system.

We shall now consider some of the system properties that are related intimately to bandwidth. First, limiting the bandwidth can result in the attenuation of transmitted noise whereas, conversely, excessive bandwidth not only increases the transmitted noise but may easily cause unwanted saturation in the system by raising the internal signal levels.

Limiting the bandwidth also eases the requirements for components operating at high power levels since the required power generally increases with bandwidth. If we consider, for example, a positional servomechanism consisting of a motor driving a pure inertia load, the power output is proportional to the product of motor torque and velocity. Since the motor torque is proportional to the acceleration of the load, the output power is then proportional to the product of load acceleration and load velocity. For a sinusoidal output of frequency ω, the peak power required to drive the output is proportional to ω^3. For inputs composed of a number of frequencies, extension of this reasoning shows that the peak power required at the output is often associated largely with the higher frequencies. A low bandwidth system in these situations requires less peak power at the output than one with a large bandwidth.

Reducing the bandwidth in general simplifies the compensation necessary. For low-bandwidth applications, the high-frequency dynamics of the components have negligible effect on system performance and hence are usually neglected in the approximation of their transfer characteristics. For high-bandwidth applications, however, these dynamics must necessarily be included as they now will greatly affect system performance. The compensation effectively substitutes for the deficient characteristics of the fixed elements those characteristics that are necessary to satisfy the performance specifications. Hence the more complex the approximation for the fixed elements is, the more complex will be the form of the compensation. Compensation for wide bandwidth can be both costly from an economic point of view and much more difficult to realize from the construction standpoint.

In mechanical systems elastances and backlash in gears and compliance in supporting structures may prove troublesome if the bandwidth is large. Overcoming these difficulties can be expensive and quite involved.

It would seem desirable from an economic point of view then to minimize the cost of the system subject to constraints on the performance indices. Unfortunately such a problem is very difficult to formulate in a way amenable to analytical calculation. However from the previous discussion we have seen that cost and bandwidth are rather closely related so that by minimizing bandwidth we shall in a general way have crudely minimized cost. Hence to avoid the difficulties present because of excessive bandwidth which are latent within conventional techniques a design procedure is desired that places emphasis on minimizing bandwidth. The development of such a design procedure is the primary concern of this chapter.

8.2 DEFINITION OF BANDWIDTH IN TERMS OF A BANDWIDTH TEST

Before we can devise an analytical procedure to minimize bandwidth by adjusting the system weighting function, bandwidth must first be rigidly defined. For this situation the definition should cover as general a class of systems as possible and should be such that the measure of bandwidth can be expressed analytically without excessive difficulty. We recall that, in general, increasing the bandwidth of a system increases the amount of transmitted noise. But we have already developed methods (Chapters 5, 6, and 7) for determining the system weighting function that minimizes the mean-square value of transmitted noise. Hence if we could devise a scheme that would provide a *unique* relationship between system bandwidth and the mean-square value of transmitted noise, we could use our previously developed methods in modified form for the determination of the optimum system. A scheme that provides this relationship is termed the *bandwidth test* and is described below.

During the bandwidth test a stationary stochastic noise signal is used as the input to the control system.   The resultant output of the system to this noise input is passed through a filter whose rms output is then measured.   The filter is inserted to give the designer control of the cutoff characteristics of the system.   The rms value of the filtered output is correlated with the bandwidth of the control system by *comparison* with the filtered output of a standard system of any prescribed form but having adjustable bandwidth.   The bandwidth of the standard system is adjusted to produce an rms value of its filtered output equal to that of the control system.   Both the standard system and the control system are driven from a common noise source during this bandwidth test.   Figure 8.2–1 shows this scheme in block diagram form for defining control system bandwidth.   By definition the bandwidth

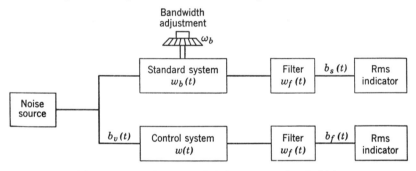

Fig. 8.2–1.   Scheme for defining system bandwidth.

of the control system is equal to the bandwidth of the standard system when the rms values of the filtered outputs are equal.

In order to assure that minimizing the filtered output of the control system shall be equivalent to minimizing its bandwidth the standard system together with the noise source and filter must produce a monotonically increasing rms output with increasing bandwidth.   Except for this requirement the choice of the noise source, the standard system, and the filter are completely arbitrary.   It is important to retain this generality in the definition of the test, as it leads to a greater flexibility in handling certain system specifications such as the rate of high-frequency cutoff.

8.3   FORMULATION OF THE PROBLEM

The basic problem to be solved is that of determining the control system weighting function $w(t)$ which satisfies certain performance requirements and which has a minimum bandwidth according to the specified bandwidth test.   The test is so designed that there exists a unique relation between the bandwidth of the control system and the rms value of the filtered output $b_f(t)$ (Fig. 8.2–1). This relation is such that increasing the bandwidth of the standard system always results in an increase in the rms value of its filtered output. By virtue of this definition of bandwidth the basic problem of minimizing bandwidth is equivalent to the problem of determining the control system weighting function $w(t)$ that minimizes the mean-square value of its *filtered* output during the bandwidth test subject to constraints on its performance indices for normal input signals. This equivalent formulation of the problem is identical in general form with the basic problem considered in Chapter 7, where now the constraints are placed on the system performance indices rather than on the mean-square values of saturating signals. Thus the form of the entire development in Chapter 7 can be used to solve our problem of minimizing bandwidth.

The control systems we consider can be either free or semi-free in configuration. Choosing the free-configuration system gives us the necessary latitude in determining the most nearly optimum system according to our specifications. The specifications for the problem are divided into two groups. The first group includes the requirements for the performance indices which may be in terms of integral-square error for transient signals or mean-square error for stochastic signals. The second group of specifications comprises those required for the description of the bandwidth test. These include the filter function $W_f(s)$, the noise source, and the standard system. For a discussion of the performance indices we refer to Chapters 2 and 4, where their use and justification are described in detail.

The question next arises, "With the bandwidth test defined as in Art. 8.2 how does one go about choosing a noise source, standard system, and filter so as to complete the problem specification?" First, we recall that the bandwidth test furnishes us a *calibration* for our control system in terms of a bandwidth parameter. This calibration depends on the choice of noise source, standard system, and filter. Second, these must be so chosen that a mean-square filtered output results which increases monotonically in value with increase in bandwidth.

The choice of noise source is arbitrary and can be chosen with regard to the noise that the actual system may encounter. In many situations the choice of the noise source as a white noise generator is suitable because white noise has components of all frequencies and is not confined therefore to a fixed range of frequencies. It also has the advantage of having a very simple autocorrelation function and power-density spectrum which makes it very amenable to analytical calculation.

Once the noise source has been specified, the choice of a suitable filter can be made with regard to the cutoff characteristics desired in the optimum control system. The filter form has full control of the cutoff rate to be imposed on the system. The criterion is that the mean-square value of filtered output must have a finite value since it is this signal that is to be minimized. Now if a white noise source is used, the combination of control system and filter must cut off at least as fast as $1/\omega$ in order to assure a finite value of mean-square filtered output. Then by making the filter a pure differentiator of the $(n-1)$th order we automatically require the system to cut off at the rate of at least $1/\omega^n$. The main justification for the choice of a pure differentiator as the filter lies in its simplicity. By suitable choice of the filter we can specify, as an additional requirement for the control system, its minimum rate of cutoff for high frequencies.

With the complete specification of noise source and filter the standard system is chosen also to produce a finite value of mean-square filtered output. Other than this requirement the choice of the standard system is arbitrary as its use is only to provide a calibration for the control system in terms of its bandwidth parameter. The form of the standard system is usually chosen with simplicity of calculation and ease of visualization in mind.

One choice might be that of a simple binomial filter of the form

$$W_b(s) = \frac{1}{\left(1 + \dfrac{s}{\omega_b}\right)^n} \tag{8.3–1}$$

where n is the order of the system and ω_b is the bandwidth parameter. This form is very amenable to calculation in the frequency domain and has frequency response characteristics that are easily visualized. Figure 8.3–1 presents the gain and phase characteristics of such a filter.

Another choice for a standard system could be a Butterworth filter of the nth order such as

$$W_b(s) = \frac{1}{B_n\left(\dfrac{s}{\omega_b}\right)} \tag{8.3–2}$$

where the first four orders are given by

$$B_1 = 1 + \frac{s}{\omega_b} \tag{8.3–3}$$

$$B_2 = 1 + 1.41\left(\frac{s}{\omega_b}\right) + \left(\frac{s}{\omega_b}\right)^2 \tag{8.3–4}$$

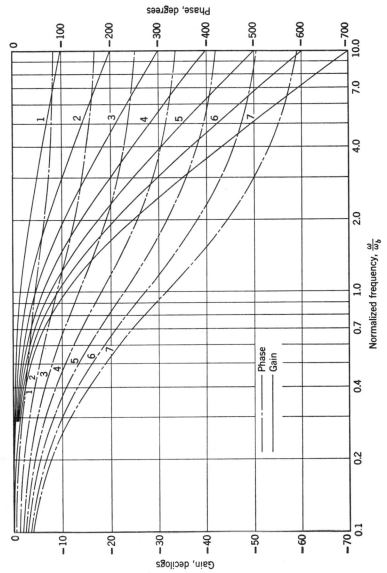

Fig. 8.3–1. Binomial filter characteristics. The order of the filter is shown on the curves.

221

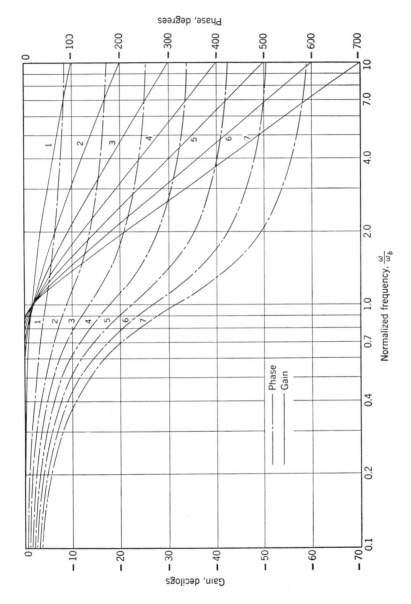

Fig. 8.3-2. Butterworth filter characteristics. The order of the filter is shown on the curves.

222

$$B_3 = 1 + 2\left(\frac{s}{\omega_b}\right) + 2\left(\frac{s}{\omega_b}\right)^2 + \left(\frac{s}{\omega_b}\right)^3 \qquad (8.3\text{--}5)$$

$$B_4 = 1 + 2.61\left(\frac{s}{\omega_b}\right) + 3.41\left(\frac{s}{\omega_b}\right)^2 + 2.61\left(\frac{s}{\omega_b}\right)^3 + \left(\frac{s}{\omega_b}\right)^4 \qquad (8.3\text{--}6)$$

This filter has amplitude and phase characteristics that are somewhat more centered about the critical frequency ω_b than they are for the binomial form. Its gain and phase characteristics are given in Fig. 8.3–2.

8.4 SOLUTION FOR SYSTEM WEIGHTING FUNCTION HAVING MINIMUM BANDWIDTH SUBJECT TO SPECIFIED LIMITS ON THE VALUES OF THE PERFORMANCE INDICES

Since, as explained in Art. 8.3, minimizing the bandwidth is equivalent to minimizing the noise transmitted by the control system, we seek the system weighting function that will minimize the rms value of the filtered noise transmitted through the control system within the constraints imposed by the specified values of the performance indices. This is an isoperimetric problem in the calculus of variations, and hence we shall apply a variational procedure in finding a solution.

The procedure for solution is first to formulate the expression for the mean-square value of filtered noise transmitted through the system. Next, expressions are obtained for the performance indices for the system in terms of the system weighting function when the system is acted upon by either transient or stochastic signals. By using the Lagrangian multiplier procedure a functional is constructed as the linear combination of the mean-square value of filtered noise and a sum of terms each equal to a performance index times a Lagrangian multiplier. The variational procedure is then applied to this functional to determine the integral equation whose solution is the optimum system weighting function in terms of the Lagrangian multipliers. This integral equation will, in general, be of the Wiener-Hopf form. If the given functions in the integral equation are analytic and hence transformable then a closed form for the solution may be obtained by the spectrum factorization procedure as outlined in Art. 5.4. If the given functions are not analytic, either they may be approximated by analytic functions and the spectrum factorization procedure used or the integral equation may be solved numerically. In either situation the weighting function so obtained will be a function of the Lagrangian multipliers. The Lagrangian multipliers are then evaluated by adjusting them to satisfy the constraints on the performance indices. Finally, using these values for the multipliers, the optimum system transfer function is determined. This transfer function can then be expressed in terms of bandwidth by using the calibration provided by the bandwidth test. This completes the solution of the problem.

In order to show how this procedure is carried out, we shall consider the problem in which the performance index is the integral-square error for a specified transient input and where we wish to find the system weighting function having minimum bandwidth. This specification of a single performance index for a transient input is not a serious restriction of the general method. It is done to reduce the length of the

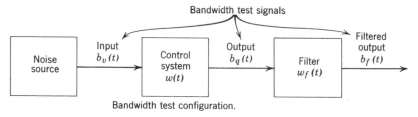

Bandwidth test configuration.

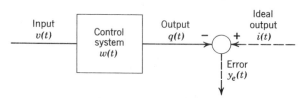

Configuration for normal operation.

Fig. 8.4–1. The variational problem. Find $w(t)$ which makes $\overline{b_f{}^2(t)}$ a minimum within constraints on performance indices.

equations so as to show clearly the development of the required integral equation. The generalization of the procedure is indicated in verbal form only and it is left to the reader to apply the method to his particular problem.

The terminology used in the development is clearly indicated in Fig. 8.4–1, which shows the general form of the problem. Since the development to be carried out here is so similar in form to that in Chapter 7, only the salient parts of the derivation are included.

First, the mean-square value of the filtered output during the bandwidth test is found as a functional of $w(t)$ by use of convolution as

$$b_f(t) = \int_{-\infty}^{\infty} dt_1 \, w_f(t_1) \int_{-\infty}^{\infty} dt_2 \, w(t_2) b_v(t - t_1 - t_2) \qquad (8.4\text{--}1)$$

Upon squaring, we get

$$b_f{}^2(t) = \int_{-\infty}^{\infty} dt_1 \, w_f(t_1) \int_{-\infty}^{\infty} dt_2 \, w(t_2) \int_{-\infty}^{\infty} dt_3 \, w_f(t_3)$$
$$\int_{-\infty}^{\infty} dt_4 \, w(t_4) b_v(t - t_1 - t_2) b_v(t - t_3 - t_4) \quad (8.4\text{--}2)$$

Recalling

$$\varphi_{bvv}(\tau) \triangleq \lim_{T \to \infty} \frac{1}{2T} \int_{-T}^{T} dt \, b_v(t) b_v(t + \tau) \quad (8.4\text{--}3)$$

and that

$$\overline{b_f{}^2(t)} \triangleq \lim_{T \to \infty} \frac{1}{2T} \int_{-T}^{T} dt \, b_f{}^2(t) \quad (8.4\text{--}4)$$

there results the desired expression in the time domain for the mean-square value of filtered output

$$\overline{b_f{}^2(t)} = \int_{-\infty}^{\infty} dt_1 \, w_f(t_1) \int_{-\infty}^{\infty} dt_2 \, w(t_2) \int_{-\infty}^{\infty} dt_3 \, w_f(t_3)$$
$$\int_{-\infty}^{\infty} dt_4 \, w(t_4) \varphi_{bvv}(t_1 + t_2 - t_3 - t_4) \quad (8.4\text{--}5)$$

Here we seek $w(t)$ which minimizes $\overline{b_f{}^2(t)}$ subject to the specified constraint on the integral-square error. In order to introduce this constraint the integral-square error is determined as a functional of $w(t)$ as follows. Since

$$y_e(t) \triangleq i(t) - q(t) \quad (8.4\text{--}6)$$

hence

$$y_e{}^2(t) = i^2(t) - 2i(t)q(t) + q^2(t) \quad (8.4\text{--}7)$$

where

$$q(t) = \int_{-\infty}^{\infty} dt_2 \, w(t_2) v(t - t_2) \quad (8.4\text{--}8)$$

and therefore

$$q^2(t) = \int_{-\infty}^{\infty} dt_2 \, w(t_2) \int_{-\infty}^{\infty} dt_4 \, w(t_4) v(t - t_2) v(t - t_4) \quad (8.4\text{--}9)$$

Recalling the definitions of the translation functions

$$I_{ii}(\tau) \triangleq \int_{-\infty}^{\infty} dt \, i(t) i(t + \tau) \quad (2.4\text{--}1)$$

$$I_{vi}(\tau) \triangleq \int_{-\infty}^{\infty} dt \, v(t) i(t + \tau) \quad (2.4\text{--}2)$$

$$I_{vv}(\tau) \triangleq \int_{-\infty}^{\infty} dt \, v(t) v(t + \tau) \quad (2.4\text{--}1)$$

there follows

$$I_y \triangleq \int_{-\infty}^{\infty} dt \, y_e{}^2(t) \quad (8.4\text{--}10)$$

Hence

$$I_y = I_{ii}(0) - 2 \int_{-\infty}^{\infty} dt_2\, w(t_2) I_{vi}(t_2)$$
$$+ \int_{-\infty}^{\infty} dt_2\, w(t_2) \int_{-\infty}^{\infty} dt_4\, w(t_4) I_{vv}(t_2 - t_4) \quad (8.4\text{--}11)$$

The functional to be minimized is then

$$F = \overline{b_f^{\,2}(t)} + \rho I_y \qquad (8.4\text{--}12)$$

In Eq. 8.4–12, $w(t)$ is replaced by $w_m(t) + \epsilon w_\epsilon(t)$, and the operation

$$\left. \frac{\partial F}{\partial \epsilon} \right|_{\epsilon = 0} = 0 \qquad (8.4\text{--}13)$$

is carried out. The resulting integral equation that arises from this operation is then

$$\int_{-\infty}^{\infty} dt_4\, w_m(t_4)$$
$$\left\{ \int_{-\infty}^{\infty} dt_1\, w_f(t_1) \int_{-\infty}^{\infty} dt_3\, w_f(t_3) \varphi_{bvv}(t_1 + t_2 - t_3 - t_4) \right.$$
$$\left. + \rho I_{vv}(t_2 - t_4) \right\} - \rho I_{vi}(t_2) = 0 \quad \text{for } t_2 \geq 0 \quad (8.4\text{--}14)$$

This equation is of the Wiener-Hopf form

$$\int_{-\infty}^{\infty} dt_4\, \psi(t_4)\, \Delta(t_2 - t_4) - \Gamma(t_2) = 0 \quad t_2 \geq 0 \qquad (5.4\text{--}1)$$

where the associations

$$\psi(t_4) \triangleq w_m(t_4) \qquad (8.4\text{--}15)$$

$$\Delta(t_2 - t_4) \triangleq \int_{-\infty}^{\infty} dt_1\, w_f(t_1) \int_{-\infty}^{\infty} dt_3\, w_f(t_3) \varphi_{bvv}(t_1 + t_2 - t_3 - t_4)$$
$$+ \rho I_{vv}(t_2 - t_4) \qquad (8.4\text{--}16)$$

$$\Gamma(t_2) \triangleq \rho I_{vi}(t_2) \qquad (8.4\text{--}17)$$

are made.

The solution of this integral equation is then the system weighting function $w_m(t)$ expressed as a function of the Lagrangian multiplier ρ. If the given functions $w_f(t)$, $\varphi_{bvv}(\tau)$, $I_{vv}(\tau)$, and $I_{vi}(\tau)$ are not analytic functions, then one is usually forced either to solve for $w_m(t)$ by numerical procedures or first to approximate the given functions by known analytic functions and then to use the spectrum factorization procedure after Fourier-transforming the given functions. If the given functions are analytic at the outset, then the spectrum factorization procedure is applied directly to their Fourier transforms.   By Fourier-transforming Eqs. 8.4–15, 8.4–16, and 8.4–17 there results

$$\Psi(s) = W_m(s) \tag{8.4--18}$$

$$\Delta(s) = 2\pi W_f(s) W_f(-s) \Phi_{bvv}(s) + \rho I_{vv}(s) \tag{8.4--19}$$

$$\Gamma(s) = \rho I_{vi}(s) \tag{8.4--20}$$

The solution for the optimum weighting function can then be expressed as

$$W_m(s) = \frac{\left[\dfrac{\Gamma(s)}{\Delta^-(s)}\right]_+}{\Delta^+(s)} \tag{5.4--28}$$

where the terminology is that used in Chapter 5.

The solution obtained for $W_m(s)$ is a function of the Lagrangian multiplier ρ.   The value of ρ is then determined so as to satisfy the constraint placed on the value of integral-square error.   By using this calculated value of ρ in Eq. 5.4–28 the optimum system weighting function becomes completely defined.

The system weighting function can now be written in terms of a bandwidth parameter when the calibration procedure as defined in the bandwidth test is used.   Here the mean-square value of filtered output from the control system is found in terms of ρ and equated to the mean-square value of the filtered output of the standard system. This provides a fixed relation between ρ and ω_b, the bandwidth parameter of the standard system.   From application of the constraint, ρ and hence ω_b can be expressed in terms of the limiting value of the performance index.   This relationship shows clearly the effect on the system bandwidth of changing the specification for the integral-square error and thus adds much insight into our understanding of the system.

The result of our development is the system weighting function that satisfies the integral-square error requirements for the specified transient input and which does so with the least possible bandwidth.   To illustrate the procedure as outlined above we shall next consider several examples.

8.5 EXAMPLES ILLUSTRATING THE METHOD

For the first example a simple positional servomechanism is considered in which the desired output is the input and the input is a ramp applied at time equal to zero.   The problem is to determine the system weighting function that minimizes the bandwidth while keeping the value of integral-square error to the transient input below a fixed limit. For the bandwidth test a white noise source is used; that is, the power-density spectrum of the noise generator output is a constant independent of frequency. Also for the bandwidth test the transfer function of the filter is unity, and the standard system has a first-order binomial form. This choice of noise source and filter makes the optimum system have a cutoff rate of at least 10 decilogs* per decade since a smaller cutoff rate fails to ensure a finite rms value of filtered output. The standard system is assigned a binomial form because then the filtering action is easily visualized, the cutoff characteristics are centered about a single frequency, and the rms filtered output is easily calculated as a function of bandwidth. The foregoing verbal statement of the problem is now put in terms of mathematical symbols.

Given.

$$v(t) = \Omega_v \delta_{-2}(t) \qquad (8.5\text{--}1)$$

$$i(t) = v(t) \qquad (8.5\text{--}2)$$

$$\Phi_{bvv}(s) = \frac{A^2}{2\pi} \qquad (8.5\text{--}3)$$

$$W_f(s) = 1 \qquad (8.5\text{--}4)$$

$$W_b(s) = \frac{1}{1 + (s/\omega_b)} \qquad (8.5\text{--}5)$$

$$I_y = \int_{-\infty}^{\infty} y_e^2(t)\, dt \qquad (8.5\text{--}6)$$

$$I_y \leq I_{ym} \qquad (8.5\text{-}7)$$

Find. We wish to find $W_m(s)$ which has minimum bandwidth and which satisfies the constraint on the integral-square error.

Solution. The general solution of Art. 8.4 is now applied to the particular situation represented by this example. Since the problem specifications are in terms of analytic functions, we choose to form the solution in the frequency domain.

The transform of the input autotranslation function is found as

$$I_{vv}(s) = v(s)v(-s) \qquad (8.5\text{--}8)$$

This follows from Eq. 2.4–30. But

$$v(s) = \frac{\Omega_v}{s^2} \qquad (8.5\text{--}9)$$

* A decilog (abbreviated dg) is a logarithmic unit such that the magnitude of a number N in decilogs is given by $10 \log_{10} N$.

and hence

$$I_{vv}(s) = \frac{\Omega_v{}^2}{s^2(-s)^2} \qquad (8.5\text{--}10)$$

Since the desired output is equal to the input the cross-translation function $I_{vi}(\tau)$ is equal to the autotranslation function $I_{vv}(\tau)$. Thus

$$I_{vi}(s) = \frac{\Omega_v{}^2}{s^2(-s)^2} \qquad (8.5\text{--}11)$$

Now

$$\Gamma(s) = \rho I_{vi}(s) \qquad (8.4\text{--}20)$$

Hence

$$\Gamma(s) = \frac{\rho\Omega_v{}^2}{s^2(-s)^2} \qquad (8.5\text{--}12)$$

Also

$$\Delta(s) = 2\pi W_f(s)W_f(-s)\Phi_{bvv}(s) + \rho I_{vv}(s) \qquad (8.4\text{--}19)$$

Therefore

$$\Delta(s) = A^2 + \rho\frac{\Omega_v{}^2}{s^2(-s)^2} \qquad (8.5\text{--}13)$$

This can be written more simply as

$$\Delta(s) = A^2\frac{(s^4 + 4b^4)}{s^2(-s)^2} \qquad (8.5\text{--}14)$$

where

$$4b^4 = \frac{\rho\Omega_v{}^2}{A^2} \qquad (8.5\text{--}15)$$

Next $\Delta(s)$ is factored into $\Delta^+(s)$ and $\Delta^-(s)$ as

$$\Delta^+(s) = \frac{(s + b + jb)(s + b - jb)}{(+s)^2} \qquad (8.5\text{--}16)$$

$$\Delta^-(s) = A^2\frac{(s - b + jb)(s - b - jb)}{(-s)^2} \qquad (8.5\text{--}17)$$

Here the factoring was accomplished symmetrically with the pole at $+s = 0$ associated with the LHP and the pole at $-s = 0$ associated with the RHP.

We now form

$$\frac{\Gamma(s)}{\Delta^-(s)} = \frac{\rho\Omega_v{}^2}{A^2}\frac{(-s)^2}{s^2(-s)^2(s - b + jb)(s - b - jb)} \qquad (8.5\text{--}18)$$

Simplifying this expression by using Eq. 8.5–15 gives

$$\frac{\Gamma(s)}{\Delta^-(s)} = \frac{4b^4}{(+s)^2(s - b + jb)(s - b - jb)} \tag{8.5–19}$$

A partial fraction expansion is made of the right-hand side as

$$\frac{1}{s^2(s - b + jb)(s - b - jb)} = \frac{a_1}{(+s)^2} + \frac{a_2}{(+s)} + \frac{a_3 s + a_4}{(s^2 - 2bs + 2b^2)} \tag{8.5–20}$$

Only a_1 and a_2 need be determined as they are the coefficients of the terms with singularities in the LHP. a_1 is found simply as

$$a_1 = \left\{ s^2 \left[\frac{1}{s^2(s^2 - 2bs + 2b^2)} \right] \right\}_{s=0} = \frac{1}{2b^2} \tag{8.5–21}$$

It is noticed that a_2 is the residue of the pole at the origin; hence by residue theory for multiple-order poles (Appendix A)

$$a_2 = \frac{d}{ds} \left\{ s^2 \left[\frac{1}{s^2(s^2 - 2bs + 2b^2)} \right] \right\}_{s=0} \tag{8.5–22}$$

Hence

$$a_2 = \frac{1}{2b^3} \tag{8.5–23}$$

Therefore

$$\left[\frac{\Gamma(s)}{\Delta^-(s)} \right]_+ = \frac{2b(s + b)}{(+s)^2} \tag{8.5–24}$$

Now, by inserting Eq. 8.5–16 and Eq. 8.5–24 into Eq. 5.4–28, the transform of the desired optimum weighting function $w(t)$ is found as

$$W_m(s) = \frac{2b(s + b)}{(s^2 + 2bs + 2b^2)} \tag{8.5–25}$$

or

$$W_m(s) = \frac{(s/b) + 1}{\frac{1}{2}(s/b)^2 + (s/b) + 1} \tag{8.5–26}$$

where b is defined by Eq. 8.5–15 in terms of the Lagrangian multiplier.

It now remains to find the value of b that satisfies the constraint on the integral-square error. By use of Parseval's theorem and the integral tables given in Appendix E, we find

$$I_y = \frac{\Omega_v^2}{8b^3} \tag{8.5–27}$$

Therefore

$$\frac{\Omega_v{}^2}{8b^3} \leq I_{ym} \qquad (8.5\text{–}28)$$

In order to decide whether to use the equality or the inequality in Eq. 8.5–28 the expression for mean-square filtered noise must first be evaluated in terms of the parameter b. The power-density spectrum of the filtered output is given by

$$\Phi_{bff}(s) = W_m(s)W_f(s)W_m(-s)W_f(-s)\Phi_{bvv}(s) \qquad (8.5\text{–}29)$$

By using

$$\overline{b_f{}^2} = \frac{1}{j}\int_{-j\infty}^{j\infty} ds\, \Phi_{bff}(s) \qquad (8.5\text{–}30)$$

there results

$$\overline{b_f{}^2} = \tfrac{3}{2}A^2 b \qquad (8.5\text{–}31)$$

It is now apparent that, for minimum $\overline{b_f{}^2}$, b should be as small as possible and hence the equality is chosen. Solving Eq. 8.5–28 for b gives

$$b = \frac{1}{2}\left(\frac{\Omega_v{}^2}{I_{ym}}\right)^{\!1/3} \qquad (8.5\text{–}32)$$

The parameter b can be expressed in terms of the bandwidth parameter ω_b by making use of the bandwidth test as the calibration mechanism. The mean-square value of the filtered noise from the standard system, expressed in terms of the standard system parameter ω_b and the noise amplitude, is given by

$$\Phi_{bss} = W_f(s)W_b(s)W_f(-s)W_b(-s)\Phi_{bvv}(s) \qquad (8.5\text{–}33)$$

For this example the general result is

$$\overline{b_s{}^2} = \frac{A^2}{2}\,\omega_b \qquad (8.5\text{–}34)$$

By equating the right members of Eqs. 8.5–31 and 8.5–34 there results

$$b = \frac{\omega_b}{3} \qquad (8.5\text{–}35)$$

and hence the minimum bandwidth system is

$$W_m(s) = \frac{3(s/\omega_b) + 1}{4.5(s/\omega_b)^2 + 3(s/\omega_b) + 1} \qquad (8.5\text{–}36)$$

where

$$\omega_b = \frac{3}{2}\left(\frac{\Omega_v^2}{I_{ym}}\right)^{\frac{1}{3}} \tag{8.5-37}$$

or

$$I_y = \frac{27}{8}\frac{\Omega_v^2}{\omega_b^3} \tag{8.5-38}$$

This system has a damping ratio of $\sqrt{2}/2$ associated with its impulse response. It is interesting to see that this method gives us a damping ratio that is considered very reasonable by practical standards. It is also interesting to note that the 10-decilog-per-decade cutoff rate of this minimum bandwidth system is the least value possible under the specified conditions of the bandwidth test.

For our second example we consider the same problem as that specified for the first example except that we now require a cutoff rate of at least 20 decilogs per decade. This specification can be imposed simply by choosing the bandwidth test filter to be a first-order differentiator. Thus we choose

$$W_f(s) = s \tag{8.5-39}$$

To ensure a finite rms value of the filtered output from the standard system during the bandwidth test, the standard system is chosen as

$$W_b(s) = \frac{1}{[1 + (s/\omega_b)]^2} \tag{8.5-40}$$

so as to make the product $W_f(s)W_b(s)$ behave at least as $1/s$ for large s.

The solution for the optimum system weighting function for this example is carried out directly as in the first example, and therefore the details of the solution are omitted. The final result is given as

$$W_m(s) = \frac{3.63(s/\omega_b) + 1}{6(s/\omega_b)^3 + 6.61(s/\omega_b)^2 + 3.63(s/\omega_b) + 1} \tag{8.5-41}$$

where

$$\omega_b = 2.08\left(\frac{\Omega_v^2}{I_{ym}}\right)^{\frac{1}{3}} \tag{8.5-42}$$

or

$$I_y = 9\frac{\Omega_v^2}{\omega_b^3} \tag{8.5-43}$$

Regarding the bandwidth as fixed, we see from Eqs. 8.5–38 and 8.5–43 that the required cutoff rate of 20 decilogs per decade has been obtained at the expense of increased integral-square error.

Figure 8.5–1, which shows the error response of the two examples as a function of time, clearly indicates the effect of demanding a higher cutoff rate. Another aspect of this effect is the increased peaking in the frequency response of the control system as shown in Fig. 8.5–2. Looking at this another way, for a fixed limit on the integral-square error, the bandwidth required for the increased cutoff rate in the second example is 40 percent greater than for the first example.

As our third illustration we shall consider the basic problem as outlined in the first example except that the desired output is the input delayed by T seconds. This is a practical problem since a time delay

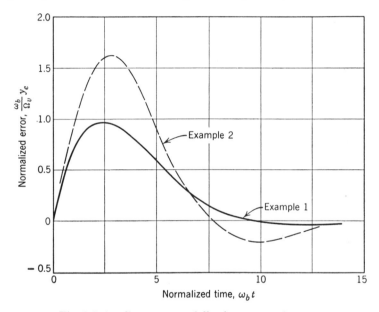

Fig. 8.5–1. System error following a ramp input.

can often be associated with the desired output. For example, in signal reproducing systems where only wave shape is important the desired output can be the input delayed by a fixed amount of time. We shall be interested in seeing how this time delay affects the optimum control system transfer function and how it affects the system bandwidth.

The mathematical statement of this problem is as follows:

Given.

$$v(t) = \Omega_v \delta_{-2}(t) \qquad (8.5\text{–}44)$$

$$i(t) = v(t - T) \qquad (8.5\text{–}45)$$

$$I_y = \int_{-\infty}^{\infty} dt \, y_e^2(t) \tag{8.5-6}$$

$$I_y \leq I_{ym} \tag{8.5-7}$$

$$W_f(s) = 1 \tag{8.5-46}$$

$$W_b(s) = \frac{1}{1 + (s/\omega_b)} \tag{8.5-47}$$

$$\Phi_{bvv}(s) = \frac{A^2}{2\pi} \tag{8.5-48}$$

Find. We wish to find the optimum system weighting function $W_m(t)$ that minimizes the mean-square value of the filtered output subject to the constraint on the value of the integral-square error I_y.

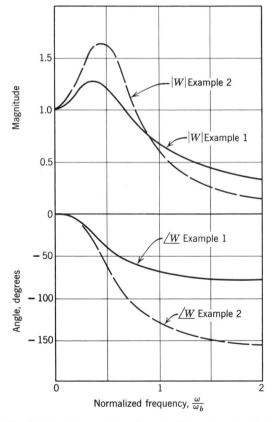

Fig. 8.5-2. System functions for Examples 1 and 2.

Solution. Again we can use the results of the derivation in Art. 8.4 to obtain the transform of the optimum system weighting function directly from the problem specifications. The form of the solution is therefore

$$W_m(s) = \frac{\left[\dfrac{\Gamma(s)}{\Delta^-(s)}\right]_+}{\Delta^+(s)} \qquad (5.4\text{--}28)$$

where

$$\Gamma(s) = \rho I_{vi}(s) \qquad (8.4\text{--}19)$$

and

$$\Delta(s) = 2\pi W_f(s) W_f(-s)\Phi_{bvv}(s) + \rho I_{vv}(s) \qquad (8.4\text{--}18)$$

From application of Eq. 2.4–30 there results

$$I_{vv}(s) = v(-s)v(s) \qquad (8.5\text{--}49)$$

$$I_{vi}(s) = v(-s)i(s) \qquad (8.5\text{--}50)$$

with

$$v(s) = \frac{\Omega_v}{s^2} \qquad (8.5\text{--}9)$$

and

$$i(s) = \frac{\Omega_v e^{-sT}}{s^2} \qquad (8.5\text{--}51)$$

we then have

$$I_{vv}(s) = \frac{\Omega_v{}^2}{(-s)^2 s^2} \qquad (8.5\text{--}52)$$

$$I_{vi}(s) = \frac{\Omega_v{}^2 e^{-sT}}{(-s)^2 s^2} \qquad (8.5\text{--}53)$$

Hence

$$\Gamma(s) = \frac{\rho \Omega_v{}^2 e^{-sT}}{(-s)^2 s^2} \qquad (8.5\text{--}54)$$

We obtain the expression for $\Delta(s)$ as in the first example as

$$\Delta(s) = \frac{A^2(s^4 + 4b^4)}{s^2(-s)^2} \qquad (8.5\text{--}14)$$

where

$$4b^4 = \frac{\rho \Omega_v{}^2}{A^2} \qquad (8.5\text{--}15)$$

The factors of $\Delta(s)$ are then

$$\Delta^+(s) = \frac{s^2 + 2bs + 2b^2}{s^2} \tag{8.5-16}$$

$$\Delta^-(s) = \frac{A^2(s^2 - 2bs + 2b^2)}{(-s)^2} \tag{8.5-17}$$

Then we form $\left[\dfrac{\Gamma(s)}{\Delta^-(s)}\right]$ as

$$\frac{\Gamma(s)}{\Delta^-(s)} = \frac{4b^4 e^{-sT}}{s^2(s^2 - 2bs + 2b^2)} \tag{8.5-55}$$

The presence of the e^{-sT} factor in Eq. 8.5–55 makes the expression irrational. Hence to find $\left[\dfrac{\Gamma(s)}{\Delta^-(s)}\right]_+$ the technique defined by Eq. 5.4–26 and Eq. 5.4–27 could be used. The result so obtained however, still involves the e^{-sT} factor and is rather complex in form. To gain more insight into the problem we shall choose to approximate the delay factor e^{-sT} by the first few terms of its power series expansion.

$$e^{-sT} \cong 1 - sT + \frac{(sT)^2}{2} - \frac{(sT)^3}{6} \tag{8.5-56}$$

For this approximation to represent the delay e^{-sT} within 10 percent the magnitude of sT must be less than unity. We shall see the effect of this approximation later.

Using Eq. 8.5–56 in Eq. 8.5–55 we have

$$\frac{\Gamma(s)}{\Delta^-(s)} = \frac{4b^4\left(1 - sT + \dfrac{s^2 T^2}{2} - \dfrac{s^3 T^3}{6}\right)}{s^2(s^2 - 2bs + 2b^2)} \tag{8.5-57}$$

To find $\left[\dfrac{\Gamma(s)}{\Delta^-(s)}\right]_+$ we expand Eq. 8.5–57 into partial fractions and keep only the terms corresponding to poles in the LHP, namely, the pole at $s = 0$. Hence we have

$$\left[\frac{\Gamma(s)}{\Delta^-(s)}\right]_+ = \frac{a_3}{s^2} + \frac{a_4}{s} \tag{8.5-58}$$

The constants are found to be

$$a_3 = 2b^2 \tag{8.5-59}$$

$$a_4 = 2b(1 - bT) \tag{8.5-60}$$

Using these values in Eq. 8.5–58 we have

$$\left[\frac{\Gamma(s)}{\Delta^-(s)} \right]_+ = \frac{2b[b + (1 - bT)s]}{s^2} \qquad (8.5\text{–}61)$$

Finally, by substituting Eq. 8.5–16 and Eq. 8.5–61 into Eq. 5.4–28 there results

$$W_m(s) = \frac{2b[b + s(1 - bT)]}{s^2 + 2bs + 2b^2} \qquad (8.5\text{–}62)$$

As a check on our result we notice that for $T = 0$ Eq. 8.5–62 reduces to Eq. 8.5–25, the result of the first example, as it should.

We next determine the integral-square error of the system defined by Eq. 8.5–62 for the ramp input. After a moderate calculation there results

$$I_y = \frac{\Omega_v^2}{b^3} \left[-\frac{7}{8} + \frac{3}{2} bT - \frac{5}{4} (bT)^2 + \frac{(bT)^3}{3} \right.$$
$$\left. + e^{-bT}(bT \sin bT - bT \cos bT + \cos bT) \right] \qquad (8.5\text{–}63)$$

Next the mean-square value of the filtered noise is found to be

$$\overline{b_f^2} = \frac{A^2}{2} b(3 - 4bT + 2b^2 T^2) \qquad (8.5\text{–}64)$$

For the standard system the mean-square value of the filtered output was found previously to be

$$\overline{b_s^2} = \frac{A^2}{2} \omega_b \qquad (8.5\text{–}34)$$

Therefore, by equating Eq. 8.5–64 and Eq. 8.5–34, we determine the bandwidth calibration as

$$\omega_b = b(3 - 4bT + 2b^2 T^2) \qquad (8.5\text{–}65)$$

Using the values of T and I_y/Ω_v^2 as specified in the statement of the problem, we can calculate from Eq. 8.5–63 the value of b, and then by use of Eq. 8.5–65 we find the value of the bandwidth parameter ω_b. The question now might naturally arise, since the parameters in the approximate optimum system transfer function are a function of T (Eq. 8.5–62), is there a certain value of T which will result in a minimum bandwidth for a fixed value of integral-square error? The answer to this question is shown by Fig. 8.5–3 where bandwidth is plotted as a function of T. We see that increasing T from zero up to the value T_o

results in a decrease in bandwidth by a factor of 6 but that further increase in T causes the bandwidth and hence transmitted noise to increase.   The optimum choice of T, designated by T_o, is found to be

$$T_o = 3.83 \left(\frac{I_y}{\Omega_v^2}\right)^{1/3} \tag{8.5-66}$$

The minimum bandwidth, ω_{b0}, corresponding to this value of T is

$$\omega_{b0} = 0.261 \left(\frac{\Omega_v^2}{I_y}\right)^{1/3} \tag{8.5-67}$$

and

$$b_0 = \omega_{b0} \tag{8.5-68}$$

We must caution the reader at this point.   The above conclusions are based on the optimum system as obtained by approximating the

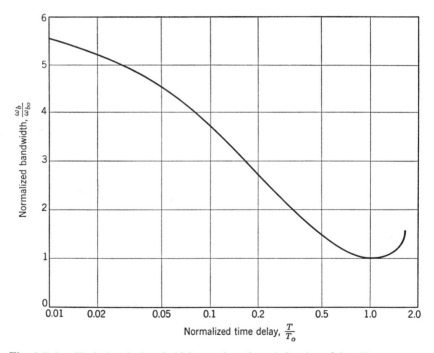

Fig. 8.5–3.   Variation in bandwidth as a function of the time delay T

where
$$T_o = \frac{1}{\omega_{b0}} = 3.83 \left(\frac{I_y}{\Omega_v^2}\right)^{1/3}$$

delay factor by its power series expansion. Had we chosen an approximation of the form

$$e^{-sT} \cong \frac{1 - \dfrac{T}{2}s}{1 + \dfrac{T}{2}s} \tag{8.5-69}$$

or any other Padé approximate (Reference T.7, p. 550) involving a denominator other than unity, the form of $W_m(s)$ would have been much more complex since the LHP poles of the approximation to e^{-sT} appear in the optimum system weighting function $W_m(s)$. We could have used the procedure described by Eq. 5.4–26 and Eq. 5.4–27 to evaluate $\left[\dfrac{\Gamma(s)}{\Delta^-(s)}\right]_+$ directly without making any approximations but again the result so obtained for $W_m(s)$ is very complex and involves the factor e^{-sT}. The series approximation was used to show clearly the basic effect on system bandwidth of permitting a time delay between input and desired output, namely, that of decreasing bandwidth with increased value of time delay. The approximate optimum system showed an optimum choice for T as indicated in Fig. 8.5–3. If, however, no approximations are made the relation between bandwidth and time delay, though very complex mathematically, shows no minimum for finite T but is a monotonically decreasing function with increasing T. This is what we would expect by intuition. Thus having justified our approach we shall proceed with the remaining part of the solution.

Using Eqs. 8.5–66 and 68 in Eq. 8.5–62, the optimum system transfer function becomes

$$W_m(s) = \frac{1}{0.5(s/\omega_{b0})^2 + (s/\omega_{b0}) + 1} \tag{8.5-70}$$

To see what advantages or disadvantages are associated with the introduction of the time delay we shall compare the results of this to the first example where there was no time delay. In Fig. 8.5–4 we notice that the system with time delay has no perceptible resonant peaking as against the peak magnification of approximately 1.3 for the first example. The normalized error responses are shown in Fig. 8.5–5 and indicate a reduction in peak error by a factor of 5. We also see that the error for the third example has a much smaller mean value over the first four units of normalized time. An error that tends to average itself out is often more desirable than an error that is pre-

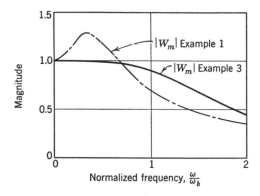

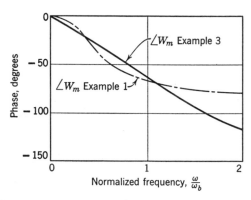

Fig. 8.5–4.   Comparison of frequency characteristics.

dominantly of one sign.   It is well to note that the reduction in peak error and integral-square error for a fixed bandwidth was possible only because we could accept a time delay between input and output information.

If we choose to realize the optimum system weighting function $W_m(s)$ by a simple unity feedback system, we have the relation between the open-loop transfer function $G(s)$ and the closed-loop transfer function $W_m(s)$:

$$G(s) = \frac{W_m(s)}{1 - W_m(s)} \qquad (8.5\text{–}71)$$

For the first example there results

$$G_1(s) = \frac{3(s/\omega_b) + 1}{4.5(s/\omega_b)^2} \qquad (8.5\text{–}72)$$

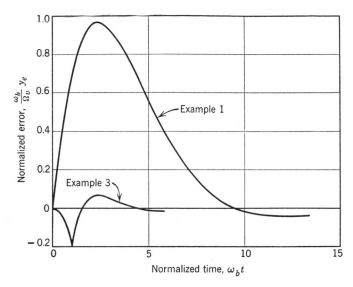

Fig. 8.5–5.   Error response to a ramp input.

For the third example the open-loop transfer function becomes

$$G_3(s) = \frac{1}{(s/\omega_{b0})[0.5(s/\omega_{b0}) + 1]} \qquad (8.5\text{--}73)$$

From a practical viewpoint it is much easier to realize a transfer function of the form of $G_3(s)$ which contains only a single integration than it is to realize a transfer function having a double integration such as $G_1(s)$.

Hence we see that, by accepting a time delay between input and desired output, the integral-square error and peak error are appreciably reduced for a fixed bandwidth, the realization of the system weighting function by a feedback system is more simply accomplished, and the time integral of the error is reduced.   Table 8.5–1 presents a summary of the important results of the three examples.

8.6   CONCLUSION

This chapter has concerned itself with the importance of system bandwidth as a design consideration.   A general discussion pointed out the close relation that exists between system bandwidth and system performance, design complexity, and economics.   Upon realizing the importance of designing a minimum-bandwidth system, we chose to define bandwidth in such a way that the problem of minimizing band-

Table 8.5–1.   Summary of Examples

	GIVEN DATA					
	Noise Spectrum $\Phi_{bvv}(s)$	Standard System $W_b(s)$	Filter $W_f(s)$	Input $v(t)$	Ideal Output $i(t)$	Constraint
Example 1	Constant	$\dfrac{1}{\left(1 + \dfrac{s}{\omega_b}\right)}$	1	$\Omega_v\, \delta_{-2}(t)$	$\Omega_v\, \delta_{-2}(t)$	Integral-square error
Example 2	Constant	$\dfrac{1}{\left(1 + \dfrac{s}{\omega_b}\right)^2}$	s	$\Omega_v\, \delta_{-2}(t)$	$\Omega_v\, \delta_{-2}(t)$	Integral-square error
Example 3	Constant	$\dfrac{1}{\left(1 + \dfrac{s}{\omega_b}\right)}$	1	$\Omega_v\, \delta_{-2}(t)$	$\Omega_v\, \delta_{-2}(t - T)$	Integral-square error

	RESULT		
	System Function $W_m(s)$	Integral Square Error I_y	Peak Error $y_e(t)_{\max}$
Example 1	$\dfrac{3(s/\omega_b) + 1}{4.5(s/\omega_b)^2 + 3(s/\omega_b) + 1}$	$3.375\, \dfrac{\Omega_v^{\,2}}{\omega_b^{\,3}}$	$0.97\, \dfrac{\Omega_v}{\omega_b}$
Example 2	$\dfrac{3.63(s/\omega_b) + 1}{6(s/\omega_b)^3 + 6.61(s/\omega_b)^2 + 3.63(s/\omega_b) + 1}$	$9\, \dfrac{\Omega_v^{\,2}}{\omega_b^{\,3}}$	$1.61\, \dfrac{\Omega_v}{\omega_b}$
Example 3	$\dfrac{1}{0.5(s/\omega_{b0})^2 + (s/\omega_{b0}) + 1}$	$0.018\, \dfrac{\Omega_v^{\,2}}{\omega_{b0}^{\,3}}$	$0.20\, \dfrac{\Omega_v}{\omega_{b0}}$

width was transposed to that of minimizing the mean-square value of a transmitted signal. Thus we were able to utilize the analytical techniques developed in the earlier chapters to find the optimum system weighting function. The definition of bandwidth was made suitably general in order to cover a wide variety of systems and to provide a control on the cutoff rate of the system. The performance specifications for the system for normal input signals were introduced into the problem as constraints in the minimization procedure.

Although a solution formula was worked out only where the performance specification was on the allowable integral-square error to a transient signal, the method is easily extended to a specification for mean-square error and to more than one constraint. Examples were included to demonstrate the application of the method of minimizing bandwidth and to illustrate how the results may be used to increase our understanding of the basic problem.

Often practical considerations may interfere with the realization of a control system that truly minimizes the bandwidth for a specified performance. In complex problems the design method discussed in this chapter may be applied to simplified mathematical models, yielding results that can serve as useful guides or standards against which the designer can assess his detailed design arrived at by trial-and-error techniques. In the next chapter a complex practical design problem is solved by utilizing the analytical design method in this manner.

9

AN APPLICATION OF
ANALYTICAL DESIGN THEORY
TO A PRACTICAL PROBLEM

9.1 HOW ANALYTICAL DESIGN THEORY IS APPLIED
TO PRACTICAL PROBLEMS

The preceding chapters have developed some of the basic elements for an approach to feedback-control-system design. This approach we call the *analytical design method*. By this method we proceed from the system specifications directly to the determination of the compensation for the system that minimizes (or maximizes) the chosen performance index. Evaluation of the performance index for this compensation tells us immediately whether the specifications imposed on the system can or cannot be met. The ability of the analytical design method to determine once and for all whether a given set of specifications can be met is one of its chief advantages over the conventional trial-and-error design procedure.

Another advantage of the analytical design theory is the insight that it gives us into the features of linear systems which inherently impose limitations on over-all performance. In Chapter 6 we saw that non-minimum-phase characteristics in the fixed elements definitely limited system performance. The effect of limited linear ranges for signals in the fixed elements was studied in Chapter 7. There it was found that operation of the fixed elements so as to avoid saturation is another source of performance limitation. Finally, in Chapter 8 we saw how a restriction on the bandwidth of a linear system necessarily limited its performance.

The above advantages of the analytical design method over the trial-and-error design procedure are so great that, unless there are off-setting disadvantages, we should expect control systems of the future to be designed almost exclusively by these newer techniques. However, the reader should by now be well aware of at least two disadvantages of the analytical design theory that offset to some degree its enormous advantages. These disadvantages are: (1) the limited number of performance indices that permit analytical solution of the design problem; and (2) the relatively complicated algebra that must be employed in working out all but the simplest problems.

With respect to the first disadvantage, the preceding chapters have given the reader a picture of the kind of analysis that is required to implement the integral-square-error performance index for transient signals and the mean-square-error performance index for stochastic signals. These performance indices have been used in this book because they are the only ones of engineering usefulness that lead to reasonably straightforward mathematical analysis. Many other performance indices might have engineering usefulness but they lead to formulations of the design problem that are not tractable by analysis. An example of such a class of performance indices involves the absolute value of the error. The reader can supply many other examples.

With respect to the second disadvantage of the analytical design method, the reader, as the result of going through the examples of Chapters 7 and 8, is already aware of the mathematical detail necessary to solve some relatively simple problems. The mathematical complexity increases very rapidly as a function of the order of the fixed elements, the amount of detail in the transient signals or spectra, and the number of constraints. In fact, the mathematical labor involved in applying the analytical design method to practical problems has discouraged most engineers who have made the attempt.

The purpose of this chapter is to show how the analytical design method can be applied to practical problems without requiring excessive mathematical labor. First, we shall make a few general remarks on how the analytical design method may be applied most efficiently to practical problems. These general remarks will be followed in the remaining articles of this chapter by an application to a practical example.

Obviously when a practical problem leads into excessively complicated mathematics we idealize it in one or more ways. If the specification of the fixed elements is causing the complexity, perhaps this specification can be replaced by a simpler model for the fixed elements which retains some of the more important features of the original specification. For example, replacing the transfer function of a pure delay by a simple rational function frequently simplifies the mathematics without much sacrifice of accuracy. Similarly, if the input-signal description introduces excessive mathematical complexity into the problem, we frequently can make simplifications in this description and still retain the main features of a more elaborate solution.

The solutions of idealized or simplified versions of practical problems serve as very effective guideposts or bench marks for judging the quality of the trial-and-error designs that are actually used. It is desirable to use a design arrived at by the trial-and-error procedure since the compensation obtained by this technique is frequently simpler in form and easier to realize, even for idealized versions of the actual problems, than the compensation called for by the analytical design procedure. A trial-and-error design can usually come very close to yielding the same performance-index value as could be obtained using the compensation indicated by the analytical design theory because the minima (or maxima) of a performance index are usually rather broad with respect to variations in the parameters and in the form of the compensation. However, without the guideposts established by use of the analytical design procedure for the purpose of telling us approximately what performance index is achievable, we are at a loss to know how far to carry a trial-and-error design. With the guideposts furnished by the analytical design theory, we know when to terminate the trial-and-error design sequence. Furthermore, if the problem specifications are inherently not achievable, the analytical design method will tell us so and thereby save us the trouble of even initiating a trial-and-error design. Thus we conclude that the most important function to be performed by the analytical design theory in practical applications is that of guiding the trial-and-error design procedure in the sense of providing standards by which to judge the effectiveness of a particular trial. At the same time, we conclude that it is usually inadvisable to use the compensation determined by the analytical procedure since in all probability this compensation is more complex than another form which will result in almost as good performance.

In applying the above ideas to his own problems the reader may find that he needs to extend the formulas derived in the preceding chapters or to derive altogether new formulas appropriate to his particular circumstances. It is inappropriate in this book, where we are attempting to set forth the basic principles of the analytical design theory, for us to attempt to foresee all the possible applications and to develop formulas sufficiently general to encompass them. Nevertheless, with the basic ideas presented in the preceding chapters the reader should be able to extend, modify, or derive altogether new equations for handling his particular problems.

We now turn our attention to a practical problem that will illustrate some of the above ideas. The problem to be considered is the design of the azimuth drive for a large radio telescope. During the spring of 1956 staff members of the Servomechanisms Laboratory, Electrical Engineering Department, Massachusetts Institute of Technology, were asked to look into the problem of controlling the 140-foot-diameter parabolic reflector to be used in the proposed National Science Foundation radio telescope. The remaining articles of this chapter discuss one aspect of the design problem posed by the azimuth drive for this telescope.

9.2 THE PROBLEM OF THE AZIMUTH DRIVE FOR A RADIO TELESCOPE

A radio telescope is a system for receiving electromagnetic radiation from outer space. Radio astronomers are currently interested in that part of the radiation spectrum corresponding to wavelengths ranging from a few meters down to a few centimeters. The radiation coming to an observer is intercepted by an antenna system where it is converted to an electrical signal which is then detected and amplified for further processing or recording. Even though the resolving power of radio telescopes is small compared to optical instruments, they have aroused great scientific interest because they represent a new communication link between the scientist and the universe. The range of frequencies that characterizes the radio waves capable of traversing the earth's atmosphere is far greater than the corresponding frequency range for light waves. Furthermore, radio waves are received from parts of the universe from which no visible light comes. Such waves indicate the presence of matter in locations and amounts heretofore unsuspected on the basis of optical observations. We are now told, for example, that perhaps as much as 25 percent of the mass of the universe lies in interstellar regions, that most of this matter is hydrogen gas, and that new stars appear to be evolving from it.

For wavelengths in the centimeter range the most effective antenna is a parabolic dish arranged to focus incoming radiation to a central point from which it is piped by means of wave guides to the radio receiver. The resolving power of such an antenna is directly proportional to its diameter and inversely proportional to the wavelength.

As a consequence, we find the radio astronomers seeking larger and larger paraboloids for focusing the radio signals. The proposed National Science Foundation radio telescope with its 140-foot-diameter antenna will be the largest in the United States. Even though this proposed telescope seems enormous, larger ones are being built in England and Australia. However, it is hoped the National Science Foundation telescope will be positioned more accurately than the larger instruments being built elsewhere. When operated at 3 centimeters this telescope will have a beam width of about 3 minutes of arc provided the reflector surface deviates no more than $\frac{1}{8}$ inch from the true paraboloid. By working at the edge of the beam pattern radio astronomers can detect the angular location of a source of radiation within about 5 percent of the antenna beam width, provided they can position the antenna with that accuracy. For the National Science Foundation telescope this requires positioning to about 10 seconds of arc. This consideration leads to the rather stringent specifications, listed below, which are imposed on the azimuth and elevation drives for the proposed telescope.

Several structural plans for the 140-foot-diameter radio telescope have been developed in a preliminary way. One of these is shown in Fig. 9.2-1. Here the 140-foot-diameter paraboloid is suspended on its altitude (elevation) axis between two steel towers approximately 100 feet high. The towers are supported on a base structure carried on wheels which run on a circular track. The azimuth motion of the antenna is obtained through rotation of the base, and the altitude motion is obtained by rotation of the antenna dish about the horizontal axis. The total structure is estimated to weigh 1.2 million pounds. Of this the antenna dish represents 0.67 million pounds.

Although the radio telescope's structure, shown in Fig. 9.2-1, moves the antenna dish in altitude and azimuth coordinates, astronomical data for telescope-pointing directions are ordinarily worked out in terms of equatorial coordinates. In equatorial coordinates one axis is parallel to the earth's axis; the other axis is perpendicular. The advantage of equatorial coordinates is that the earth's rotation can be compensated for by adding an angle (hour-angle) proportional to time into one axis only. Although many optical telescopes operate in equatorial coordinates, the large structure required for radio telescopes usually necessitates the use of altitude-azimuth coordinates in order to reduce expense. When altitude-azimuth coordinates are used, some means for converting astronomical data given in terms of equatorial coordinates into altitude-azimuth coordinates must be provided. For the 140-foot-diameter radio telescope the coordinate conversion may be accomplished by a digital computer.

Some means for measuring the direction along which the antenna is pointing has to be provided.   Optical telescopes employ extremely precise gearing for positioning the reflector.   This enables synchro devices, geared to rotate many times for 1 degree of reflector movement, to be used to transmit position data to the operator.   The position data are often presented on three dials reading degrees, minutes, and seconds.   The radio telescope with its enormous structure exposed to the weather may not be able to depend upon the gearing for its directional accuracy.   When gears are larger than a certain

Fig. 9.2–1.   One design for the antenna structure of the 140-foot-diameter radio-telescope project sponsored by the National Science Foundation.   Designed by Jacob Feld, New York.   (Reproduced by courtesy of Associated Universities, Inc.)

optimum size their precision decreases.   Also, the deflections in the mountings for the gear train, in the antenna structure, and also in the base structure can contribute appreciable errors.   For example, consider the effect of a 1-degree centigrade difference between the two tower temperatures.   Under this condition one tower will be 1.2×10^{-3} foot longer than the other, thereby causing the elevation axis to tilt 8×10^{-6} radian.   Since 1 second of arc corresponds to 4.85×10^{-6} radian, this tilt amounts to almost 2 seconds of arc.   This gives an idea of how serious temperature effects can be in the structure for a radio telescope.   Similar problems exist with respect to elastic deflections caused by gravitational deflections as the antenna rotates in altitude or caused by unbalanced wind forces. In view of the difficulty of obtaining accurate gearing for the azimuth and altitude power drives and also out of consideration for thermal and elastic deflections in the structure itself, some thought has been given to the measurement of the antenna dish angles by means of a stabilized platform. In such a scheme a platform, supported by gimbals fixed to the antenna dish, would be driven by auxiliary optical tracking servomechanisms to maintain a constant direction with respect to light sources on the earth's surface. With such a platform altitude and azimuth angles could be measured directly at the one-speed shafts of the platform by means of analogue-to-digital encoder disks. With this arrangement there is some possibility of measuring the altitude and azimuth angles of the radio telescope to the order of 3 seconds of arc.

The next contribution to the antenna pointing error that we must consider is the drive system which couples the output of the coordinate converter to the antenna. This drive system comprises the two servomechanisms for controlling the altitude and the azimuth angles of the radio telescope. These servomechanisms utilize the differences between the coordinate-converter outputs and the measured antenna signals as their actuating signals. For the reasons mentioned above, it is assumed that the antenna position will be measured by means of stabilized platforms. We now review those factors that are of particular importance in the design of the servomechanisms that drive the antenna in elevation and azimuth. Three factors of prime importance in the design of these devices are:

1. The structural elastance.
2. The moments of inertia of the various parts.
3. Disturbance torques caused by wind gusts.

These factors will be discussed with particular reference to the azimuth drive since the design of this drive is the subject of the articles to follow.

A detailed consideration of the structural design of the antenna dish itself and also the base and towers indicates that, of the large number of possible modes of vibration, the one of particular importance for the azimuth servomechanism design is that which involves the moment of inertia of the base, the torsional elastance resulting from cantilever bending of the towers, and the moment of inertia of the antenna dish. Figure 9.2–2 shows an assumed equivalent mechanical system for the antenna structure so far as the azimuth drive is concerned. Here the base is characterized by a lumped moment of inertia J_b which is turned through an angle θ by means of the servomotor which acts through suitable gearing. The antenna dish, represented by a moment of inertia J_d, is coupled to the base by an equivalent spring constant k which represents the elastance introduced by the towers. The azimuth angle of the antenna dish is denoted by the symbol q; wind torque is indicated by the symbol u. The wind torque is produced by unbalanced forces associated with the flow of air around the antenna dish. These forces depend upon the velocity of the wind and the position of the dish relative to the wind. Table 9.2–1 summarizes the values for the quantities shown in Fig. 9.2–2.

Table 9.2–1.   Important Constants for the Azimuth Drive

Moment of inertia of dish (maximum)	$J_d = 6.0 \times 10^7$ slug ft^2
Moment of inertia of base	$J_b = 12.0 \times 10^7$ slug ft^2
Effective spring constant of towers	$k = 0.7 \times 10^{10} \dfrac{\text{ft-lb}}{\text{rad}}$
Maximum wind torque (for 30 mph wind velocity and worst dish position)	$u_{\text{max}} = 0.60 \times 10^6$ ft-lb

The azimuth moment of inertia of the dish varies with its altitude angle and has the maximum value indicated in the table for 90 degrees elevation above the horizontal. The maximum wind torque indicated in the table is for a wind velocity of 30 mph and for a dish angle different from the condition of maximum moment of inertia. Accurate operation of the radio telescope for wind velocities up to 30 mph is required. For purposes of designing the azimuth power drives, the maximum moment of inertia of the dish will be assumed even though it does not agree with the value of the inertia for the condition of maximum wind torque. This is done because the inertia of the dish is a factor tending to lower the gains that can be used in the azimuth drive. Therefore, in order to have a conservative design, the maximum moment of inertia should be used.

In order to understand the importance of wind-torque disturbance in the design of the azimuth drive, observe that the maximum wind torque is capable of

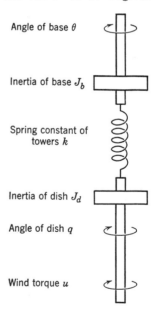

Fig. 9.2–2.   Equivalent mechanical system for azimuth drive.

deflecting the elastance associated with the towers 0.86×10^{-4} radian or 18 seconds of arc. Since the wind velocity fluctuates in a manner to be discussed in more detail in Art. 9.4, it is evident that the azimuth power drive must continually operate to compensate for the elastic deflections caused by the wind load. But the bandwidth of the azimuth power drive is severely restricted by the natural frequency associated with the inertia of the dish and the tower elastance. This natural frequency, from the data given in Table 9.2–1, is 10.8 radians per second or 1.72 cycles per second. Thus we see that a major problem in the design of the azimuth drive for the radio telescope is the minimization of errors caused by wind torques in the presence of fixed elements which contain a mechanical resonance having a low natural frequency. Unfortunately, mechanical resonances of the type encountered here have very little damping associated with them.

Other specifications are imposed on the design of the azimuth drive such as tracking rates and slewing rates and maximum tracking error. However, analysis of these specifications indicates that the requirements that they impose are much less severe than those associated with the wind disturbance problem.

We now wish to summarize the above discussion of the operational requirements for the radio telescope in the form of a set of specifications pertaining to the azimuth drive. The over-all pointing error for the radio telescope should be of the order of 10 seconds of arc. (This is based on 5 percent of the beam width at 3 centimeters wavelength.) If the azimuth drive is allowed to have 7 seconds of over-all error and the same is allowed for the elevation drive, the maximum pointing error will not exceed 10 second of arc. However, from the 7 seconds of allowable azimuth error, deductions must be made for the coordinate converter and the position-measuring system. If the coordinate converter is allowed to have an error of 2 seconds of arc and the antenna position-measuring system an error of 2 seconds then 3 seconds of error are permitted for the servomechanism controlling the azimuth angle of the antenna. It is doubtful if either the coordinate converter or the position-measuring system can be built with errors of only 2 seconds of arc but if these errors are increased the already tight tolerance on the servomechanism becomes even tighter. However this analysis is pessimistic since it represents the extreme case of all the errors adding. A more realistic approach is the statistical one in which we may have the errors adding as the square root of the sum of the squares of the individual errors. If this approach is used and if we allow 3 seconds of rms error for both the coordinate converter and the position-measuring system, we find that the azimuth servomechanism is allowed to have 5.5 seconds of rms error.

The foregoing error specification plus the data contained in Table 9.2–1 represent an incomplete set of specifications for the azimuth drive of the radio telescope. Even though we are ignoring all requirements other than those resulting from the wind loading (on the supposition that they can be made to result in errors that are negligible relative to those caused by the wind), we lack adequate statistical data on wind velocity fluctuations. However, the designer of a feedback control system more often than not must proceed with incomplete specifications, and where data are lacking he must make reasonable assumptions. Article 9.4 will discuss the wind-torque specifications in more detail after the fixed elements of the system are defined in the next article.

9.3 BLOCK DIAGRAM OF THE AZIMUTH DRIVE

In order to proceed with the design of the azimuth drive, the fixed elements must be completely specified. In the preceding article data on the antenna structure itself have been presented. What remains is the specification of the servomotor to be used with the azimuth drive. After the servomotor is selected the gear ratio between the servomotor and the base of the antenna structure must be established. Once this information relating to the fixed elements has been obtained, an overall block diagram of the azimuth drive can be derived. This block diagram will show in detail the nature of the fixed elements.

Under low-speed tracking conditions even in the presence of wind gusts the power requirements are very small. At a maximum tracking rate of 200 seconds of arc per second the maximum power required to overcome wind load is of the order of 1 horsepower. If another horsepower is allowed for gear friction and a factor of safety, we arrive at a 2-horsepower rating for the servomotor. Very satisfactory hydraulic or electric drives exist in this power range. Rather arbitrarily it is decided to use a hydraulic drive in the form of a constant-displacement, piston-type, hydraulic motor coupled to an electrically actuated four-way control valve supplied with high-pressure oil. The principal reason for selecting the hydraulic drive in preference to an electric drive is that the former can most certainly be made to have an output velocity proportional to electrical signal input to the valve actuator over the frequency range of interest in the design of this servomechanism. The same could not be said with absolute certainty for an electric drive. The hydraulic motor (together with its associ-

ated control valve) that is selected for purposes of this design is characterized by the data contained in Table 9.3–1. The only item that

Table 9.3–1. Important Constants for Hydraulic Servomotor

Maximum speed $|\dot{\theta}_m|_{max} = 3{,}000$ rpm

Moment of inertia $J_m = 1.09 \times 10^{-4} \dfrac{\text{in-lb sec}^2}{\text{rad}}$

Coefficient of viscous damping $f = 0.634 \dfrac{\text{in -lb sec}}{\text{rad}}$

needs explanation in this table is the coefficient of viscous damping f.
This coefficient expresses the fact that the speed-torque curves of the
hydraulic servomotor for constant electrical signal applied to the valve

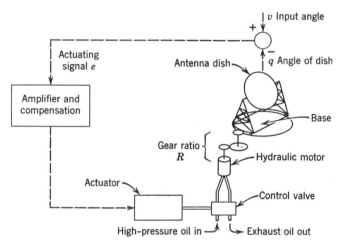

Fig. 9.3–1. Schematic diagram of azimuth drive.

fall off with increasing torque because of oil leakage past the pistons of
the motor and past the lands of the control valve.

Figure 9.3–1 shows a schematic diagram of the azimuth drive using
the hydraulic servomotor. In this diagram it should be understood
that the actuating signal e is obtained from digital-to-analogue conversion equipment operating on the difference in the digital representa-
tions for the desired antenna position as determined by the coordinate
converter and the measured antenna position obtained from the
stabilized platform. The least significant digit in the difference is
expected to be of the order of 1 second of arc. On the basis of experience with other systems employing actuating signals derived from
digital information, it is anticipated that, because of the small size of
the quanta used, the quantized nature of this feedback signal can be

ignored for purposes of preliminary design. Accordingly, the analysis to follow assumes the actuating signal to be the instantaneous difference between the input v (output of the coordinate converter) and the measured angle of the dish q.

The gear ratio R (which is the ratio of the angle of the servomotor to the angle of the base) is taken to be the ratio of maximum motor speed to maximum base speed at the highest tracking rate. For a maximum tracking rate of 200 seconds of arc per second this gear ratio turns out to be 3.24×10^5. This approach for determining the gear ratio is justified when the accelerations required of the motor and the load result in negligible torques referred to the motor. Once the gear ratio is determined, it is convenient to refer all quantities to the motor shaft in order to reduce the size of the numbers used to describe the

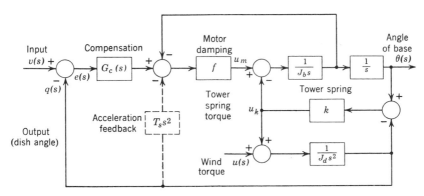

Fig. 9.3–2.   Detailed block diagram of azimuth drive.

antenna structure. It will be recalled that moments of inertia and spring constants reflected through a gear train are divided by the square of the gear ratio whereas load torques are divided by the first power of the gear ratio. Angles, of course, are multiplied by the gear ratio when they are reflected to the motor end of the gear train. In the block diagrams and analyses that follow all quantities are referred to the servomotor shaft.

Figure 9.3–2 shows the detailed block diagram of the azimuth drive. The summing point at the output of the compensation block in this figure represents the angular velocity of the hydraulic servomotor as if it were free of all load torque. Subtracted from this idealized motor velocity is the actual motor velocity which is the same as the base velocity when it has been reflected through the gear train. The difference in these two velocities is associated with the leakage of the motor and the valve. Multiplication of this difference in velocities by the motor damping f yields the motor torque u_m. The motor torque is used to overcome the spring torque u_k associated with the twist of the towers and to accelerate the base inertia.* The spring torque in cooperation with the wind torque drives the antenna dish by accelerating its inertia. Shown in dotted lines in Fig. 9.3–2 is an acceleration feedback path used to help stabilize the azimuth drive in one of the compensation schemes described in Art. 9.7.

The next step in the analysis of the azimuth drive is to simplify the block diagram of Fig. 9.3–2. Using standard procedures for reducing block diagrams, we arrive at the equivalent single-loop block diagram of the azimuth drive shown in Fig. 9.3–3. This simplified block dia-

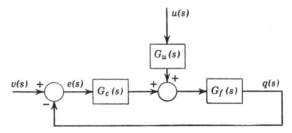

Fig. 9.3–3.   Equivalent single-loop block diagram of azimuth drive.

$$G_u(s) = \left[\left(\frac{J_b}{k} \right) s^2 + \left(\frac{f}{k} \right) s + 1 \right] \left(\frac{1}{f} \right)$$

$$G_f(s) = \cfrac{1}{\left[\left(\frac{J_b J_d}{f \; k} \right) s^3 + \left(\frac{J_d}{k} \right) s^2 + \left(\frac{J_b + J_d}{f} + T_s \right) s + 1 \right] s}$$

gram is exactly equivalent to that of Fig. 9.3–2. It has been obtained in such a way that the identity of the output signal from the compensation has been retained. In both block diagrams this signal corresponds to the angular velocity that the antenna base structure would have if the hydraulic motor and valve had no leakage so that they produce an output velocity proportional to the electrical signal driving the valve actuator.

The single-loop block diagram of Fig. 9.3–3 places in evidence the transfer function $G_f(s)$ of the fixed elements and also an auxiliary transfer function $G_u(s)$ through which the wind torque disturbance $u(s)$ enters the system. Expressions for these transfer functions in terms of the system parameters are given in this figure. In the next article we seek a more detailed description of the wind-torque disturb-

---

* The motor inertia is included in the base inertia in this block diagram and in all subsequent calculations.

ance. Then we develop a further modification of the system block diagram, using as the starting point Fig. 9.3–3. On the basis of this new block diagram a general formula is established for the compensation that minimizes the mean-square error caused by applying simultaneously to the system a stochastic input signal and a stochastic disturbance.

9.4 AN ESTIMATE FOR THE VARIATIONS IN WIND TORQUE

As mentioned in the preceding article, our first task is to determine a suitable description for the disturbance caused by the wind torque. Aerodynamic considerations indicate that the wind torque is proportional to the square of the wind velocity so that we may write

$$u_g = c_w V^2(t) \qquad (9.4\text{--}1)$$

Here u_g stands for the gross wind torque caused by a wind velocity V. The proportionality constant c_w depends upon the position of the dish and the direction of the wind; under the worst operating condition the data in Table 9.2–1 give the following value for c_w

$$c_w = 0.667 \times 10^3 \text{ ft-lb } (\text{mph})^{-2} \qquad (9.4\text{--}2)$$

The basic problem now is to characterize the wind velocity as a function of time. It is common knowledge that the wind velocity is seldom constant in magnitude or direction over even short periods of time. Since direction effects will come in as a cosine function, they can be ignored for the size of wind direction variations likely to be encountered over intervals of time of interest to us here. But the same cannot be said for the variations in the magnitude of the wind velocity. We shall therefore represent the instantaneous wind velocity by

$$V(t) = V_0 + V_1(t) \qquad (9.4\text{--}3)$$

where V_0 is the average value of the wind velocity and $V_1(t)$ is the instantaneous variation of the wind velocity from its mean value. When we speak of the wind velocity as being, say, 30 miles per hour, we are ordinarily referring to V_0. For many purposes it is only this average velocity that is of interest. In the radio telescope, however, it is primarily the variation in the wind velocity that is of interest. This can be seen by substituting the right side of Eq. 9.4–3 in Eq. 9.4–1. We then find the gross wind torque to be given by

$$u_g(t) = c_w[V_0^2 + 2V_0V_1(t) + V_1^2(t)] \qquad (9.4\text{--}4)$$

The average value of the wind torque is given by

$$\overline{u_g(t)} = c_w[V_0^2 + \overline{V_1^2(t)}] \tag{9.4–5}$$

The average value of the wind torque presents no problem to the control system since it can be compensated for either by a manual adjustment or by making the static stiffness of the system sufficiently high. We therefore shall give no further consideration to the component of the gross wind torque corresponding to its average value.

From Eq. 9.4–4 we can write the following expression for the instantaneous deviation $u_1(t)$ of the gross wind torque from its mean value:

$$u_1(t) = c_w[2V_0V_1(t) + V_1^2(t) - \overline{V_1^2(t)}] \tag{9.4–6}$$

In order to determine the statistical character of this wind-torque fluctuation, recourse must be had to experimental meteorological data. Fluctuations in wind velocity having rms values of the order of 25 percent of the mean wind velocity have been observed at sites similar to those proposed for the 140-foot-diameter radio telescope (Reference S.3). With fluctuations of this order the contribution of the last two terms on the right side of Eq. 9.4–6 most of the time is small relative to the first term. We shall therefore approximate the fluctuation in the wind torque by the first term only and write

$$u(t) = 2c_wV_0V_1(t) \tag{9.4–7}$$

where $u(t)$ is the approximate value of $u_1(t)$. According to Eq. 9.4–7 the wind-torque fluctuation is simply the fluctuation in the wind velocity multiplied by a constant. Thus our problem of characterizing the wind-torque fluctuation is simply that of finding a statistical description for the wind-velocity fluctuation $V_1(t)$.

At this point we run into a paucity of appropriate experimental data. Obviously the structure of the wind is considerably influenced by the terrain over which it passes. Furthermore, the apparent structure will depend upon the observation interval since the wind is influenced by many factors that can introduce long-term fluctuations. For the purposes at hand we are interested in the structure of the wind over observation intervals of the order of minutes to hours but not days or years. Reference M.25 gives several autocorrelation functions for wind-velocity fluctuations. Comparing this information with the power-density spectra quoted in Reference S.3 indicates that the autocorrelation function of the velocity fluctuation can be approximated by

$$\varphi_{vv1}(\tau) = [\overline{V_1^2(t)}]e^{-\nu|\tau|} \tag{9.4–8}$$

On the basis of these references the frequency ν ranges from 0.4 to 3 radians per second. For purposes of this analysis we shall take ν as 1 radian per second.

We are now in a position to write an expression for the power-density spectrum for the fluctuation in the wind torque. On the basis of the autocorrelation function of Eq. 9.4–8 and the wind-torque relation of Eq. 9.4–7, we see that the power-density spectrum for the wind torque is given by

$$\Phi_{uu}(s) = \frac{\beta^2}{\pi}\frac{\nu}{(-s^2 + \nu^2)} \qquad (9.4\text{--}9)$$

where β is $2\,c_w V_0[\overline{V_1^2(t)}]^{\frac{1}{2}}$. For an average wind velocity of 30 mph, a wind-velocity fluctuation of 7.5 mph rms, the value of c_w given by Eq. 9.4–2, and the value of the gear ratio given in Art. 9.3 (namely, 3.24 $\times$ 10^5), we find that the value of β is

$$\beta = 11.1 \text{ in.-lb} \qquad (9.4\text{--}10)$$

when the wind torque is referred to the servomotor shaft. From the discussion in the preceding paragraph we take the frequency ν to be

$$\nu = 1.0 \text{ rad sec}^{-1} \qquad (9.4\text{--}11)$$

Equations 9.4–9 through 9.4–11 summarize our best estimate for the power-density spectrum of the wind-torque fluctuation corresponding to the worst condition under which accurate tracking is desired. This information is the data that was missing in the specifications summarized at the end of Art. 9.2.* A plot of the power-density spectrum for

---

* The reader may question the foregoing analysis of wind-torque fluctuation since it assumes that the wind is uniform over an area larger than the 140-foot paraboloid. The wind-velocity data used in the analysis are derived from instruments that measure the wind velocity almost at a single point. Observations have been made on the spatial structure of the wind as well as the time structure. Unfortunately, the data on the spatial structure that are known to the authors are for a single dimension only rather than the two dimensions necessary for torque calculations. Qualitatively, a two-dimensional spatial structure for the wind in addition to a one-dimensional time structure would appear to have two effects. In the first place, there would be a tendency to reduce the rms velocity variation of the wind when averaged over areas of a few square feet. This effect would tend to decrease the wind-torque fluctuation. But, in the second place, there is the possibility of torque production by large-scale shearing phenomena in the wind structure. This effect would tend to increase the wind-torque fluctuation. Therefore, without further information, it would appear that the power-density spectrum of Eq. 9.4–9 is not an unreasonable estimate.

the wind-torque disturbance is shown in Fig. 9.4–1.   Only the positive-frequency portion of the spectrum is shown since spectra corresponding to autocorrelation functions are even functions of frequency.

9.5   WIND-GUST ERROR FOR SYSTEM WITH SEMI-FREE CONFIGURATION

With the completion of the specifications by the establishment of a power-density spectrum for the wind-torque disturbance, we are in a position to ask what the control-system compensation should be in order to minimize its rms error.   Since none of the formulas for compensation derived in the preceding chapters apply to this particular

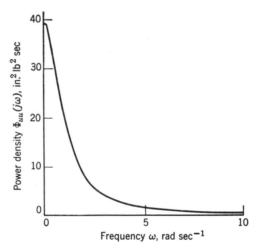

Fig. 9.4–1.   Power-density spectrum for wind-torque variations.   Mean wind velocity = 30 mph.

problem, it is necessary to derive a new one.   From the new compensation formula it will be evident that the rms error caused by wind-torque disturbances alone can be made arbitrarily small provided the fixed elements are minimum phase.   This theoretical result will be modified in Art. 9.6 to take into account the practical limitation imposed by the elastance and inertia of the antenna structure.

The compensation problem for which we seek an answer can be stated as follows.   Given information about the input signal, the desired output signal, the disturbance signal, and the fixed elements of a control system, find the compensation that minimizes the mean-square error between the desired output and the actual output.   The general solution to this problem is outlined in the following paragraphs.

One approach to the problem of disturbances was discussed in Art. 1.7. There it was indicated that the disturbance signal could be moved through the fixed elements to the periphery of the control-system block diagram and then combined with the input, desired output, and actual output. These manipulations transformed the problem back into one free of disturbances. A similar approach will be used here except that the identity of the disturbance signal always will be retained. Figure 9.5–1 shows block diagrams of a system with a single disturbance. Starting with diagram A of this figure which

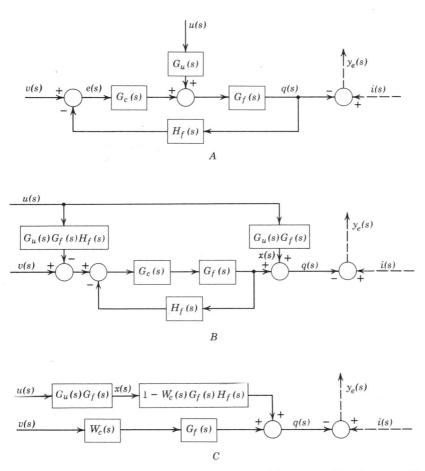

Fig. 9.5–1. Block diagrams of a control system with a single disturbance. (A) with disturbance brought to input of fixed elements. (B) with disturbance moved to periphery of diagram through fixed elements. (C) With feedback loop replaced by equivalent cascade.

shows the disturbance brought to the input of the fixed elements, we proceed to diagram B where the disturbance has been moved to the periphery of the system through the fixed elements. Once this has been done, the feedback loop can be replaced by an equivalent cascade configuration as shown in diagram C. On the basis of diagram C we obtain the following fundamental relationship among the output $q(s)$, the input $v(s)$, and the disturbance $u(s)$:

$$q(s) = W_c(s)G_f(s)v(s) + [1 - W_c(s)G_f(s)H_f(s)]x(s) \quad (9.5\text{–}1)$$

In this equation the signal $x(s)$ is related to the disturbance $u(s)$ by the following definition

$$x(s) \triangleq G_u(s)G_f(s)u(s) \quad\quad\quad (9.5\text{–}2)$$

Use of the signal $x(s)$ or $x(t)$ in place of the actual disturbance simplifies the formulas to follow.

By working in the time domain we can derive an expression for the mean-square error from which, by the standard variational procedure, an integral equation for the compensation can be obtained. The steps in this procedure are entirely analogous to those followed in Art. 6.1; therefore we shall omit many intermediate steps in establishing the integral equation for the compensation. From Eq. 9.5–1 we observe that the actual output can be expressed in the time domain as

$$
\begin{aligned}
q(t) = w_c(t_1)\star g_f(t_3)\star v(t - t_1 - t_3) &+ x(t)\\
- w_c(t_1)\star g_f(t_3)\star h_f(t_5)&\star x(t - t_1 - t_3 - t_5) \quad (9.5\text{–}3)
\end{aligned}
$$

In this equation we have introduced a new notation for integration of a dummy variable from minus infinity to plus infinity. The star has the meaning defined in the following equation

$$w_c(t_1)\star[\;\;] = \int_{-\infty}^{\infty} dt_1\, w_c(t_1)[\;\;] \quad\quad (9.5\text{–}4)$$

In other words, a star following a weighting function always means integration with respect to the argument of the weighting function from minus infinity to plus infinity of the product of the weighting function and that which follows the star. Introduction of this notation will considerably simplify the writing of the formulas to follow.

Recalling that the error $y_e(t)$ is by definition the difference between the desired output $i(t)$ and the actual output $q(t)$, we can proceed from the time-domain expression for the actual output given by Eq. 9.5–3 to the following expression for the mean-square error in terms of the correlation functions of the several signals:

$$
\begin{aligned}
\overline{y_e{}^2(t)} \ = \ & \varphi_{ii}(0) \\
& + w_c(t_1) \star w_c(t_2) \star g_f(t_3) \star g_f(t_4) \star \varphi_{vv}(t_1 + t_3 - t_2 - t_4) \\
& + \varphi_{xx}(0) \\
& + w_c(t_1) \star w_c(t_2) \star g_f(t_3) \star g_f(t_4) \star h_f(t_5) \star h_f(t_6) \star \\
& \qquad\qquad \varphi_{xx}(t_1 + t_3 + t_5 - t_2 - t_4 - t_6) \\
& + 2w_c(t_1) \star g_f(t_3) \star \varphi_{vx}(t_1 + t_3) \\
& + 2w_c(t_1) \star g_f(t_3) \star h_f(t_5) \star \varphi_{xi}(t_1 + t_3 + t_5) \\
& - 2\varphi_{xi}(0) \\
& - 2w_c(t_1) \star g_f(t_3) \star \varphi_{vi}(t_1 + t_3) \\
& - 2w_c(t_1) \star g_f(t_3) \star h_f(t_5) \star \varphi_{xx}(t_1 + t_3 + t_5) \\
& - 2w_c(t_1) \star w_c(t_2) \star g_f(t_3) \star g_f(t_4) \star h_f(t_6) \star \\
& \qquad\qquad \varphi_{vx}(t_1 + t_3 - t_2 - t_4 - t_6)
\end{aligned}
$$

(9.5–5)

From this equation we can derive the integral equation for the compensation that minimizes the mean-square error by letting $w_c(t) = w_{cm}(t) + \epsilon w_\epsilon(t)$ where $w_{cm}(t)$ is the weighting function of the compensation that minimizes the mean-square error and $w_\epsilon(t)$ is an arbitrary realizable weighting function. Substituting this expression for the weighting function of the compensation into Eq. 9.5–5 makes the mean-square error a function of ϵ. Differentiating the mean-square error with respect to ϵ and setting $d\left(\overline{y_e{}^2}\right)/d\epsilon = 0$ with $\epsilon = 0$ yield the desired integral equation which can be written as

$$
\begin{aligned}
w_{cm}(t_2) \star & [g_f(t_3) \star g_f(t_4) \star \varphi_{vv}(t_1 + t_3 - t_2 - t_4) \\
& + g_f(t_3) \star g_f(t_4) \star h_f(t_5) \star h_f(t_6) \star \\
& \qquad\qquad \varphi_{xx}(t_1 + t_3 + t_5 - t_2 - t_4 - t_6) \\
& - g_f(t_3) \star g_f(t_4) \star h_f(t_6) \star \varphi_{vx}(t_1 + t_3 - t_2 - t_4 - t_6) \\
& - g_f(t_3) \star g_f(t_4) \star h_f(t_6) \star \varphi_{vx}(t_2 + t_3 - t_1 - t_4 - t_6)] \\
& + [-g_f(t_3) \star \varphi_{vi}(t_1 + t_3) \\
& - g_f(t_3) \star h_f(t_5) \star \varphi_{xx}(t_1 + t_3 + t_5) \\
& + g_f(t_3) \star h_f(t_5) \star \varphi_{xi}(t_1 + t_3 + t_5) \\
& + g_f(t_3) \star \varphi_{vx}(t_1 + t_3)] = 0 \quad \text{for } t_1 \geq 0
\end{aligned}
$$

(9.5–6)

For transformable correlation functions the explicit solution formula derived in Art. 5.4 may be employed. This formula is repeated here for convenience.

$$
W_{cm}(s) = \frac{\left[\dfrac{\Gamma(s)}{\Delta^-(s)} \right]_+}{\Delta^+(s)}
$$

(5.4–28)

For the problem at hand we have

$$\Gamma(s) = 2\pi G_f(-s)[\Phi_{vi}(s) + H_f(-s)\Phi_{xx}(s) - \Phi_{vx}(s)$$
$$- H_f(-s)\Phi_{xi}(s)] \quad (9.5\text{-}7)$$

and

$$\Delta(s) = 2\pi G_f(-s)G_f(s)[\Phi_{vv}(s) + H_f(-s)H_f(s)\Phi_{xx}(s)$$
$$- H_f(s)\Phi_{vx}(s) - H_f(-s)\Phi_{xv}(s)] \quad (9.5\text{-}8)$$

Substitution of these two expressions in Eq. 5.4–28 gives us an explicit solution for the transfer function of the equivalent cascade compensation for the control system that minimizes the mean-square error under the condition in which the system is excited by an input signal and a disturbance simultaneously.

Let us now apply the general result given in the preceding paragraph to the problem of the radio telescope. Here, according to the specifications, the input signal is negligible, the desired output is also negligible, and the problem is merely one of suppressing the error caused by the wind-torque disturbance. In addition, we know from Fig. 9.3–3 that the fixed elements for the radio telescope are minimum phase and that the feedback elements have a transfer function $H_f(s)$ equal to unity. Thus Eq. 9.5–7 becomes

$$\Gamma(s) = 2\pi G_f(-s)\Phi_{xx}(s) \quad (9.5\text{-}9)$$

and Eq. 9.5–8 reduces to

$$\Delta(s) = 2\pi G_f(-s)G_f(s)\Phi_{xx}(s) \quad (9.5\text{-}10)$$

Substitution of these expressions in Eq. 5.4–28 yields for the system compensation

$$W_{cm}(s) = \frac{1}{G_f(s)} \quad (9.5\text{-}11)$$

In other words, the compensation that minimizes the mean-square error when a disturbance only is acting is simply the reciprocal of the transfer function of the fixed elements provided the fixed elements are minimum phase and the feedback elements have a transfer function of unity.

If the compensation indicated by Eq. 9.5–11 is employed in the radio telescope drive, the mean-square error turns out to be zero. This can be easily seen by substituting the transfer function of the compensation in Eq. 9.5–1 and remembering that $H_f(s)$ is equal to unity. The reader who is uninitiated in feedback-control design would conclude from this that we have arrived at a very satisfactory solution for the compensation design. However, we have only shown that as far as linear theory is concerned it is theoretically possible to achieve errors below any assigned limit provided the system is excited by a disturbance only and provided the fixed elements are linear and minimum phase. In practice, an attempt to realize the compensation of Eq. 9.5–11 can only lead to failure.

Let us examine a little more closely the implications of Eq. 9.5–11. It will be recalled that the compensation $G_c(s)$ to be used inside the feedback loop of a control system is related to the equivalent cascade compensation $W_c(s)$ by Eq. 1.7–4 which is repeated here for convenience.

$$G_c(s) = \frac{W_c(s)}{1 - G_f(s)H_f(s)W_c(s)} \tag{1.7–4}$$

Now suppose that as an approximation to the desired equivalent cascade compensation we use

$$W_c(s) = \frac{1}{(as + 1)G_f(s)} \tag{9.5–12}$$

In the limit as a approaches zero this compensation approaches that of Eq. 9.5–11. Reference to Fig. 9.3–3 shows that the transfer function for the fixed elements is given by

$$G_f(s) = \frac{1}{s\,b(s)} \tag{9.5–13}$$

where $b(s)$ is a polynomial in s of the third degree. The constant term of this polynomial is unity. Substitution of the right members of Eqs. 9.5–12 and 9.5–13 in Eq. 1.7–4 yields

$$G_c(s) = \frac{b(s)}{a} \tag{9.5–14}$$

Here we see that the transfer function of the compensating elements to be used inside the feedback loop is a polynomial in s divided by a constant which approaches zero as the effect of this compensation on the closed loop approaches the desired result. In the limit when a equals zero we have a requirement for an infinite gain together with a requirement for proportional, first, and higher derivative control. Of course, this kind of compensation is impossible to realize in practice even though it does not violate the realizability condition that we have imposed on weighting functions. As an approximation to the $G_c(s)$ of Eq. 9.5–14 we may employ

$$G_c(s) = \frac{b_1(s)}{a\,b_2(s)} \tag{9.5–15}$$

Here the polynomial $b_2(s)$ is at least of the same degree as $b_1(s)$. Such compensation corresponds to a higher-order lead network. By making the coefficients in the $b_2(s)$ polynomial orders of magnitudes smaller than the corresponding coefficients of the $b_1(s)$ polynomial, we can begin to achieve the desired compensation effect provided the constant a can be made small enough. But let us examine the over-all system function that results when compensation of the form of Eq. 9.5–15 is used. The over-all system function is of the form

$$W(s) = \frac{b_1(s)}{asb(s)b_2(s) + b_1(s)} \qquad (9.5\text{--}16)$$

Substitution of numerical values for the coefficients of the polynomials in this expression will quickly reveal that severe restrictions are imposed on the smallness of the constant a if the over-all system is to remain stable. These restrictions are least severe when the polynomial $b_1(s)$ is equal to $b(s)$. This condition corresponds to zeros of the compensation canceling poles in the fixed elements. Such canceling action is very difficult to maintain in practice with a system like the radio telescope. With the poorly damped mechanical resonance that this structure exhibits, small changes in the damping of the hydraulic servomotor can disturb the pole-zero cancellation very markedly. When the poles and zeros do not cancel, the order of the denominator $w(s)$ increases and the restriction on the smallness of a (that is, on the largeness of the gain) becomes more severe.

From the foregoing considerations we conclude that the compensation called for by Eq. 9.5–11 is very impractical. We therefore turn our attention in the next article to the introduction of a constraint on the solution for the compensation with the objective of making it easier to realize in practice.

9.6 WIND-GUST ERROR WITH BANDWIDTH LIMITATION

In this article we introduce a constraint on the bandwidth of the over-all control system during the process of minimizing the mean-square error through adjustment of the compensation. The motivation for introducing this constraint is simply to avoid the impractical result derived in the preceding section. We select bandwidth as the factor to be constrained because we wish to force the over-all system to operate at frequencies below the lowest resonant frequency of the mechanical structure. This objective seems reasonable in view of the tremendous practical difficulties that one encounters when an attempt is made to make the servomechanism bandwidth comparable to or larger than the lowest mechanical resonant frequency in the load.

For purposes of this chapter, bandwidth is defined in exactly the same manner as in Chapter 8. In Art. 8.2 bandwidth is defined in terms of the response of the control system to an arbitrary stochastic input. A bandwidth rating is assigned to the control system by setting the bandwidth of a standard system so that the responses of the two systems are equal under the same conditions. Figure 8.2–1 illustrates this technique for assigning a bandwidth rating to the control system. The introduction of the standard system is the means whereby the response of the control system to an arbitrary stochastic input is made to be significant in terms of bandwidth. The standard system and signal source are both chosen so as to make the bandwidth increase monotonically with increasing mean-square response of the control system. As explained in Chapter 8, an additional filter with weighting function $w_f(t)$ is provided on the output of both the standard system and the control system in order to provide a mechanism for adjusting the rate of cutoff of the control system.

From Fig. 8.2–1 the mean-square response of the control system, as measured after the filter, is seen to be

$$\overline{b_f{}^2(t)} = w_c(t_1) \star w_c(t_2) \star g_f(t_3) \star g_f(t_4) \star w_f(t_5) \star w_f(t_6)$$
$$\star \varphi_{bvv}(t_1 + t_3 + t_5 - t_2 - t_4 - t_6) \quad (9.6\text{–}1)$$

Here $\varphi_{bvv}(\tau)$ represents the autocorrelation function of the signal source or noise generator used for bandwidth determination. This equation is the same as Eq. 8.4–5 except for the change to the new notation for integration from minus infinity to plus infinity. Also, in Eq. 9.6–1 the over-all system weighting function (represented by $w(t)$ in Eq. 8.4–5) has been replaced by the convolution of the weighting function of the compensation $w_c(t)$ and the weighting function for the fixed elements $g_f(t)$. In view of the way in which bandwidth is defined, placing a constraint on the bandwidth is the same as placing a constraint on the mean-square value of the filtered response of the control system. Both the mean-square error as given by Eq. 9.5–5 and the mean-square value of the filtered output of the control system under bandwidth test conditions are functionals involving the weighting function of the compensation. Therefore, using the procedure developed by Lagrange, we introduce the constraint on bandwidth by minimizing the functional

$$F = \overline{y_e{}^2(t)} + \rho \overline{b_f{}^2(t)} \quad (9.6\text{–}2)$$

instead of simply the mean-square error alone. When this functional is minimized by application of the standard variational procedure, a new integral equation results for $w_c(t)$. It is not difficult to see that this new integral equation is formed by adding the following term to Eq. 9.5–6.

$$\rho w_c(t_2) \star g_f(t_3) \star g_f(t_4) \star w_f(t_5) \star w_f(t_6) \star \varphi_{bvv}(t_1 + t_3 + t_5 - t_2 - t_4 - t_6) \quad (9.6\text{--}3)$$

Adding this term to the integral equation means that the function $\Delta(s)$ appearing in the explicit solution formula of Eq. 5.4–28 is changed from that given by Eq. 9.5–8 to

$$\Delta(s) = 2\pi G_f(-s)G_f(s)[\Phi_{vv}(s) + H_f(-s)H_f(s)\Phi_{xx}(s)$$
$$- H_f(s)\Phi_{vx}(s) - H_f(-s)\Phi_{xv}(s) + \rho W_f(-s)W_f(s)\Phi_{bvv}(s)] \quad (9.6\text{--}4)$$

The function $\Gamma(s)$ which appears in the explicit solution formula is unchanged from Eq. 9.5–7. This completes the general discussion of the solution for the compensation when the bandwidth is limited.

Let us now apply the general result derived above to the problem of the azimuth drive for the radio telescope. Certain simplifications can be made in the general result since the specifications for the radio telescope drive state that the input signal and the desired output signal are both zero. Furthermore, the fixed elements employed in the radio telescope drive are minimum phase, and, in accordance with the discussion in Art. 6.3, the compensation can be found by solving for the over-all system function and then dividing by the transfer function for the fixed elements. The solution for the over-all system function is obtained by setting $G_f(s) = 1$ in the functions $\Gamma(s)$ and $\Delta(s)$. Thus for the radio telescope problem we have

$$\Gamma(s) = 2\pi\Phi_{xx}(s) \quad (9.6\text{--}5)$$

$$\Delta(s) = 2\pi[\Phi_{xx}(s) + \rho W_f(-s)W_f(s)\Phi_{bvv}(s)] \quad (9.6\text{--}6)$$

In view of the fact that we now are constraining the bandwidth, three additional specifications need to be introduced into the radio telescope problem. First, the power-density spectrum of the noise source used for the bandwidth test must be given. We shall take this to be white noise with the spectrum

$$\Phi_{bvv}(s) = \eta/\pi \quad (9.6\text{--}7)$$

Next, in order to force the control system to have a cutoff rate of at least 20 decilogs per decade of frequency change, we set the transfer function for the filter equal to

$$W_f(s) = s \quad (9.6\text{--}8)$$

Finally, we specify the form of the standard system used in the bandwidth test to be

$$W_b(s) = \frac{1}{[(1/\omega_b)s + 1]^2} \tag{9.6-9}$$

As pointed out in Chapter 8, the form for the standard system is not particularly important so long as it cuts off at the rate required by the input-signal specification and the filter used for the bandwidth test.

Next we must evaluate the power-density spectrum $\Phi_{xx}(s)$. By reference to Eq. 9.5–2 we observe that

$$\Phi_{xx}(s) = G_u(-s)G_u(s)G_f(-s)G_f(s)\Phi_{uu}(s) \tag{9.6-10}$$

From Fig. 9.3–3 we see that

$$G_u(s) = \left(\frac{J_b}{k}s^2 + \frac{f}{k}s + 1\right)\frac{1}{f} \tag{9.6-11}$$

$$G_f(s) = \frac{1}{\left(\dfrac{J_b}{f}\dfrac{J_d}{k}s^3 + \dfrac{J_d}{k}s^2 + \dfrac{J_b + J_d}{f}s + 1\right)s} \tag{9.6-12}*$$

The power-density spectrum of the wind-torque disturbance is given in Eq. 9.4–9. Upon substitution of the value of $\Phi_{xx}(s)$, given by Eq. 9.6–10 together with Eqs. 9.6–11, 9.6–12, and Eq. 9.4–9, in the general solution formula for the system function, we find that we are faced with a fairly involved computation. The computation is made difficult because of the order of $G_u(s)$ and of $G_f(s)$. We therefore examine the possibility of simplifying the computation by reducing the complexity of these transfer functions.

With a view to simplification let us examine the shape of the power-density spectrum for the wind-torque disturbance. As shown in Fig. 9.4–1, the power density at 5 radians per second is of the order of 4 percent of the zero-frequency value or, considering both positive and negative frequencies, the total power density at plus and minus 5 radians per second is 8 percent of the zero-frequency value. Considering the power between the limits minus 5 radians per second to plus 5 radians per second, we observe that 88 percent of the total power is located in this interval. Substitution of the numerical values for the coefficients in the expressions for $G_u(s)$ and $G_f(s)$ yields

$$G_u(s) = (0.0172s^2 + 0.792s + 1)\frac{1}{f} \tag{9.6-13}$$

$$G_f(s) = \frac{1}{(0.186 \times 10^{-3}s^3 + 0.857 \times 10^{-2}s^2 + 0.0326s + 1)s} \tag{9.6-14}$$

* $T_s = 0$ when acceleration feedback is not used in Fig. 9.3–2.

Since there is very little power in the disturbance at frequencies beyond 5 radians per second, let us see what terms we can drop from $G_u(s)$ and $G_f(s)$. In the former, the term in s^2 contributes very little relative to the term in s up to 5 radians per second. With respect to the latter, all terms except the constant unity inside the parentheses can be ignored. Of course, the pole at the origin in $G_f(s)$ is very significant at low frequencies and must be retained. From these considerations we may approximate $G_u(s)$ as

$$G_u(s) \cong (T_u s + 1)\frac{1}{f} \qquad (9.6\text{--}15)$$

where

$$T_u = f/k \qquad (9.6\text{--}16)$$

The transfer function $G_f(s)$ is approximated as

$$G_f(s) \cong 1/s \qquad (9.6\text{--}17)$$

The mathematical model of the azimuth drive represented by these approximations will be referred to as Model I in order to distinguish it from another model introduced in the next article.

Using the Model I approximations for $G_u(s)$ and $G_f(s)$, we find that $\Phi_{xx}(s)$ can be approximated by the relatively simple function

$$\Phi_{xx}(s) = \frac{\beta^2 \nu(-T_u{}^2 s^2 + 1)}{\pi f^2(-s^2 + \nu^2)(-s^2)} \qquad (9.6\text{--}18)$$

Physically, the approximations that have been used here for purposes of computing the power-density spectrum $\Phi_{xx}(s)$ correspond to ignoring the inertia terms in the fixed elements and in $G_u(s)$. This is reasonable to do in view of the relatively low frequencies involved in the wind-torque disturbance. At these low frequencies reduction of the mean-square values of the output is effected principally by means of the closed-loop stiffness of the system and not through attenuation of the disturbance by the fixed elements. In fact, if the control loop is opened, the leakage associated with the servomotor would result in an infinite mean-square value for the error associated with the disturbance. This is indicated by the pole at the origin in the transfer function for the fixed elements.

We are now in a position to evaluate the over-all system function $W_m(s)$ that minimizes the mean-square error subject to the constraint on the bandwidth. Substituting the value for $\Phi_{xx}(s)$ given by Eq. 9.6–18 into the general solution formula, together with the value for

$W_f(s)$ given by Eq. 9.6–8 and the value of $\Phi_{bvv}(s)$ given by Eq. 9.6–7, we ultimately find that $W_m(s)$ has the relatively simple form

$$W_m(s) = \frac{bs + 1}{a_3s^3 + a_2s^2 + a_1s + 1} \quad (9.6\text{–}19)$$

In this expression the coefficient a_3 is related to the square root of the Lagrangian multiplier ρ. However, the algebraic work is considerably reduced if we regard a_1 as a new Lagrangian multiplier and solve for the other coefficients in terms of a_1. Doing this yields

$$a_2 = \frac{a_1^2 - T_u^2}{2} \quad (9.6\text{–}20)$$

$$a_3 = -\frac{a_1}{\nu^2} + \left[\left(\frac{a_1}{\nu^2}\right)^2 + \frac{a_2^2}{\nu^2}\right]^{\frac{1}{2}} \quad (9.6\text{–}21)$$

$$b = \frac{a_3\nu^2 + (a_2 + T_u^2)\nu + a_1}{a_3\nu^3 + a_2\nu^2 + a_1\nu + 1} \quad (9.6\text{–}22)$$

These three equations show how the parameters of the over-all system function are controlled by the specifications imposed on the azimuth drive.

The next step is to establish the bandwidth of the control system in terms of the master coefficient a_1. It will be recalled that the mean-square value $\overline{b_f^2(t)}$ of the filtered output of the control system during the bandwidth test can be evaluated by

$$\overline{b_f^2(t)} = \frac{1}{j} \int_{-j\infty}^{j\infty} ds\, W(-s)\,W(s)\,W_f(-s)\,W_f(s)\Phi_{bvv}(s) \quad (9.6\text{–}23)$$

Substitution of the system function into this expression yields

$$\overline{b_f^2(t)} = \eta\left[\frac{(b^2a_1 + a_3)}{a_3(a_2a_1 - a_3)}\right] \quad (9.6\text{–}24)$$

The filtered output of the standard system under bandwidth test conditions is obtained by substituting in Eq. 9.6-23 the over-all system function for the standard system in place of that for the control system. Doing this and evaluating show that the mean-square value $\overline{b_s^2(t)}$ of the filtered output of the standard system is given by

$$\overline{b_s^2(t)} = \frac{\eta\omega_b^3}{2} \quad (9.6\text{–}25)$$

Equating the mean-square values given by Eqs. 9.6–24 and 9.6–25 gives us the following relation for the bandwidth of the control system

$$\omega_b = \left[\frac{2(b^2 a_1 + a_3)}{a_3(a_2 a_1 - a_3)}\right]^{\frac{1}{4}} \qquad (9.6\text{--}26)$$

This expression gives us the desired functional relationship between the master coefficient a_1 and the bandwidth ω_b since the other coefficients are expressed in terms of a_1 by means of Eqs. 9.6–20 through 9.6–22.

We next seek the relationship between the mean-square error caused by the disturbance and the master parameter a_1 in the over-all system function. From Eq. 9.5–1 we see that, for the case of no input signal and zero desired-output signal, the power-density spectrum of the error is given by

$$\Phi_{yy}(s) = [1 - W(-s)H_f(-s)][1 - W(s)H_f(s)]\Phi_{xx}(s) \qquad (9.6\text{--}27)$$

Here the system function $W(s)$ is used for the product $W_c(s)G_f(s)$. This equation follows since the error is the negative of the output under these conditions. The mean-square error is found by integrating the power-density spectrum as follows

$$\overline{y_e^2(t)} = \frac{1}{j} \int_{-j\infty}^{j\infty} ds\ \Phi_{yy}(s) \qquad (9.6\text{--}28)$$

Substituting $H_f(s) = 1$, the value of $W(s)$ given by Eq. 9.6–19, and the power-density spectrum given by Eq. 9.6–18 in Eq. 9.6–27 and applying Eq. 9.6–28, we find the mean-square error to be given by

$$\overline{y_e^2(t)} = \left(\frac{2\beta^2 \nu}{f^2}\right)\left(\frac{1}{2\pi j}\right) \int_{-j\infty}^{j\infty} ds\ \frac{c(-s)c(s)}{d(-s)d(s)} \qquad (9.6\text{--}29)$$

Here the polynomials $c(s)$ and $d(s)$ turn out to be

$$c(s) = a_3 T_u s^3 + (a_2 T_u + a_3)s^2 + [(a_1 - b)T_u + a_2]s + a_1 - b \qquad (9.6\text{--}30)$$

and

$$d(s) = a_3 s^4 + (a_2 + a_3 \nu)s^3 + (a_1 + a_2 \nu)s^2 + (1 + a_1 \nu)s + \nu \qquad (9.6\text{--}31)$$

In terms of these polynomials the mean-square error can be evaluated using the table of integrals given in Appendix E. Computation proceeds most expeditiously if numerical values for the coefficients of the polynomials are evaluated for each of a series of values for a_1. In this way the mean-square error can be found as a function of a_1.

As the final step in our analysis of wind-gust error under conditions of bandwidth limitation, we plot the root-mean-square error caused by the wind-torque disturbance as a function of the control-system bandwidth. By Eq. 9.6–26 the system bandwidth ω_b can be tabulated as a function of a_1. Equation 9.6–29, together with Eqs. 9.6–30 and 9.6–31, allows us to tabulate the mean-square error as a function of a_1. Through the use of these two tables it is then possible to plot the mean-square or rms error as a function of bandwidth. This has been done in Fig. 9.6–1, which shows the rms error as a function of the system

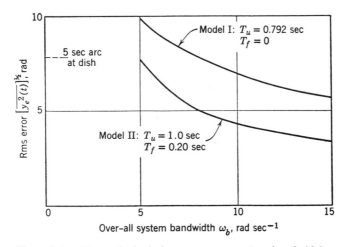

Fig. 9.6–1. Theoretical wind error versus system bandwidth.

bandwidth. The upper curve of this figure corresponds to the Model I approximations used in this article. The lower curve corresponds to another set of approximations for $G_u(s)$ and $G_f(s)$, which will be discussed in the next article.

As pointed out at the beginning of this chapter it is not our intention to use the compensation indicated by Eq. 9.6–19 in the design of the actual control system. Rather, we use the system function given by this equation to establish a relationship between the bandwidth and the minimum possible rms error caused by the wind disturbance. Because of the approximations used in the derivation of the rms-error-to-bandwidth relationship, Fig. 9.6–1 can serve only as a guide which is valid at low frequencies. In the next article we shall show how the guidance offered by this figure is employed in a trial-and-error design of compensation that might actually be used for the azimuth drive of the radio telescope.

9.7 TRIAL-AND-ERROR DESIGNS

The purpose of this article is to show how the results from analytical design theory are used to guide trial-and-error designs and to indicate when the trial-and-error procedure should be terminated. In order to accomplish our purpose we outline three trial designs for the compensation to be used in the azimuth drive of the radio telescope. For each of these designs we determine the over-all system bandwidth ω_b and the rms error caused by the stochastic wind disturbance. By comparing the rms error for a given trial design with the theoretical error achievable within its bandwidth as indicated by Fig. 9.6–1, we determine the margin available for system improvement. If this margin is small and the bandwidth of the system under consideration is approaching the natural frequency of the antenna structure, we know that further improvement through additional trial designs will be practically impossible to obtain. Conversely, if a large margin exists between the theoretical and realized rms errors or if the realized system bandwidth is small relative to the natural frequency of the mechanical structure, we know that additional trials are worthwhile because further improvement in system performance is theoretically possible.

The trial-and-error designs of this section are developed by means of gain-phase plots of the open-loop transfer function for the system. This design technique is discussed in Appendix D. In this article we consider three trial designs for the unknown compensation $G_c(s)$ shown in Fig. 9.3–2. Compensation A employs simple gain only in accordance with the equation

$$G_c(s) = K_v \qquad (9.7\text{–}1)$$

where K_v is the velocity constant of the system. Compensation B also uses simple gain for $G_c(s)$ but, in addition, uses a parallel feedback path from the antenna position as shown in dotted lines in Fig. 9.3–2. By this parallel path a signal proportional to the output acceleration is subtracted from the output of the compensating elements to form the net signal which controls the hydraulic valve. The parallel feedback compensation is intended to improve system performance by increasing the effective damping associated with the mechanical structure. Compensation C is the same as compensation B except for the addition of a lag network as part of the cascade compensation.   This makes the transfer function of the compensating elements for compensation C have the following form

$$G_c(s) = \left(\frac{T_c s + 1}{\alpha T_c s + 1}\right) K_v \qquad (9.7\text{--}2)$$

We now discuss how the parameter values for the three forms of compensation are established.

In applying the trial-and-error design procedure to the problem of the radio telescope drive the specification on the degree of stability is taken to be a peak magnification M_p of the over-all frequency response of 1.3.   From this specification on the degree of stability the velocity constant (gain) for compensation A is immediately established from the gain-phase plot of the open-loop frequency response since this plot has been normalized with respect to gain.   The top curve in Fig. 9.7–1 shows the gain-normalized, open-loop frequency response for the azimuth drive of the radio telescope for compensation A.   By setting the closed-loop $M = 1.3$ contour tangent to the frequency-response locus in a manner similar to the construction shown for the bottom curve we find the velocity constant to be 0.69 second^{-1}.*   This relatively low gain is the consequence of the poorly damped mechanical resonance corresponding to the inertia of the antenna dish and the elastance of the supporting towers.   The deficiency in damping is clearly exhibited by the excessive rise in the magnitude of the open-loop frequency response in the vicinity of -180 degrees of phase shift.

A considerable improvement in the velocity constant could be effected if the magnitude rise of the open-loop transfer function in the neighborhood of -180 degrees of phase shift could be suppressed.   By employing acceleration feedback from the output as indicated in the dotted lines of Fig. 9.3–2, additional damping is introduced, in effect, into the mechanical structure through the action of the acceleration signal on the servomotor.   This additional damping shows up as an increase in the coefficient of the term involving the first power of s within the denominator brackets of the transfer function $G_f(s)$ (Fig. 9.3–3).   The parameter T_s, which is proportional to the gain of the auxiliary feedback, is adjusted by trial and error until the open-loop frequency response of the over-all system will permit the maximum possible improvement in gain.   A value of T_s of 0.167 second is

---

* In setting the gain K_v by this method, a preliminary check must always be made to ensure that the value of gain so selected is within a range of gain values corresponding to stable system operation.   Nyquist's stability criterion, discussed in Appendix B, can be used for this check.   Although the details of the stability check are omitted here, the selected gain does yield a stable system.

approximately correct for the auxiliary feedback gain in the sense of providing maximum improvement in the velocity constant of the over-all system.   The middle curve of Fig. 9.7–1 is the open-loop frequency response of the system for this adjustment of the auxiliary feedback. As a consequence of the improved damping, the velocity constant is increased to 5 second^{-1}.

In order to compare the performance of the over-all system with compensations A and B as just described, the band width of the system with each form of compensation must be determined.   The bandwidth is found by using Eq. 9.6–23 to determine the mean-square filtered

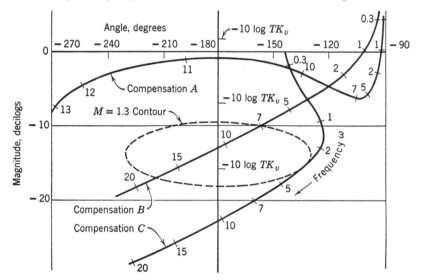

Fig. 9.7–1.   Gain-phase plots of $\left(\dfrac{1}{TK_v}\right)\dfrac{q}{e}(j\omega)$ for three compensation trials. $T = 1.0$ second.

response under bandwidth-test conditions.   The integration is carried out graphically on plots of the square of the product of the magnitudes of the over-all system function and the filter function.   Figure 9.7–2 shows such plots.   By comparing the mean-square response so deter-mined with the mean-square response of the standard system as given by Eq. 9.6–25, the bandwidth of the over-all system is established. In this way we find the bandwidth for the system with compensation A to be 6.5 radians per second and that with compensation B to be 7.3 radians per second.

Next we determine the mean-square errors for the two systems. The mean-square error is found by graphical integration of the power-

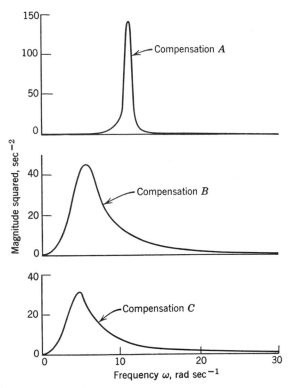

Fig. 9.7–2.   Plots of $|W(j\omega)W_f(j\omega)|^2$ used to determine bandwidth.

density spectrum for the error as indicated by Eq. 9.6–28.   The power-
density spectrum of the error can be found by Eq. 9.6–27 but it is
somewhat more convenient to rewrite this in another form.   Because
the transfer function for the feedback elements is unity, Eq. 9.6–27
can be written as

$$\Phi_{yy}(s) = \left[\frac{1}{1 + G_c(-s)G_f(-s)}\right]\left[\frac{1}{1 + G_c(s)G_f(s)}\right]\Phi_{xx}(s) \quad (9.7\text{--}3)$$

Substituting the right member of Eq. 9.6–10 for $\Phi_{xx}(s)$, multiplying
and dividing by $G_c(s)G_c(-s)$, and identifying the over-all system function permit us to write Eq. 9.7–3 in the form

$$\Phi_{yy}(s) = W(-s)W(s)\frac{G_u(-s)}{G_c(-s)}\frac{G_u(s)}{G_c(s)}\Phi_{uu}(s) \quad (9.7\text{--}4)$$

Figure 9.7–3 shows plots for the error power-density spectra as determined by this equation.   From the areas underneath these plots we

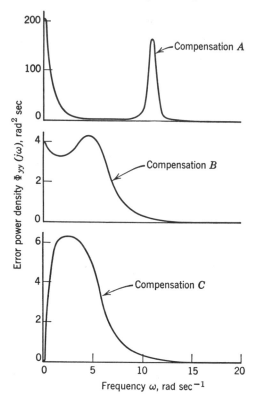

Fig. 9.7–3.   Error power-density spectra.

find the rms error for compensation A to be 29 radians and that for compensation B to be 7.5 radians.

Comparison of the above results for trial-and-error compensation with the theoretical limits of performance derived in the preceding article is facilitated by Table 9.7–1.   The first conclusion to be drawn

Table 9.7–1.   Comparison of Realized and Theoretical Performance for Wind-Torque Fluctuations

TRIAL-AND-ERROR DESIGN	BANDWIDTH (rad sec^{-1})	REALIZED RMS ERROR (radians at servomotor)	THEORETICAL RMS ERROR (radians at servomotor)	
			Model I	Model II
Compensation A	6.5	29	8.7	—
Compensation B	7.3	7.5	8.2*	5.4
Compensation C	6.4	8.4	—	6.1

   * Model I does not apply since the approximation for $G_f(s)$ is not satisfactory when the acceleration feedback of compensations B and C is used.

from this table is that the bandwidths obtained with both compensations A and B are reasonable since they are better than 50 percent of the structural natural frequency of 10.8 radians per second. However, for compensation A the rms error is over four times as large as the theoretical error for Model I as determined by the analytical design method in the preceding article. This would indicate that improvement through additional trials should be obtainable. This leads one to compensation B where the rms error turns out to be 7.5 radians, a value less than the 8.2 radians theoretically indicated by Model I. This apparent anomaly is explained when it is recalled that compensation B effectively alters the fixed elements so that the Model I approximation of Eq. 9.6–17 no longer applies. Even without further analysis, however, we see that compensation B appears to give us error performance approaching theoretical limits and that further trials are not likely to lead to much improvement.

In order to be even more certain that there is little room for improvement through additional trials, it is desirable to determine a new theoretical limit on performance, using a more satisfactory approximation for the fixed elements. Therefore as a new approximation, which we shall denote as Model II, we use

$$G_f(s) = \frac{1}{(T_f s + 1)s} \tag{9.7–5}$$

The parameter T_f accounts for the increase in the significance of the coefficient of the term involving the first power of s within the brackets of $G_f(s)$ shown in Fig. 9.3–3. This increase is caused by the addition of $T_s = 0.167$ second to the original 0.033 second existing before acceleration feedback was introduced. This makes $T_f = 0.200$ second for Model II, a value that makes this term significant for the important frequencies of the power-density spectrum of the wind-torque disturbance as shown in Fig. 9.4–1. By setting T_u in the approximation for $G_u(s)$ given by Eq. 9.6–15 to a new value of 1.0 second instead of the value of 0.792 second used in Art. 9.6, we avoid any increase in the complexity of the theoretical solution for the over-all system function. This comes about since the $(T_u s + 1)$ factor cancels an $(s + \nu)$ factor in Eq. 9.6–18 for $\Phi_{xx}(s)$. The increase in T_u is postulated to result from an increase in the damping of the hydraulic servomotor from $f = 0.634$ to $f = 0.801$ inch-pound second per radian. This parameter is quite variable and is strongly dependent on the viscosity of the hydraulic fluid.

For Model II the theoretical system function that minimizes the rms error is given by Eq. 9.6–19 as before. However, the parameters are changed to

$$a_2 = \tfrac{1}{2}a_1{}^2 \qquad\qquad\qquad (9.7-6)$$

$$a_3 = -\; T_f{}^2 a_1 + (T_f{}^4 a_1{}^2 + \tfrac{1}{4}T_f{}^2 a_1{}^4)^{\frac{1}{2}} \qquad (9.7-7)$$

$$b = \left[\frac{(a_3/T_f{}^3) + (a_2/T_f{}^2) + (a_1/T_f)}{(a_3/T_f{}^3) + (a_2/T_f{}^2) + (a_1/T_f) + 1} \right] T_f \qquad (9.7-8)$$

Using these modified coefficients the rms error for a given bandwidth is evaluated in the same way as for Model I. The result is plotted as the lower curve of Fig. 9.6–1. From this we see that Model II gives lower rms errors than Model I as we should expect because of the increased filtering action of the fixed elements when acceleration feedback is employed.

On the basis of Model II we see that, for the system bandwidth corresponding to compensation B, the theoretical rms error is 5.4 radians. This error is below the realized error of 7.5 radians for compensation B, indicating that no anomaly exists when the proper approximation for the fixed elements is used. Nevertheless the realized error is close enough to the theoretical limit so that we can conclude that we are in the region of diminishing returns as far as additional compensation trials are concerned.

Although compensation B gives a satisfactory rms error for wind-torque variations, the steady-state error corresponding to the average wind torque is 7.0 radians. Also, the steady-state error for a constant input velocity of maximum value (200 seconds of arc per second or 314 radians per second at the servomotor) is 62.8 radians, an excessive value. These considerations are outside the scope of this chapter but are mentioned in order to explain why the performance with compensation B could still be considered unsatisfactory on grounds other than the errors caused by wind-velocity fluctuations. In order to reduce the steady-state errors, compensation C is employed. The gain-phase plot for compensation C using $\alpha = 10$ and $T_c = 2.0$ seconds is shown as the bottom curve in Fig. 9.7–1. With this compensation, the velocity constant K_v is raised to 38 second^{-1} and the steady-state errors are reduced to 13 percent of the values quoted for compensation B. With these new values the steady-state errors are satisfactory. But, as shown in Table 9.7–1, this has been accomplished at the expense of an increase in the rms error for wind-torque fluctuations. Some increase in this error is to be expected since the bandwidth has been reduced. The ratio of the realized error to Model II theoretical error is practically unchanged in going from compensation B to compensation C. Thus the principal criticism of compensation C is the bandwidth reduction. However, this reduction is practically unavoidable with simple lag compensation if a reasonable settling time to transients is desired.

The major conclusion to be drawn from the application of analytical and trial-and-error design techniques to the wind-torque disturbance problem encountered in the azimuth drive of the radio telescope is simply this: Theory says the rms error cannot be much lower than 3.4 seconds of arc (5.4 radians at the motor). Trial-and-error techniques show that errors of the order of 4.8 seconds of arc (7.5 radians at the motor) are realizable with simple compensation. To the wind error must be added steady-state errors and a safety factor. We therefore conclude that a total rms error for the azimuth servomechanism (exclusive of measuring errors) will exceed 5.5 seconds, the value specified in Art. 9.2. Therefore, the specifications should be relaxed or another antenna structure should be investigated.

9.8 CONCLUSIONS

This chapter represents a rather detailed and exhaustive study of one aspect of the azimuth drive for a large radio telescope. This study has shown us many of the steps that may be necessary in applying analytical design theory to practical problems. Let us recapitulate these steps in order to summarize what we have learned through this example.

The first step in solving a design problem by either analytical means or by trial-and-error procedure is to formulate the problem by gathering together the performance specifications and the description of the fixed elements. This part of the problem solution for the radio telescope drive is covered in Art. 9.2, 9.3, and 9.4. In Art. 9.2 we went from the general operational requirements to rather detailed specifications on the azimuth drive. In Art. 9.3 the fixed elements for the azimuth drive were established through analysis of a schematic diagram and block diagrams for the system. In Art. 9.4 a study was made of the missing specification, namely, a statistical description for the wind-torque disturbance.

The second step in applying analytical theory to a practical problem is the development of an appropriate formula for the compensation. Although many problems can be handled by formulas derived in this book or in the literature, we must always be prepared for new situations. The radio telescope problem represented such a new situation, and in Art. 9.5 a new compensation formula was derived and shown to lead to impractical results. In Art. 9.6 a modification of this design formula was developed.

The third step in applying analytical design theory is the making of reasonable approximations so as to reduce the complexity of the computation needed to determine the compensation and to compute the resultant performance. With respect to the radio telescope drive, the key for making these approximations is the concentration of the power density of the disturbance at low frequencies. As shown in Art. 9.6, this permitted considerable simplification of the analysis.

Even with appropriate approximations the compensation determined by analytical theory is usually unduly complex and difficult to realize. Often simpler forms of compensation determined by the trial-and-error design procedure can be found which will yield performance almost identical with that determined theoretically. This comes about because minima (or maxima) in the performance indices of control systems tend to be broad just as they are in other engineering problems. Therefore, the fourth step in applying analytical theory is to find simpler forms of compensation that yield results almost as good as those obtained theoretically. By using the trial-and-error design procedure a number of possible forms of compensation can be found. These compensations can be checked for their efficiency by comparing the performance figures that they make possible with guide figures established by the analytical design theory. This step for the radio telescope problem was carried out in Art. 9.7.

THE FOURIER AND
LAPLACE TRANSFORMATIONS

This appendix concerns itself first with a verification of the Fourier transform pair. The conditions that must be met by a function $f(t)$ in order to be Fourier transformable are then set forth. The discussion is extended to the Laplace transform as a special case of the Fourier transform. A short listing of some of the operational properties of the Fourier and Laplace transforms are then included in table form. The process of inverse transformation is discussed with emphasis on the use of the theory of residues. Several examples are included to illustrate the application of the inverse transform methods and also to bring out the basic restrictions on the Fourier and Laplace transformations. Finally, the class of Fourier transformable functions is extended by use of a convergence factor to cover such functions as steps and ramps. The discourse on transforms closes with a discussion of the restrictions imposed by use of the convergence factor.

A.1 INTRODUCTION TO THE FOURIER TRANSFORMATION

The Fourier transform pair as used in this book is defined by the relations

$$F(s) = \int_{-\infty}^{\infty} dt \, e^{-st} f(t) \qquad (A.1\text{--}1)$$

$$f(t) = \frac{1}{2\pi j} \int_{-j\infty}^{j\infty} ds\ e^{st} F(s) \qquad (\text{A.1--2})$$

where $s = j\omega$.* The proof that performing the integral operations as defined by Eqs. A.1–1 and A.1–2 on $f(t)$ yields the original function $f(t)$ is presented by a plausibility argument. Combining Eqs. A.1–1 and A.1–2 and replacing t by x in Eq. A.1–2, there results the Fourier transform theorem

$$f(x) = \frac{1}{2\pi j} \int_{-j\infty}^{j\infty} ds\ e^{sx} \int_{-\infty}^{\infty} dt\ f(t) e^{-st} \qquad (\text{A.1--3})$$

The conditions imposed on $f(t)$ in order that it be Fourier transformable are the so-called Dirichlet conditions (1), (2), and (3) and the convergence condition (4), as follows:

1. Function $f(t)$ can have only a finite number of discontinuities in the finite interval $t_1 < t < t_2$.
2. Function $f(t)$ can have only a finite number of points at which the function becomes infinite in the finite interval $t_1 < t < t_2$.
3. Function $f(t)$ can have only a finite number of maxima and minima in any finite interval $t_1 < t < t_2$.
4. The integral $\int_{-\infty}^{\infty} dt\ |f(t)|$ must be convergent.

Assuming that these conditions are met by $f(t)$ we must now prove that the function $f(x)$ as obtained from Eq. A.1–3 is truly the same function as $f(t)$. To do this we first define a new function $f_1(x)$ by

$$f_1(x) = \frac{1}{2\pi j} \int_{-j\infty}^{j\infty} ds\ e^{sx} e^{-\epsilon|s|} \int_{-\infty}^{\infty} dt\ f(t) e^{-st} \qquad (\text{A.1--4})$$

which in the limit as $\epsilon \to 0$ approaches $f(x)$

$$f(x) = \lim_{\epsilon \to 0} f_1(x) \qquad (\text{A.1--5})$$

But $s = j\omega$ in the integral over s and therefore there is no need to consider s other than purely imaginary in either integral. Therefore,

$$|s| = |\omega| \qquad (\text{A.1--6})$$

and

$$ds = jd\omega \qquad (\text{A.1--7})$$

---

* The variable s in this book is used for the general complex variable $\sigma + j\omega$. However, unless otherwise indicated, s as used in the direct Fourier transform is understood to have an imaginary part only, i.e., $s = j\omega$.

Hence Eq. A.1–4 becomes upon substitution and an interchange in the order of integration

$$f_1(x) = \frac{1}{2\pi} \int_{-\infty}^{\infty} dt \, f(t) \int_{-\infty}^{\infty} d\omega \, e^{-\epsilon|\omega|} e^{(x-t)j\omega} \tag{A.1-8}$$

The integration with respect to ω on the right side is carried out by splitting the integral into two parts as follows

$$f_1(x) = \frac{1}{2\pi} \int_{-\infty}^{\infty} dt \, f(t) \left\{ \int_{-\infty}^{0} d\omega \, e^{[\epsilon + j(x-t)]\omega} + \int_{0}^{\infty} d\omega \, e^{-[\epsilon - j(x-t)]\omega} \right\}$$

Integrating

$$f_1(x) = \frac{1}{2\pi} \int_{-\infty}^{\infty} dt \, f(t) \left[\frac{1}{\epsilon + j(x - t)} + \frac{1}{\epsilon - j(x - t)} \right]$$

and collecting terms there results

$$f_1(x) = \frac{1}{\pi} \int_{-\infty}^{\infty} dt \, f(t) \left[\frac{\epsilon}{\epsilon^2 + (x - t)^2} \right] \tag{A.1-9}$$

Now the term in brackets on the right has the general shape shown in Fig. A.1–1. As ϵ tends toward zero this function becomes infinite in

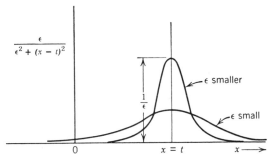

Fig. A.1–1.   Behavior of the function $\dfrac{\epsilon}{\epsilon^2 + (x - t)^2}$ as ϵ is decreased.

magnitude at $t = x$ and zero elsewhere.   Its behavior is very similar to that of the impulse function.   Therefore the product of $f(t)$ and the term involving ϵ can be non-zero only for $t = x$ as ϵ tends to zero.   This permits us to write

$$f_1(x) \doteq \frac{1}{\pi} f(x) \int_{-\infty}^{\infty} dt \, \frac{\epsilon}{\epsilon^2 + (x - t)^2} \tag{A.1-10}$$

for very small ϵ.   The integral on the right side is easily evaluated by the substitution

$$u = x - t \tag{A.1-11}$$

to become

$$f_1(x) = \frac{1}{\pi} f(x) \int_{-\infty}^{\infty} du \frac{\epsilon}{\epsilon^2 + u^2} \tag{A.1-12}$$

and then

$$f_1(x) = \frac{1}{\pi} f(x) \tan^{-1} \frac{u}{\epsilon} \Big]_{-\infty}^{\infty} \tag{A.1-13}$$

but

$$f(x) = \lim_{\epsilon \to 0} f_1(x) \tag{A.1-5}$$

therefore

$$f(x) = \lim_{\epsilon \to 0} \frac{1}{\pi} f(x) \tan^{-1} \frac{u}{\epsilon} \Big]_{-\infty}^{\infty} \tag{A.1-14}$$

and thus

$$f(x) = \frac{1}{\pi} f(x) \left(\frac{\pi}{2} - \frac{-\pi}{2} \right) \tag{A.1-15}$$

whence

$$f(x) = f(x)$$

and hence the theorem of Eq. A.1–3 is verified. This verification using the plausibility argument is due originally to Cauchy.

A.2 EXTENSION TO THE LAPLACE TRANSFORMATION

The requirement that the integral

$$\int_{-\infty}^{\infty} dt \, |f(t)|$$

converge for the Fourier transform to exist places a definite restriction on the class of functions that are Fourier transformable. Hence engineering functions such as the step, the ramp, or any periodic wave are not Fourier transformable in the strict sense. If one relaxes this convergence requirement by the admission of an exponential convergence factor, the class of transformable functions is greatly extended. In this manner we shall show how the Laplace transform evolves as a special case of the Fourier transform.

First, we shall assume that we have chosen our scale of t such that we are interested only in the function $f(t)$ for $t > 0$. With this assumption and with the introduction of the convergence factor $e^{-\sigma t}$ the convergence condition that the function $f(t)$ must satisfy becomes

$$\int_{0}^{\infty} dt \, |f(t)| e^{-\sigma t} \text{ converges} \tag{A.2-1}$$

The greatest lower bound of the set of numbers σ that renders the integral convergent is defined as the abscissa of absolute convergence and is denoted by σ_a. The Fourier transform theorem then becomes

$$f(x)e^{-\sigma x} = \frac{1}{2\pi j} \int_{-j\infty}^{j\infty} d(j\omega)e^{j x\omega} \int_0^\infty dt\, e^{-j\omega t}f(t)e^{-\sigma t} \qquad \text{(A.2-2)}$$

Multiplying both sides of the equation by $e^{\sigma x}$ and changing the variable in the frequency integral from $j\omega$ to $\sigma + j\omega$ there results

$$f(x) = \frac{1}{2\pi j} \int_{\sigma - j\infty}^{\sigma + j\infty} d(\sigma + j\omega)e^{(\sigma + j\omega) x} \int_0^\infty dt\, f(t)e^{-(\sigma + j\omega)t} \qquad \text{(A.2-3)}$$

Now to ensure that the convergence condition is fulfilled the limits on the integration with respect to $\sigma + j\omega$ must have their real part σ greater than σ_a. This value of $\sigma > \sigma_a$ is denoted by c. Further, we can treat $\sigma + j\omega$ as a complex variable and replace it by s. There follows directly

$$F(s) = \int_0^\infty dt\, e^{-st}f(t) \qquad \text{(A.2-4)}$$

$$f(t) = \frac{1}{2\pi j} \int_{c - j\infty}^{c + j\infty} ds\, e^{st}F(s) \qquad \text{(A.2-5)}$$

where $s = \sigma + j\omega$ and $c > \sigma_a$. These two equations then constitute the Laplace transform pair as used in this book.

A.3 SOME USEFUL PROPERTIES OF THE LAPLACE AND FOURIER TRANSFORMATIONS

Both the Laplace transform pair as just defined and the Fourier transform pair as defined by Eqs. A.1–1 and A.1–2 possess the property of uniqueness. This property can be stated as follows: a transformable function has one and only one transform and conversely a transform has one and only one inverse transform. Fortunately, the large majority of the functions used in engineering work are Laplace transformable. The processes of transformation as defined by Eqs. A.1–1 and A.2–4 are straightforward and hence can be handled by the general techniques used in integration. Often the labor involved in the integration of a complicated function can be reduced by either breaking the function down into its simpler parts or by application of some of the operational properties of the transform or both. Extensive tables of both Fourier and Laplace transform pairs exist in the literature. See References C.1, C.55, E.7, and G.2. A few of the more useful operational properties of the Laplace transform and the Fourier transform (S.5, T.4) are listed in Tables A.3–1 and A.3–2, respectively.

Table A.3–1. Some Properties of the Laplace Transform

	FUNCTION	LAPLACE TRANSFORM
1	$f(t)$	$F(s)$
2	$f\left(\dfrac{t}{a}\right)$	$aF(as)$
3	$f(t-a)$ where $f(t-a) = 0,\ 0 < t < a$	$e^{-as}F(s)$
4	$e^{-at}f(t)$	$F(s+a)$
5	$\dfrac{df(t)}{dt}$	$sF(s) - f(0^+)$
6	$\displaystyle\int_0^t \cdots \int_0^t (dt)^n f(t)$	$\dfrac{F(s)}{s^n}$
7	$t^n f(t)$	$(-1)^n \dfrac{d^{(n)}}{ds^n} F(s)$
8	$\dfrac{f(t)}{t^n}$	$\displaystyle\int_s^\infty \cdots \int_s^\infty (ds)^n F(s)$ nth repeated integral
9	$\displaystyle\int_0^t d\tau\, f_1(t-\tau)f_2(\tau)$	$F_1(s)F_2(s)$
10	$f_1(t)f_2(t)$	$\dfrac{1}{2\pi j}\displaystyle\int_{c-j\infty}^{c+j\infty} dw\, F_1(s-w)F_2(w)$
11	$\displaystyle\lim_{t\to 0} f(t)$	$= \displaystyle\lim_{s\to\infty} sF(s)$
12	$\displaystyle\lim_{t\to\infty} f(t)$	$= \displaystyle\lim_{s\to 0} sF(s)$

provided $F(s)$ is analytic on the imaginary axis and in the right half-plane

Table A.3–2. Some Properties of the Fourier Transform

	FUNCTION	FOURIER TRANSFORM
1	$f(t)$	$F(s)$
2	$f\left(\dfrac{t}{a}\right)$	$aF(as)$ for $a > 0$
3	$f(t-a)$	$e^{-as}F(s)$
4	$e^{-at}f(t)$ if a is a pure imaginary number only	$F(s+a)$
5	$\dfrac{d^r f(t)}{dt^r}$	$s^r F(s)$ provided first $(r-1)$ derivatives of $f(t)$ vanish as $t \to \pm\infty$
6	$\displaystyle\int_{-\infty}^\infty d\tau\, f_1(t-\tau)f_2(\tau)$	$F_1(s)F_2(s)$

A.4 SOME DEFINITIONS AND RELATIONS FROM COMPLEX VARIABLE THEORY

At this point we recall some fundamental definitions from the theory of functions of a complex variable. We denote $F(s)$ as a function of the complex variable s where s has σ as its real part and ω as its imaginary part. The function $F(s)$ is said to be analytic in a region R if, at each point in the region, $F(s)$ has a finite derivative and is single valued. Consequently, if a function $F(s)$ is analytic at a point and in some finite region, however small, about this point, then $F(s)$ can be expanded in a Taylor series about this point.

Points at which $F(s)$ is not analytic are called singular points. The singularities of a function of a complex variable are important since they determine the behavior of the function throughout the complex plane. An analytic function with no singularities of any kind is merely a constant. At a singular point the derivative of $F(s)$ either does not exist or has a value that depends on how this point is approached. There are three types of singular points—poles, essential singularities, and branch points. A singularity at $s = a$ is said to be a pole of order n if n is the smallest positive integer that can cause the product $(s - a)^n F(s)$ to be analytic at point a. A singular point a of $F(s)$ is said to be an essential singularity if the function $F(s)$ is single valued, if the derivative $\dfrac{dF(s)}{ds}$ does not exist, and if there is no integer n for which $(d/ds)[(s - a)^n F(s)]$ exists at $s = a$. Therefore an essential singularity can be thought of as a pole of infinite order. For example, the function e^{sT} has an essential singularity at infinity.

A third type of isolated singular point is the branch point which occurs in multivalued functions. A branch point has the characteristic that, if the function is evaluated at points along a closed path surrounding the branch point, the value of the function after completely traversing the path will differ from the initial value. At this branch point it can be shown that a derivative of some order will not exist. Examples of functions having branch points are the logarithm function $[\ln f(s)]$ and the power function $[f(s)]^k$, where k is a non-integer and where, for both function types, $f(s)$ is an entire function excluding a mere constant. These two types of functions have branch points at the points at which the argument $f(s)$ vanishes. By a suitable geometrical construction a hypothetical surface, called the Riemann surface, can be defined on which the function becomes single valued. Since a further discussion of singularities is beyond the scope of this appendix, the reader is referred to standard references on the subject (C.5, H.25, and K.5) for more information.

Single-valued analytic functions of a complex variable may be classed according to the singularities they possess. A function whose only singularity is the point at infinity is analytic everywhere in the finite plane and is called an entire function. This type of function is further classified as an entire rational function or an entire transcendental function according to whether the singularity at infinity is a pole of finite order or an essential singularity. The entire function admits to a power-series expansion of the form

$$f(s) = \sum_{n=0}^{\infty} a_n s^n$$

which is convergent everywhere in the finite plane. Hence an entire rational function has an expansion with a finite number of terms and is therefore a finite polynomial in s. An entire transcendental function has an infinite number of terms in its expansion. Sinh s, e^{sT}, and cos s are examples of entire transcendental functions.

Another important and more general class of functions are those which are single valued (excluding infinity) and which have no singularities other than, at most, poles in the entire finite plane. Functions of such a class are said to be meromorphic functions. It follows then that a meromorphic function is the quotient of two entire functions and has in every finite region at most a finite number of poles. Examples of meromorphic functions are $\sin s/(1 - e^{-sT})$, cot s, and $G(s)/H(s)$ where $G(s)$ and $H(s)$ are polynomials in s. If $G(s)$ and $H(s)$ are finite polynomials, the function is called a rational function. This completes the discussion of classes of functions.

A.5   THE INVERSE FOURIER TRANSFORMATION

The process of inverse transformation involves the evaluation of an integral of the form given in Eq. A.1–2 and in Eq. A.2–5. These equations are recalled here

$$f(t) = \frac{1}{2\pi j} \int_{-j\infty}^{j\infty} ds\, e^{st} F(s) \qquad (A.1-2)$$

for the inverse Fourier transform and

$$f(t) = \frac{1}{2\pi j} \int_{c-j\infty}^{c+j\infty} ds\, e^{st} F(s) \qquad (A.2-5)$$

for the inverse Laplace transform. In these line integrals the integration is carried out over the infinite length of the imaginary axis for the Fourier case and, for the Laplace case, over an infinite line parallel to the imaginary axis and displaced so that all the singularities of $F(s)$ lie to the left of this line. The evaluation of these line integrals can be simplified if the results of Cauchy's residue theorem are employed. The procedure is to represent the line integral along the infinite imaginary axis as the difference between the line integral over the closed path including both the imaginary axis and the arc of a semicircle of infinite radius and the integral over the semicircle of infinite radius. It can be shown that under certain restrictions on $F(s)$ and t the value of the integral along the infinite semicircle vanishes and hence the value of the line integral is given by direct application of the residue theorem to the closed contour.

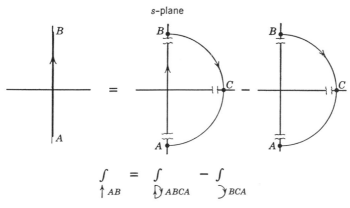

$$\int_{AB} = \int_{ABCA} - \int_{BCA}$$

Fig. A.5-1a. Equivalent contours used for evaluating the inverse Fourier transform for $t < 0$.

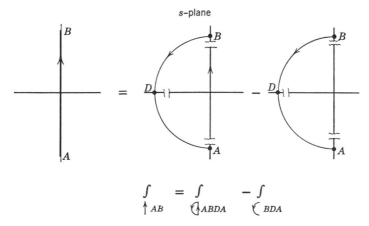

$$\int_{AB} = \int_{ABDA} - \int_{BDA}$$

Fig. A.5-1b. Equivalent contours used for evaluating the inverse Fourier transform for $t > 0$.

We consider first the inverse Fourier transform. We notice that the infinite semicircle can be taken about either the right half-plane or the left half-plane. Now the singularities of the Fourier transform $F(s)$ can in general lie in both half-planes. It will be shown that the line integral around the contour enclosing the left half-plane defines $f(t)$ for $t > 0$ and the line integral around the contour enclosing the right half-plane likewise defines $f(t)$ for $t < 0$. The two sets of contours are shown in Fig. A.5–1.

We consider first the integral representation as shown in Fig. A.5–1a. The value of the line integral about the infinite semicircle enclosing the right half-plane is evaluated as follows. Its magnitude is given by the inequality

$$\left| \int ds\, e^{st} F(s) \right| \leq \int |ds|\, |e^{st}|\, |F(s)| \tag{A.5–1}$$

Now consider that the semicircle has a finite radius R. Then along the contour we have

$$s = Re^{j\theta}$$
$$= R \cos \theta + jR \sin \theta \tag{A.5–2}$$

Therefore

$$ds = Rje^{j\theta}\, d\theta \tag{A.5–3}$$

and

$$e^{st} = e^{tR \cos \theta} e^{jRt \sin \theta} \tag{A.5–4}$$

We also assume that

$$\lim_{s \to \infty} |F(s)| \leq \lim_{s \to \infty} K \left| \frac{1}{s} \right| \tag{A.5–5}$$

Using these expressions in Eq. A.5–1 there results

$$\left| \int ds\, e^{st} F(s) \right| \leq \int_{-\pi/2}^{\pi/2} R\, d\theta\, e^{tR \cos \theta} \left(\frac{K}{R} \right)$$
$$\leq K \int_{-\pi/2}^{\pi/2} d\theta\, e^{tR \cos \theta} \tag{A.5–6}$$

In the range from $-\pi/2$ to $\pi/2$, $\cos \theta$ is positive, and hence, if $t > 0$, the value of the integral on the right side of Eq. A.5–6 becomes infinite as R tends toward infinity and a solution does not exist. However, if we restrict t to have negative values only, the integral can possess a finite value. In order to evaluate this integral in terms of elementary functions we approximate the exponential term by

$$\exp tR \cos \theta \leq \exp tR \left(1 - \frac{2}{\pi} |\theta| \right) \tag{A.5–7}$$

to ensure no violation of the inequality in Eq. A.5–6. Substituting this expression in Eq. A.5–6, there results

$$\left| \int ds \ e^{st} F(s) \right| \le K e^{tR} \left[\int_{-\pi/2}^{0} d\theta \ e^{+(2/\pi) tR\theta} + \int_{0}^{\pi/2} d\theta \ e^{-(2/\pi) tR\theta} \right]$$

$$\le \frac{K\pi}{tR} (e^{tR} - 1) \quad \text{for } t < 0 \qquad (A.5\text{–}8)$$

Now passing R to its limit of infinity

$$\left| \int ds \ e^{st} F(s) \right| \le \lim_{R \to \infty} \left[\frac{K\pi}{tR} (e^{tR} - 1) \right]$$

$$\le 0 \quad \text{for } t < 0 \qquad (A.5\text{–}9)$$

Clearly the solution of this inequality is that the magnitude of the line integral about the infinite semicircle must be zero. This is written as

$$\int ds \ e^{st} F(s) = 0 \quad \text{for } t < 0 \qquad (A.5\text{–}10)$$

provided $|F(s)|$ behaves at least as $|K/s|$ for large s. Therefore the solution of Eq. A.2–5 is given directly by the application of Cauchy's residue theorem to the closed contour as shown in Fig. A.5–1a. Cauchy's residue theorem states, "If C is the boundary of a simply connected* region within which and on which $g(s)$ is analytic except at a finite number of poles within, then the value of $\int_C ds \ g(s)$ is $2\pi j$ times the sum of the residues at the poles of $g(s)$ which lie within the region C."

It merely remains to calculate the value of the residue at each of the poles of $F(s)e^{st}$ lying within the closed contour. Of the several methods available for calculating the residue at a pole the following expression is preferred because of its simplicity and completeness. For a pole of order m at $s = s_k$ of the function $g(s)$ the residue at this pole is given by

$$\text{Residue } (s_k) = \frac{1}{(m-1)!} \left\{ \frac{d^{m-1}}{ds^{m-1}} [(s - s_k)^m g(s)] \right\}_{s=s_k} \qquad (A.5\text{–}11)$$

Summarizing, the inverse Fourier transform as defined by Eq. A.1–2 may be evaluated as

$$f(t) = - \sum_{k\text{RHP}} \frac{1}{(m-1)!} \left\{ \frac{d^{m-1}}{ds^{m-1}} [(s - s_k)^m F(s) e^{st}] \right\}_{s=s_k} \quad \text{for } t < 0$$

$$(A.5\text{–}12)$$

* A region is said to be simply connected if every simple closed path lying entirely within the region encloses only points of the region itself and hence no boundary points.

where the summation is over the residues of all poles in the right half-plane. The negative sign in Eq. A.5–12 arises as a consequence of the fact that the integration around the closed contour is taken in a direction opposite to the direction assigned to increasing positive angle and that the previous statement of Cauchy's residue theorem assumes that the direction of integration corresponds to increasing positive angle.

In a like manner it can be shown that the value of $f(t)$ for $t > 0$ can be evaluated by considering a contour (Fig. A.5–1b) enclosing the entire left half-plane. The inverse Fourier transform for $t > 0$ is then given by

$$f(t) = + \sum_{j\text{LHP}} \frac{1}{(m-1)!} \left\{ \frac{d^{m-1}}{ds^{m-1}} [(s - s_j)^m F(s) e^{st}] \right\}_{s=s_j} \quad \text{for } t > 0$$

(A.5–13)

where the summation is over the residues of all poles in the left half-plane.

As an example of the application of this method of residues to the evaluation of an inverse Fourier transform, let

$$F(s) = \frac{1}{(s-a)^2(s+b)}$$

(A.5–14)

be the Fourier transform whose inverse is required. To determine $f(t)$ for $t < 0$ we investigate the poles of $F(s)$ lying in the right half-plane. The second-order pole at $s = a$ is the only pole in the RHP. Using Eq. A.5–12 with $m = 2$ and $s_k = a$, we have

$$f(t) = -\frac{1}{1!} \left\{ \frac{d}{ds} \left[\frac{e^{st}}{s+b} \right] \right\}_{s=a} \quad t < 0$$

$$= - \left[\frac{te^{st}}{s+b} - \frac{e^{st}}{(s+b)^2} \right]_{s=a} \quad t < 0$$

Hence

$$f(t) = \frac{e^{at}}{(a+b)} \left[\frac{1}{(a+b)} - t \right] \quad \text{for } t < 0$$

(A.5–15)

To evaluate $f(t)$ for $t > 0$ we take into account the single-order pole in the LHP at $s = -b$ and use Eq. A.5–13 with $m = 1$. There follows immediately

$$f(t) = \frac{1}{0!} \left[\frac{e^{st}}{(s-a)^2} \right]_{s=-b}$$

$$f(t) = \frac{e^{-bt}}{(a+b)^2} \quad \text{for } t > 0$$

(A.5–16)

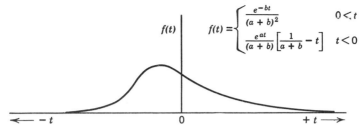

$$f(t) = \begin{cases} \dfrac{e^{-bt}}{(a+b)^2} & 0 < t \\[3mm] \dfrac{e^{at}}{(a+b)}\left[\dfrac{1}{a+b}-t\right] & t < 0 \end{cases}$$

Fig. A.5–2.   The function $f(t)$ of example.

A plot of this function of $f(t)$ as given by Eqs. A.5–15 and A.5–16 is shown in Fig. A.5–2.   This completes the discussion of the Fourier transform and its inverse.

A.6   THE INVERSE LAPLACE TRANSFORMATION

In evaluating the inverse Laplace transform we recall Eq. A.2–5

$$f(t) = \frac{1}{2\pi j} \int_{c-j\infty}^{c+j\infty} ds\, e^{st} F(s) \tag{A.2–5}$$

Here the integration is carried out along a line $\sigma = c$ parallel to the imaginary axis and so displaced that all the singularities of $F(s)$ lie to the left side of it.   By a technique similar to that used for the inverse Fourier transform, the line integral of Eq. A.2–5 is represented by the sum of a closed contour integral and four line integrals as shown in Fig. A.6–1

$$\int_{AB} = \oint_{ABCDEA} - \int_{BC} - \int_{CDE} - \int_{EA} \tag{A.6–1}$$

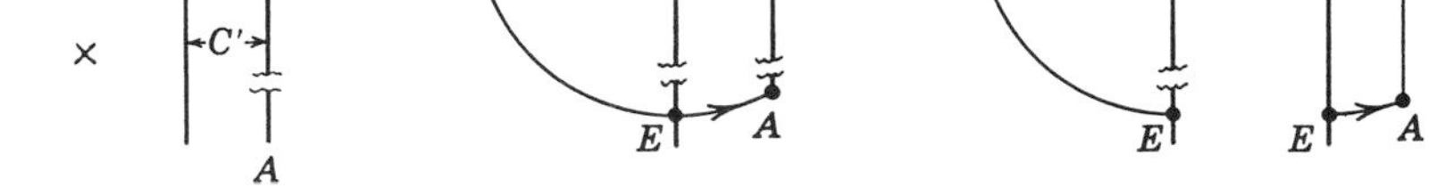

$$\int_{AB} = \int_{ABCDEA} - \int_{CDE} - \int_{BC} - \int_{EA}$$

Fig. A.6–1.   Equivalent contours for evaluating the inverse Laplace transform for $t > 0$.

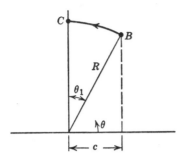

Fig. A.6–2. The geometry of the partial contour BC.

Provided that the behavior of $F(s)$ for very large s is

$$\lim_{s \to \infty} |F(s)| \leq K \left| \frac{1}{s} \right| \quad \text{(A.6–2)}$$

and that t is positive, it can be shown as in the Fourier transform that the value of the line integral along CDE, the circle of closure of large radius, tends to zero as the radius becomes infinitely large. It remains to be shown that the line integrals along segments BC and EA tend to zero for an infinite radius R. Consider first the line integral along BC as given by

$$I_{BC} = \lim_{R \to \infty} \frac{1}{2\pi j} \int_{c+jR \cos \theta_1}^{jR} ds\, e^{st} F(s) \quad \text{(A.6–3)}$$

where the symbols used are defined as shown in Fig. A.6–2. It follows as before that

$$|I_{BC}| \leq \frac{1}{2\pi} \lim_{R \to \infty} \int_{c+jR \cos \theta_1}^{jR} |ds|\, |e^{st}|\, |F(s)| \quad \text{(A.6–4)}$$

Again let

$$s = Re^{j\theta} \quad \text{(A.6–5)}$$

and impose the restriction on $F(s)$ that

$$\lim_{R \to \infty} |F(s)| \leq K \left| \frac{1}{s} \right| \quad \text{(A.6–6)}$$

It then follows that

$$|ds| = R\, d\theta \quad \text{(A.6–7)}$$

$$|e^{st}| = e^{Rt \cos \theta} \quad \text{(A.6–8)}$$

$$|F(s)| \leq \frac{K}{R} \quad \text{(A.6–9)}$$

and upon substitution of these values in Eq. A.6–4 there results

$$|I_{BC}| \leq \frac{K}{2\pi} \lim_{R \to \infty} \int_{\pi/2-\theta_1}^{\pi/2} d\theta\, e^{Rt \cos \theta} \quad \text{(A.6–10)}$$

Now since θ lies in the range $0 < \theta < \pi/2$, since R and t are positive, and in order not to violate the inequality we can approximate the exponential term by

$$\exp Rt \cos \theta \le \exp Rt \frac{\pi}{2}\left(1 - 2\frac{\theta}{\pi}\right) \qquad \text{(A.6–11)}$$

For very large values of R, θ_1 is given approximately by

$$\theta_1 \doteq \frac{c}{R} \qquad \text{(A.6–12)}$$

Using Eqs. A.6–11 and A.6–12 in Eq. A.6–10 and performing the integration yield

$$|I_{BC}| \le \lim_{R \to \infty} \frac{K}{2\pi Rt}(e^{ct} - 1) \qquad \text{(A.6–13)}$$

In this expression c and t are necessarily finite, and hence upon passing R to its limit there results

$$|I_{BC}| \le 0 \qquad \text{(A.6–14)}$$

Therefore $I_{BC} = 0$ and likewise the line integral along the path EA can be shown to be equal to zero. Hence the inverse Laplace transform can be evaluated directly from the residues of poles of $F(s)e^{st}$ in the finite part of the s-plane as

$$f(t) = \sum_k \frac{1}{(m-1)!}\left\{\frac{d^{m-1}}{ds^{m-1}}[(s-s_k)^m F(s)e^{st})]\right\}_{s=s_k} \qquad \text{for } t \ge 0 \quad \text{(A.6–15)}$$

As an example of the use of this expression we shall consider that the transform of Eq. A.5–14 is a Laplace transform and that we wish its inverse. Therefore

$$F(s) = \frac{1}{(s-a)^2(s+b)} \qquad \text{(A.6–16)}$$

The residues of the poles of $F(s)e^{st}$ at a and $-b$ were found previously (Eqs. A.5–15 and A.5–16) to be

$$\text{Res }(a) = \frac{e^{at}}{a+b}\left(t - \frac{1}{a+b}\right) \qquad \text{(A.6–17)}$$

$$\text{Res }(-b) = \frac{e^{-bt}}{(a+b)^2} \qquad \text{(A.6–18)}$$

Therefore the function $f(t)$ is given directly by

$$f(t) = \frac{e^{at}}{a+b}\left(t - \frac{1}{a+b}\right) + \frac{e^{-bt}}{(a+b)^2} \qquad t \ge 0 \qquad \text{(A.6–19)}$$

The graph of this function is shown in Fig. A.6–3 and is seen to differ considerably from the function obtained from Eq. A.6–16 when it was assumed that Eq. A.6–16 was a Fourier transform.

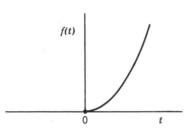

Fig. A.6–3. The function $f(t)$ of example.

From the foregoing results as well as from the uniqueness property of the transforms it can be concluded that, if a transform has poles in both right and left half-planes, then its inverse Fourier and Laplace transforms will necessarily differ. However, if the poles of the transform lie entirely in the left half-plane, then the inverse Fourier and Laplace transforms are identical.

A.7 EXTENSION OF FOURIER TRANSFORMABLE FUNCTIONS BY USE OF A CONVERGENCE FACTOR

In closing the discussion on transforms we consider the class of functions that are almost Fourier transformable in the strictest sense, i.e., the class of Laplace transformable functions having zero as the value of the abscissa of absolute convergence. This class of functions includes all functions $f(t)$ that satisfy the Dirichlet conditions, which behave no worse than t^n for large values of t where n is a finite number, and which are zero for negative values of t. The Fourier transform pair for a member of this class of functions can be found by means of a limit process as shown by the following example.

Consider that the function $f(t)$ is given by

$$f(t) = \begin{cases} t^n, & 0 \le t \\ 0, & t < 0 \end{cases} \tag{A.7–1}$$

Clearly this function is not Fourier transformable in the strictest sense, since $\int_{-\infty}^{\infty} dt\,|f(t)|$ is not finite. Now let

$$f(t) = \lim_{\epsilon \to 0} t^n e^{-\epsilon t} \tag{A.7–2}$$

The Fourier transform of $f(t)$ is then

$$F(s) = \lim_{\epsilon \to 0} \int_{-\infty}^{\infty} dt\, e^{-st} t^n e^{-\epsilon t} \tag{A.7–3}$$

and upon evaluating the integral

$$F(s) = \lim_{\epsilon \to 0} \frac{n!}{(s + \epsilon)^{n+1}} \tag{A.7-4}$$

Therefore

$$F(s) = \frac{n!}{s^{n+1}} \tag{A.7-5}$$

is the Fourier transform of $f(t)$ as ϵ approaches zero.

To perform the inverse transformation of Eq. A.7–5 according to Eq. A.1–2, we must first write the transform in the form as given by Eq. A.7–4. This is done in order to remove the singularity from the path of integration along the imaginary axis since no singularities are permitted on the contour C over which Cauchy's residue theorem is applied. The inverse Fourier transform is then given by application of Eq. A.5–13 as

$$f(t) = \lim_{\epsilon \to 0} \frac{1}{n!} \left\{ \frac{d^n}{ds^n} \left[(s + \epsilon)^{n+1} \frac{n!e^{st}}{(s + \epsilon)^{n+1}} \right] \right\}_{s=-\epsilon} \quad t \geq 0$$

$$= \lim_{\epsilon \to 0} t^n e^{-\epsilon t} \quad t \geq 0 \tag{A.7-6}$$

Therefore

$$f(t) = \begin{cases} t^n, & t \geq 0 \\ 0, & t < 0 \end{cases} \tag{A.7-7}$$

and the original time function is recovered. We must caution the reader at this point. To remove the singularity at $s = 0$ of Eq. A.7–5 from the path of integration we could equally as well have chosen the form

$$F(s) = \lim_{\epsilon \to 0} \frac{n!}{(s - \epsilon)^{n+1}} \tag{A.7-8}$$

where here we have moved the singularity into the right half-plane. The inverse Fourier transform of Eq. A.7–8 upon passing to the limit is found easily to be

$$f(t) = \begin{cases} 0, & t \geq 0 \\ -(t)^n, & 0 > t \end{cases} \tag{A.7-9}$$

Comparing Eqs. A.7–7 and A.7–9 we see that they differ entirely. The first is non-zero for t greater than zero and the second is non-zero for t less than zero. Thus by extending the Fourier transform to cover the class of functions whose Laplace transforms have poles only in the left half-plane and on the finite part of the imaginary axis, we find that the uniqueness property of the Fourier transform pair is lost in that the value of the inverse transform now depends on the direction in which the limit is taken. This restriction is not as severe as one might suspect because in general it will be obvious in which direction to take the limit since the two possible results correspond to two distinctly separate ranges of the variable t, namely, positive t and negative t. Thus with prior knowledge of the range of t the applicable inverse Fourier transform can be determined uniquely. This completes the discussion of the application of the Fourier transformation to the broad class of functions that behave for large t no worse than t^n where n is finite.

STABILITY CRITERIA

In this appendix the stability criterion of Nyquist and that of Routh and Hurwitz are set forth, and examples are given of their application to specific problems.

B.1 INTRODUCTION

If it is assumed that the system is linear, that is, the principle of superposition applies, then by Laplace-transforming the differential equations characterizing the system (assuming zero initial conditions) a quotient relating the transform of the output to the transform of the input may be obtained. This quotient is called the transform of the system weighting function or, more simply, the system function $W(s)$.

The system function will be the quotient of two polynomials in s if the system has lumped parameters, no time delays, and no time-varying parameters. If time delays are present in the system, factors of the form e^{-sT} are introduced in the system function. If the system is characterized by distributed parameters, transcendental terms such as $e^{-\sqrt{as}}$, $\cosh \sqrt{as}$, $\sinh \sqrt{as}$, $\cosh s$, and $\cosh \sqrt{s^2 + a^2}$ may also appear.

The problem is then to determine from the system function $W(s)$ whether the system is stable. A system is defined to be stable if $W(s)$ has no singularities in the right half-plane including the imaginary axis except for possibly a pole (with a finite residue) at the origin.

As can be seen from Eq. A.6–15, a pole of $W(s)$ in the right half-plane corresponds to an increasing exponential function in the time domain. Likewise, conjugate poles on the imaginary axis correspond to constant amplitude oscillations in the time domain. Thus in the time domain a system is said to be stable if, after an impulse disturbance, the system returns to a static equilibrium state which can differ from its state before the disturbance by at most a constant.

The stability problem then becomes one of determining whether there are any poles of $W(s)$ in the right half-plane; that is, for rational system functions, whether there are any zeros of the denominator polynomial in the right half-plane. The similar methods of Routh (1877) (R.5) and Hurwitz (1895) (H.9) consider the situation where the denominator of $W(s)$ is a finite polynomial in s. Nyquist (1932) (N.9) considers another method in which $W(s)$ may be extended to include meromorphic functions with the restrictions that in the RHP and on the imaginary axis there are no essential singularities. We shall treat the more general method of Nyquist first.

B.2 THE NYQUIST STABILITY CRITERION

An important theorem in the theory of functions of a complex variable states: Let $f(s)$ be a function of s, which is single valued on and within a simple closed boundary C and analytic on C. If $f(s)$ is unequal to zero along C and if there are at most a finite number of singular points (all poles) within the contour C then

$$\frac{1}{2\pi j} \int_C ds \, \frac{f'(s)}{f(s)} = Z - P \qquad \text{(B.2–1)}$$

where Z is the number of zeros and P the number of poles of $f(s)$ within C, each counted according to its multiplicity.

This theorem follows directly from Cauchy's residue theorem which states

$$\frac{1}{2\pi j} \int_C ds \, g(s) = \begin{array}{l} \text{sum of the residues of } g(s) \text{ at the poles} \\ \text{enclosed by } C \end{array} \qquad \text{(B.2–2)}$$

Replacing $g(s)$ by $f'(s)/f(s)$, and noticing that the singularities of $f'(s)/f(s)$ occur at both the poles and zeros of $f(s)$, the residues are then found at these singularities to be equal to the multiplicity of the singularity, with the residues in the zeros of $f(s)$ being positive and the residues in the poles of $f(s)$ being negative. The stated theorem then follows directly.

Now Eq. B.2–1 can also be written as

$$\frac{1}{2\pi j} \int_C ds \frac{f'(s)}{f(s)} = \frac{1}{2\pi j} \int_C d[\ln f(s)] \qquad \text{(B.2–3)}$$

Since $f(s)$ will in general have both real and imaginary parts along the boundary C, its logarithm is rewritten as

$$\ln f(s) = \ln |f(s)| + j \angle f(s) \qquad \text{(B.2–4)}$$

Provided $f(s)$ is not zero anywhere on the boundary C, the integration of Eq. B.2–3 gives directly

$$\frac{1}{2\pi j} \int_C d[\ln f(s)] = \frac{1}{2\pi j} [\ln |f(s)| + j \angle f(s)]_{s_1}^{s_2} \qquad \text{(B.2–5)}$$

$$= \frac{1}{2\pi} [\angle f(s_2) - \angle f(s_1)] \qquad \text{(B.2–6)}$$

where s_1 and s_2 denote the arbitrary beginning and end of the closed boundary C as it is followed.
Therefore

$$\frac{1}{2\pi j} \int_C ds \frac{f'(s)}{f(s)} = \frac{1}{2\pi} \times \text{net change in angle of } f(s) \qquad \text{(B.2–7)}$$
$$\text{as } s \text{ varies over } C$$

Combining the results of Eq. B.2–1 and B.2–7 we find that $1/2\pi$ times the net change in angle (net encirclements of the origin) of $f(s)$ as s is varied over a boundary C is equal to the excess of zeros over poles of $f(s)$ within the boundary C. If N is defined as the net number of encirclements of the origin by $f(s)$ as s is varied over C, then we may write

$$N = Z - P \qquad \text{(B.2–8)}$$

where the contour C is traversed in a direction corresponding to increasing positive angle and where an encirclement is termed positive if it also is in the direction corresponding to the positive angle.

We can now apply this result directly to the problem of stability

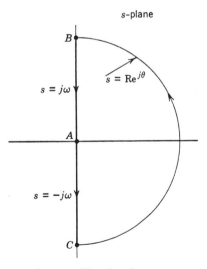

Fig. B.2–1. The closed contour enclosing the finite right half-plane.

determination. We wish to know if the denominator of the system function $W(s)$ has any zeros in the right half-plane. Hence the boundary C is chosen so as to enclose the entire finite right half-plane. This contour is shown in Fig. B.2–1 where the large semicircle enclosing the right half-plane is given by

$$s = Re^{j\theta}, \quad \frac{\pi}{2} > \theta > -\frac{\pi}{2} \qquad (B.2\text{–}9)$$

with R tending toward infinity as its limit.

It is assumed that $W(s)$ is written as

$$W(s) = \frac{A(s)}{D(s)} \qquad (B.2\text{–}10)$$

where $A(s)$ is an entire function of s and that $A(s)$ and $D(s)$ have no common factors. We then plot $D(s)$ on the complex plane by varying s over the values along C. This plot gives us a closed contour. In general $D(s)$ will be an entire function of polynomial form which clearly has no poles in the finite part of the plane. If $D(s)$ is transcendental, the number of poles P of $D(s)$ in the finite part of the right half-plane must now be determined. Knowing P and determining N from the plot of $D(s)$ as s varies over C, we can now determine the number of zeros Z of $D(s)$ in the right half-plane from Eq. B.2–8 as

$$Z = N + P \qquad (B.2\text{–}11)$$

Z must be zero for the system to be stable. Hence two separate steps are involved in the application of the criterion—first, that of determining the right half-plane poles of $D(s)$ and second, that of plotting $D(s)$ as s is varied over C. The first step is usually very simply accomplished. The second step may involve considerable labor especially if $D(s)$ is of third order or higher and if $D(s)$ involves transcendental terms.

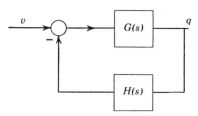

Fig. B.2–2. A simple single-loop feedback control system.

For the feedback control system of the general form shown in Fig. B.2–2 the complexity involved in the plotting can be reduced appreciably if use is made of the open-loop transfer function. For such a system the system function is related to the open-loop transfer function by

$$W(s) = \frac{G(s)}{1 + G(s)H(s)} \qquad (B.2\text{–}12)$$

where both $G(s)$ and $H(s)$ may possess both poles and zeros. For stability we wish to know if $W(s)$ has any poles in the right half-plane. This is equivalent to finding the RHP zeros of $1 + G(s)H(s)$ or the RHP -1's of $G(s)H(s)$. In order to bring into evidence the effect of a change in open-loop gain and at the same time minimize the work required to prepare the Nyquist plot, we choose to rewrite the denominator expression as $(1/K) + [G(s)H(s)/K]$ where K is the open-loop gain parameter. Again the poles of $W(s)$ are identical with the $(-1/K)$'s of $[G(s)H(s)/K]$.

To apply Nyquist's criterion to this denominator we first map $[G(s)H(s)/K]$ as s is varied over a contour C enclosing the entire right half-plane. We then count the net number of positive encirclements N around the $(-1/K) + j0$ point made by this locus. A change in gain K merely changes the location of the $(-1/K)$ point and does not affect the $[G(s)H(s)/K]$ locus. Next the number of RHP poles P of $[G(s)H(s)/K]$ is determined directly from this function by inspection if it is in factored form or by calculation if it is in polynomial or transcendental form. The stability of the system is then given directly by application of Eq. B.2–8 which when rearranged states

$$Z = N + P \qquad\qquad (B.2\text{–}13)$$

The system is therefore stable if and only if Z is zero, where Z is now the number of RHP zeros of the denominator of Eq. B.2–12.

In applying the criterion in this form care must be taken in choosing the contour C which is to enclose the right half-plane. Equation B.2–1 and hence Eq. B.2–13 require that there be no singularities of the mapping function, in our case $[G(s)H(s)/K]$, on the contour C. As is often the case, $[G(s)H(s)/K]$ may have a pole at the origin or even several pairs of conjugate complex poles on the imaginary axis. To handle these special cases the contour C is modified by passing each singularity on the imaginary axis along a very small semicircle as shown in Fig. B.2–3. The modified contour C may pass either to the right or to the left of the singularity, as shown in Figs. B.2–3a and B.2–3b, respectively, if the singularity is a pole. If the singularity is not a pole, the contour must pass always to the right of the singularity since Eq. B.2–1 admits only poles as singularities within C. Those poles on the imaginary axis that are passed on the left by the contour C now lie within the contour and hence their count must be included in P. Thus for a singularity at $s = j\omega_k$ the contour C is usually chosen as

$$s = j\omega_k + \rho_k e^{j\theta} \qquad\qquad (B.2\text{–}14)$$

in the immediate vicinity of the pole where the angle θ varies from $+\pi/2$ radians through zero to $-\pi/2$ radians and where ρ_k has zero as its limit.

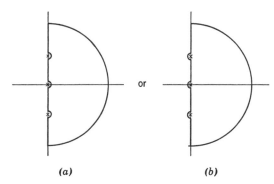

(a)   (b)

Fig. B.2–3.   Two possible contour modifications that avoid the poles on the imaginary axis.

The locus of $[G(s)H(s)/K]$ as s is varied over C consists primarily of four parts.   The behavior of $[G(s)H(s)/K]$ for $s = j\omega$ except in the vicinity of j-axis singularities is simply the open-loop frequency response of the system.   The behavior of $[G(s)H(s)/K]$ for $s = -j\omega$ is then the conjugate of the behavior for positive frequencies and hence may be obtained by reflecting that behavior about the real axis.   As s varies over the infinite semicircle the value of $[G(s)H(s)/K]$ for all physical systems is equal to zero or at most a finite constant.   Finally, the behavior of $[G(s)H(s)/K]$ on the small semicircles about any poles on the imaginary axis is determined from direct application of Eq. B.2–14 to the function.   The mapping of the contour C onto the function plane is thus completed.

In applying the criterion in this latter form the restrictions placed on the character of the open-loop transfer function $[G(s)H(s)/K]$ become apparent.   First, $[G(s)H(s)/K]$ may have at most a finite number of singularities, all poles, within the right half-plane.   Second, $[G(s)H(s)/K]$ may have at most a finite number of singularities, either poles or branch points, on the imaginary axis.   The class of functions may be extended to include those functions having branch points only if the branch points lie in the left half-plane and if the principal value of the function is used.   Third, an essential singularity of the form e^{-sT} is admissible in the numerator of $[G(s)H(s)/K]$ since the magnitude of this function attains only values between $+1$ and 0 as s is passed to the limit in the right half-plane.

The application of the Nyquist criterion is best shown by considering an example. Let a feedback control system be defined by

$$G(s) = G_c(s)G_f(s) \tag{B.2-15}$$

$$H(s) = 1 \tag{B.2-16}$$

$$G_f(s) = \frac{e^{-0.00833s}}{s(s-1)} \tag{B.2-17}$$

The transfer function $G_f(s)$ of the fixed elements corresponds to that of a 60 cps two-phase induction motor driven by a half-wave magnetic amplifier. The negative damping is present due to low rotor resist-

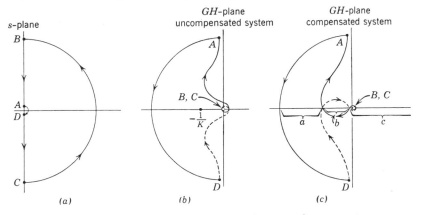

Fig. B.2–4. Nyquist plots for example.

ance. The first question posed is, "Can the fixed elements be stabilized by pure gain only?" Therefore we let

$$G_c(s) = K \tag{B.2-18}$$

The open-loop transfer function $[G(s)H(s)/K]$ becomes

$$\frac{G(s)H(s)}{K} = \frac{e^{-0.00833s}}{s(s-1)} \tag{B.2-19}$$

We first see that $[G(s)H(s)/K]$ has only one right-half-plane pole and that this pole is located at $s = 1$. A sketch of the plot of $[G(s)H(s)/K]$ along the contour C as defined by Fig. B.2–4a is shown in Fig. B.2–4b and indicates one positive encirclement of the $-1 + j0$ point for the value of gain chosen. Hence by Nyquist's criterion as expressed by Eq. B.2–13 there results

$$Z = 1 + 1$$
$$= 2 \text{ RHP zeros of } 1 + G(s)H(s)$$

Increasing K introduces the possibility of more positive encirclements due to the spiral nature of the part of the plot caused by the $e^{-0.0083s}$ factor. Hence we may conclude that the system is unstable for all positive values of K.

For negative values of K we can either rotate our plot 180° about the origin and consider encirclements of $-1/|K| + j0$ or we can use the present plot and consider encirclements of the $+1/|K| + j0$ point. The latter procedure is simpler and shows immediately that there are, as a minimum, at least no positive encirclements of $+1/|K| + j0$. This gives at least one right-half-plane zero of $(1/K) + [G(s)H(s)/K]$ for negative values of K. Therefore, we are led to the result that the system is unstable for all values of gain K both positive and negative and hence some form of compensation is required to render the system stable.

If now we choose a compensating network of the form

$$G_c(s) = \left(\frac{0.3s + 1}{0.03s + 1}\right) K_1 \qquad (\text{B.2--20})$$

the locus of $[G(s)H(s)/K_1]$ over C is modified as shown in Fig. B.2–4c. The lead network $G_c(s)$ is inserted so that its phase lead effect causes the $G(j\omega)H(j\omega)$ locus to cross over into the third quadrant, thus introducing the possibility of both positive and negative encirclements. The possible locations of the $(-1/K_1) + j0$ point are designated by a, b, and c. Table B.2–1 shows that the $(-1/K_1) + j0$ point must lie in region b for the system to be stable. This region is found to correspond to a gain setting of

$$3.84 < K_1 < 355 \qquad (\text{B.2--21})$$

Table B.2-1

REGION	N	P	Z	Result
a	$+1$	$+1$	$+2$	Unstable
b	-1	$+1$	0	Stable
c	≥ 0	$+1$	≥ 1	Unstable

Thus the application of the Nyquist criterion to this problem not only resulted in the determination of whether the system was stable but made clear what type of compensation was required to make an otherwise unstable system stable. The degree of stability (Appendix C) can also be determined from the Nyquist diagram in the form of the closed-loop frequency response by the simple construction shown in Fig. B.2–5. The closed-loop frequency response is obtained by dividing vector BC representing $(q/e)(j\omega)$ by vector AC corresponding to

$(v/e)(j\omega)$, thus giving $(q/v)(j\omega)$. Hence the closer a system locus passes to the $-1 + j0$ point, the larger will be its resonant peaking.

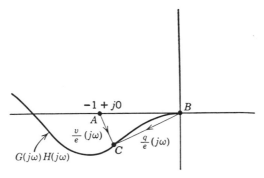

Fig. B.2–5.   Vector relationships on the open-loop polar plot.

The Nyquist criterion can also be applied where the open-loop frequency response plot is prepared from experimental data. The open-loop transfer function must then be stable and hence can have no right-half-plane poles, i.e., $P = 0$. Care must be taken to determine accurately the behavior of the system for very low frequencies in order to close correctly the Nyquist contour.

In applying the Nyquist criterion to determine the stability of multiloop systems the general procedure is to start with the innermost loop and work outward, carefully keeping track of the number of RHP poles as the criterion is applied to each successive loop. The labor involved in this method can often be reduced by elimination of some of the loops through block diagram manipulation. The choice of a precise procedure to follow for a multiloop system depends upon the block diagram configuration and upon the location of the fixed elements and the compensation elements within the loops.

B.3   ROUTH AND HURWITZ STABILITY CRITERION

The method of Routh and Hurwitz is a test that, when applied to a finite polynomial with real coefficients, yields the numbers of roots of the polynomial with positive real parts and with zero real parts. The methods of Routh and Hurwitz, although devised independently, have results that are identical in form. The discussion in this section is therefore limited to the Routh criteron.

To apply the Routh criterion to the stability determination of a system the transfer function for the entire system must first be obtained in the form of a fraction having polynomials of s in the numerator and denominator. The stability of the system is dependent on the location of the zeros of the denominator polynomial, with zeros having positive real parts corresponding to an unstable system and with zeros having zero real parts corresponding to a sustained system oscillation. The denominator polynomial will have the general polynomial form

$$D(s) = a_n s^n + a_{n-1} s^{n-1} + a_{n-2} s^{n-2} + \cdots + a_0 \quad (B.3\text{--}1)$$

the zeros of which are found as solutions of the equation

$$D(s) = 0 \quad (B.3\text{--}2)$$

The Routh procedure is first to write the coefficients a_k in an array of the form

$$
\begin{array}{c|cccccc}
s^n & a_n & a_{n-2} & a_{n-4} & a_{n-6} & a_{n-8} & \cdots \\
s^{n-1} & a_{n-1} & a_{n-3} & a_{n-5} & a_{n-7} & & \\
s^{n-2} & b_1 & b_2 & b_3 & & & \\
s^{n-3} & c_1 & c_2 & c_3 & & & \\
s^{n-4} & d_1 & d_2 & & & &
\end{array}
\quad (B.3\text{--}3)
$$

The coefficients b_k, c_k, etc., of the succeeding rows are determined from the two previous rows in the following manner

$$b_1 = \frac{a_{n-1} a_{n-2} - a_n a_{n-3}}{a_{n-1}}$$

$$b_2 = \frac{a_{n-1} a_{n-4} - a_n a_{n-5}}{a_{n-1}}$$

$$c_1 = \frac{b_1 a_{n-3} - a_{n-1} b_2}{b_1} \quad (B.3\text{--}4)$$

$$d_1 = \frac{c_1 b_2 - b_1 c_2}{c_1}$$

New rows are added to the array of Eq. B.3–3 in this manner until the array consists of $n + 1$ rows. During this procedure of obtaining the successive coefficients, the coefficients in any row may be multiplied or divided by any finite *positive* number without affecting the general character of the array.

With the array thus completely determined, the number of zeros of $D(s)$ with positive real parts is given by the number of changes in sign of the coefficients in the first column of the array. Two cases can arise that require special attention. The first arises whenever the term in the first column of any row is zero with at least one of the remaining terms in that row being non-zero. Calculation of the coefficients in the succeeding row in the routine manner would result in infinite coefficients. To avoid this the first column zero is replaced by an arbitrarily small real number ϵ, and the calculations then continued in the routine manner. The number of changes in sign of the first column coefficients is unaffected by the choice of ϵ as either a small positive or negative real number.

The second case arises when all the coefficients of the second or any succeeding row are zero. This result indicates the existence of pairs of roots lying radially opposite and equidistant from the origin. The procedure is then to take the coefficients of the last non-zero row as coefficients of an auxiliary polynomial in s^2 of order $n + 1 - k$, where n is the order of the original polynomial and k the number of the last non-zero row. The $k + 1$ row is then formed from the coefficients of the derivative with respect to s of this polynomial in s^2. The row-by-row calculation is then continued in the normal manner. The number of changes in sign of the coefficients in the first column indicates the number of roots of $D(s)$ with positive real parts. If there are any pairs of roots with zero real parts, they exist as zeros of the auxiliary polynomial.

In applying Routh's criterion to a polynomial $D(s)$, it is noted first that the presence of both negative and positive coefficients of $D(s)$ and/or the presence of zeros for the coefficients of some of the terms of $D(s)$ indicate immediately the existence of roots of $D(s)$ with positive real parts. Hence, a necessary requirement on a polynomial to ensure that its roots have negative real parts is that all the coefficients be of the same sign and that terms in all intermediate powers of s be present.

The stability requirements for third and fourth-degree polynomials are rather simple in form and are listed below. For a cubic of the form

$$a_3 s^3 + a_2 s^2 + a_1 s + a_0 = 0 \tag{B.3-5}$$

the requirements for no right-half-plane roots become

1. All coefficients of the same sign and non-zero.

2. $a_1 a_2 - a_0 a_3 > 0.$

$$\tag{B.3-6}$$

For a quartic of the form

$$a_4 s^4 + a_3 s^3 + a_2 s^2 + a_1 s + a_0 = 0 \tag{B.3-7}$$

the requirements for no right-half-plane roots become

1. All coefficients positive in sign and non-zero.

2. $a_1(a_3 a_2 - a_4 a_1) - a_3{}^2 a_0 > 0.$

$$\tag{B.3-8}$$

The verification of these requirements is left as an exercise for the reader. To illustrate the use of Routh's criterion two examples are now presented.

Given the polynomial

$$s^5 + 2s^4 + 6s^3 + 48s^2 + 8s + 160 \qquad\qquad \text{(B.3–9)}$$

we wish to know if there exist any zeros with positive real parts. To do this we write the coefficient array as

$$
\begin{array}{c|ccc}
s^5 & 1 & 6 & 8 \\
s^4 & 2 & 48 & 160 \\
s^3 & b_1 & b_2 & \\
s^2 & c_1 & c_2 & \\
s & d_1 & & \\
1 & e_1 & &
\end{array}
\qquad\qquad \text{(B.3–10)}
$$

The third-row coefficients are given by

$$b_1 = \frac{2 \times 6 - 1 \times 48}{2} = -18$$

$$b_2 = \frac{2 \times 8 - 160 \times 1}{2} = -72$$

which, after division by 18 to keep the numbers small, become

$$b_1' = -1 \quad b_2' = -4$$

The fourth-row coefficients become

$$c_1 = \frac{-1 \times 48 - (-4) \times 2}{-1} = 40$$

$$c_2 = \frac{-1 \times 160 - 0}{-1} = 160$$

which after division by 40 are

$$c_1' = 1 \quad c_2' = 4$$

The array is then

$$
\begin{array}{c|ccc}
s^5 & 1 & 6 & 8 \\
s^4 & 2 & 48 & 160 \\
s^3 & -1 & -4 & \\
s^2 & 1 & 4 &
\end{array}
\qquad\qquad \text{(B.3–11)}
$$

Calculation of the next row gives all zeros and hence indicates the presence of a pair of roots lying radially opposite the origin. The auxiliary polynomial is formed from the fourth row as

$$s^2 + 4$$

The zeros of this polynomial are located at $s = \pm j2$ and hence are a pair of roots with zero real parts. The fifth row of the coefficient array is formed from the coefficients of the derivative of the auxiliary polynomial and is simply 2, 0.

The complete coefficient array then becomes

$$
\begin{array}{c|ccc}
s^5 & 1 & 6 & 8 \\
s^4 & 2 & 48 & 160 \\
s^3 & -1 & -4 & \\
s^2 & 1 & 4 & \\
s & 2 & 0 & \\
1 & 4 & 0 &
\end{array}
\qquad \text{(B.3–12)}
$$

There are two changes of sign in the first column, thus indicating two roots of the polynomial with positive real parts. The factors of the polynomial can be shown to be

$$(s - 1 + j3)(s - 1 - j3)(s + j2)(s - j2)(s + 4) = 0 \quad \text{(B.3–13)}$$

thus verifying the result obtained by the Routh criterion.

As a second example of the application of Routh's criterion to a particular problem, we choose the system with fixed elements defined by Eq. B.2–17 and with the compensation as given by Eq. B.2–20. Hence

$$G(s)H(s) = \frac{K_1 e^{-0.00833s}(0.3s + 1)}{s(s - 1)(0.03s + 1)} \qquad \text{(B.3–14)}$$

We wish to know the limits on the range of K_1 for stable operation. Now Routh's criterion can handle only finite polynomials in s. Hence we must approximate the time delay by a polynomial. As a first approximation we choose

$$e^{-0.00833s} \doteq 1 - 0.00833s \qquad \text{(B.3–15)}$$

The open-loop transfer function then becomes

$$G(s)H(s) = \frac{K_1(1 - 0.00833s)(1 + 0.3s)}{s(s - 1)(1 + 0.03s)} \qquad \text{(B.3–16)}$$

Now the closed-loop transfer function is found by using Eq. B.2–12 as

$$W(s) = \frac{K_1(1 - 0.00833s)(1 + 0.3s)}{0.03s^3 + (0.97 - 0.0025K_1)s^2 + (-1 + 0.29167K_1)s + K_1}$$

$$\text{(B.3–17)}$$

The denominator is a cubic, and hence the criterion for stability is given by Eq. B.3–6 where

$$a_3 = 0.03$$

$$a_2 = 0.97 - 0.0025K_1$$

$$a_1 = -1 + 0.29167K_1$$

$$a_0 = K_1$$

$$\text{(B.3–18)}$$

By simple algebra the limits on the range of gain K_1 are found to be

$$3.92 < K_1 < 338.6 \qquad\qquad \text{(B.3–19)}$$

This result compares closely with the exact result given by Eq. B.2–21, namely

$$3.84 < K_1 < 355 \qquad\qquad \text{(B.2–21)}$$

and was obtained with much less effort.

If the approximation chosen for the time delay is

$$e^{-0.00833s} = \frac{1 - 0.00417s}{1 + 0.00417s} \qquad\qquad \text{(B.3–20)}$$

the denominator polynomial becomes fourth degree with the final result, obtained from the application of Eq. B.3–8, being

$$3.84 < K_1 < 365 \qquad\qquad \text{(B.3–21)}$$

which again compares favorably with the exact result.

Thus by using a suitable polynomial approximation for the transcendental term the limits on the gain K_1 for stable operation of the system are very simply determined. However, the results of the application of the Routh criterion lend little to the determination of the degree of stability of the system. The results give only the answers "stable" or "unstable."

B.4 COMPARISON OF THE TWO STABILITY CRITERIA

In summary, Routh's criterion gives the number of right-half-plane zeros of a finite polynomial. The application of the criterion is limited to polynomials and hence can handle transcendental terms and experimental data only if they are first suitably approximated by polynomials. The results of the criterion, in general, offer little insight into the problem of compensation to improve performance and give no indication of resonant frequency, peak magnification, rise time, etc., for a particular gain setting. In determining the stability of multiloop systems the over-all system transfer function must first be calculated before the criterion can be applied. This procedure may itself involve considerable labor. However, if several literal coefficients are present in the transfer functions, application of the Routh criterion generally will result in a series of rather simple relations which must be satisfied by the variable coefficients for a stable system.

The Nyquist criterion, on the other hand, can be applied only to systems where the open-loop function is known within a gain factor. A new Nyquist plot must be prepared, in general, each time that a time constant or parameter is changed. The Nyquist criterion has a distinct advantage in that it can be applied to a more general type of linear system function than those which can be treated by the Routh criterion. The system function may contain transcendental terms of specific forms in addition to polynomials. The Nyquist plots can often be accomplished by inspection if the transfer function is in factored form. However, if the transfer function is very complex, involving transcendental terms, and is not in factored form, the plot becomes much more difficult to construct. The determination of the precise range of open-loop gain for a stable system involves either an iterative or a graphical procedure for all but the simplest system functions. The degree of stability as determined by the peak magnification and resonant frequency is easily ascertained from the Nyquist plot. Experimental open-loop frequency-response data can be used to construct the Nyquist plot without resort to a mathematical model —the only assumption being made is that the system is linear.

REVIEW OF
CONVENTIONAL DESIGN TECHNIQUES

C.1 INTRODUCTION

Conventional design procedure is a combined graphical and analytical method which tests a series of trial forms of compensation to verify whether it may be possible to meet a set of specifications.   The method primarily uses the frequency domain since the labor involved in the successive trials is less than would be involved in the time domain. Usually the compensation functions that are employed are simple in form.   As pointed out in Art. 1.6, the trial-and-error design procedure neither indicates the limit of performance achievable in given circumstances nor protects the designer from an inconsistent set of performance specifications.   Thus, in the trial-and-error design procedure, intuition and experience must be relied upon to indicate when the possibility of improvement through additional trials has been exhausted.

As outlined in Table 1.6–1, the trial-and-error design procedure starts with specifications of the input signal, desired output, disturbances, allowable error, fixed elements, and the degree of stability. The objective of the designer is to find the form and parameter values of one or more compensation schemes that will enable the specifications to be met.   For a single-loop control system of the form shown in Fig. 1.7–1, the trial-and-error design procedure may be outlined as follows:

1. With pure gain compensation $[G_c(s) = K]$, the range of gain for stable closed-loop operation is determined.

2. If the system is unstable for all values of gain, a stabilization function must be introduced.

3. After a range of gains for stable operation has been found, a particular gain within this range is selected in order to produce the specified degree of stability.

4. With the gain setting found in step 3 the system error is determined to see if it is within the limit set by the specifications.

5. If the system error specifications are not met, the form of the compensation function $G_c(s)$ is modified so as to increase the accuracy of the system while maintaining the specified degree of stability.

6. After the new form of compensation is introduced, the system error is checked again to see if it is within the specifications.

7. If the error specifications are still not met, different or more complex compensation schemes are tried. Steps 5 and 6 are repeated until the design specifications are satisfied if possible. Obviously, there is no positive way of knowing that the specifications can be satisfied if the trial-and-error procedure is used exclusively.

A variety of methods are available to the designer using the conventional trial-and-error procedure. The more commonly used techniques are reviewed in this appendix and in Appendix D. After a summary of performance parameters that are used as figures of merit for steady-state behavior, the Bode diagram of the frequency response of a system is introduced. Asymptotic approximations in this diagram are then applied to the problem of feedback compensation. The Bode diagram presentation is often used as an intermediate step in the gain-phase-plane procedure. Because of its great utility, the gain-phase-plane procedure is treated separately in Appendix D along with considerations of cascade compensation.

Most of the conventional design techniques result in the establishment of the transfer function or frequency response of a system. Since error specifications are usually described in the time domain, it is necessary to determine the time response of the system to verify whether the transfer function that has been established enables one to meet specifications. Methods for determining the transient response of a system from the frequency response are described, and the error coefficient procedure is then reviewed. The error coefficient method enables one to find the response of a system to an arbitrary input. The root-locus technique is an alternate procedure that is often used in conjunction with the other techniques so that the designer may gain greater insight into the behavior of the system he is examining. After a brief discussion of the root-locus method the appendix closes with a summary of analogue computation techniques.

C.2   PERFORMANCE CONSTANTS

One of the important properties of a feedback control system is its steady-state response to simple transient inputs.   The steady-state error that is developed in response to a ramp input, an acceleration input, or a step disturbance is related to the parameters of the system by means of performance constants that are denoted by K_v, the *velocity constant;* K_a, the *acceleration constant;* and K_T, the *torque constant.* Other performance constants can be defined but for most applications these three suffice.

Referring to Fig. 1.4–3, where the block diagram of a general feedback control system is shown, let the steady-state error be defined as

$$E_{ss} \triangleq \lim_{t \to \infty} y_e(t) \qquad (C.2\text{–}1)$$

when the disturbance u and the noise v_n are equal to zero and the data signal v_d is a ramp input

$$
\begin{aligned}
v_d(t) &= \Omega_i t, \quad t \geq 0 \\
&= 0, \qquad t < 0
\end{aligned}
\qquad (C.2\text{–}2)
$$

The velocity constant of the system is then defined as

$$K_v \triangleq \frac{\Omega_i}{E_{ss}} \qquad (C.2\text{–}3)$$

If the ideal output i is equal to the input v_d, then, referring to Fig. 1.7–1, the velocity constant of the system may be found from

$$\frac{1}{K_v} = \lim_{s \to 0} \left[\frac{1 - W(s)}{s} \right] \qquad (C.2\text{–}4)$$

where

$$W(s) \triangleq \frac{q(s)}{v(s)} \qquad (C.2\text{–}5)$$

In the case of a unity feedback system where the transfer function $H_f(s)$ of the feedback elements is unity, Eq. C.2–4 for the velocity constant can be reduced to

$$K_v = \lim_{s \to 0} s G_c(s) G_f(s) \qquad (C.2\text{–}6)$$

This result shows that a unity feedback system with the ideal output equal to the input will have a finite, non-zero velocity constant only if the cascade combination $G_c(s)G_f(s)$ has exactly one pole at the origin of the s-plane. Such a system will exhibit zero steady-state error in response to a step input.

The acceleration constant K_a of a system is defined in a similar manner. Let the disturbance u and the noise v_n be zero and the data signal v_d be given by

$$v_d(t) = \tfrac{1}{2}A_i t^2, \quad t \geq 0$$
$$= 0, \qquad t < 0$$

$$(C.2{-}7)$$

The acceleration constant is defined as

$$K_a \triangleq \frac{A_i}{E_{ss}} \qquad (C.2{-}8)$$

When the ideal output is equal to the input, the acceleration constant can be found from

$$\frac{1}{K_a} = \lim_{s \to 0} \left[\frac{1 - W(s)}{s^2} \right] \qquad (C.2{-}9)$$

For a unity feedback system this equation can be reduced to

$$K_a = \lim_{s \to 0} s^2 G_c(s)G_f(s) \qquad (C.2{-}10)$$

From this equation we see that a unity feedback system with the ideal output equal to the input will have a finite, non-zero acceleration constant only if $G_c(s)G_f(s)$ has exactly a double-order pole at the origin. Such a system will exhibit zero steady-state error in response to a ramp input as well as to a step input.

The torque constant K_T should be more logically termed the disturbance constant but the study of positional servomechanisms has led to the term "torque constant" since the primary disturbance in these systems is a load-torque disturbance. Referring to Fig. 1.7–3, let the input v be zero and the disturbance be given by

$$u(t) = U_0 \delta_{-1}(t) \qquad (C.2{-}11)$$

where $\delta_{-1}(t)$ is a unit step. In this case the error y_e is equal to the actuating signal e or the negative of the output q. The torque constant is then defined as

$$K_T \triangleq -\frac{U_0}{E_{ss}} \qquad (C.2{-}12)$$

In terms of the transfer functions of the diagram of Fig. 1.7–3, the torque constant can be determined from

$$\frac{1}{K_T} = \lim_{s \to 0} \left[\frac{W(s)}{G_c(s)G_{f1}(s)} \right] \tag{C.2–13}$$

In those cases where

$$\lim_{s \to 0} W(s) = 1 \tag{C.2–14}$$

the torque constant is given by

$$K_T = \lim_{s \to 0} G_c(s)G_{f1}(s) \tag{C.2–15}$$

This result shows that for systems exhibiting the property defined by Eq. C.2–14, the torque constant is merely the gain factor associated with the cascade combination of the compensation and the predisturbance elements.

The defining equations for the performance constants (Eqs. C.2–3, C.2–8, and C.2–12) show how these constants are related to the steady-state error. In each case, a relatively high value of the performance constant implies a relatively low value of the steady-state error for a given input or disturbance. In another sense, if the performance constant is known, then the steady-state error for a given input or disturbance can be found very simply from the equations that define the performance constant.

C.3   THE BODE DIAGRAM

The frequency response of a system is the most convenient medium to use for design purposes. As a natural extension of the Nyquist criterion (Appendix B), which determines the stability of a system, the frequency response is widely used when the degree of stability of the system is specified. Although the polar-plane representation is the most direct method for studying the frequency response curve of a system, the Bode diagram and the gain-phase plane are more convenient to apply. This article briefly discusses the Bode diagram; Appendix D is devoted to the gain-phase-plane representation. For a more thorough discussion of the Bode diagram, see References B.4, B.6, B.7, C.3, and T.3.

The Bode diagram of a given frequency function consists of two curves, the magnitude curve and the phase curve. The magnitude curve is a plot of the magnitude of the function in decilogs* against

* A decilog (abbreviated dg) is a logarithmic unit such that the magnitude of a number N in decilogs is given by $10 \log_{10} N$.

the logarithm of the frequency. The phase curve is a plot of the phase angle of the function in degrees against the logarithm of the frequency. The logarithmic magnitude scale used in the Bode diagram presentation enables one to construct the magnitude of a rational frequency function as a linear combination of the magnitudes of its component factors. In addition, a logarithmic frequency scale aids in the construction of the magnitude curve owing to the asymptotic approximations that are possible.

Since a rational function can be factored into first- and second-order factors, the entire function can be constructed from a set of standard curves that represent the magnitude and phase of these simple factors.

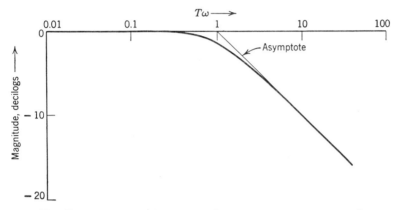

Fig. C.3–1.   Magnitude curve of first-order factor $(Tj\omega + 1)^{-1}$.

There are three basic factor types involved in any rational frequency function. These three types are:

1. $(j\omega)^{\pm n}$

2. $(Tj\omega + 1)^{\pm n}$ first order

3. $\left[\left(j\dfrac{\omega}{\omega_n}\right)^2 + 2\zeta j\dfrac{\omega}{\omega_n} + 1\right]^{\pm n}$ second order

The first type represents differentiation or integration. Its magnitude curve is a straight line having a slope of $\pm 10n$ dg per decade passing through 0 dg at 1 radian per second. The phase curve is merely a constant angle given by $\pm 90n°$.

The magnitude asymptotes and the true magnitude curves of the first- and second-order factor types for $n = -1$ are presented in Figs. C.3–1 and C.3–2, respectively. The frequency at which the

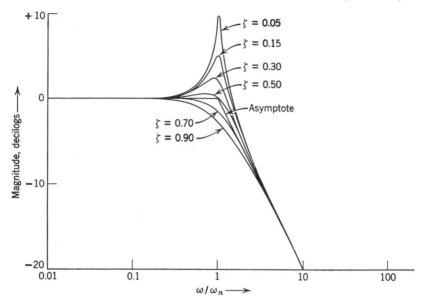

Fig. C.3–2.   Magnitude curves of second-order factor $\left[\left(j\dfrac{\omega}{\omega_n}\right)^2 + 2\zeta j\dfrac{\omega}{\omega_n} + 1\right]^{-1}$.

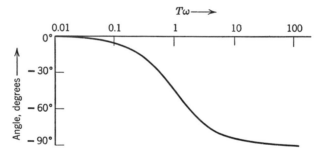

Fig. C.3–3.   Phase-angle curve of first-order factor $(Tj\omega + 1)^{-1}$.

asymptotes intersect is called the break frequency ω_b of the factor. The break frequency of the first-order factor is given by

$$\omega_b = \frac{1}{T} \qquad\qquad (C.3\text{–}1)$$

The break frequency of the second-order factor is the natural frequency ω_n.

The phase curves of the first- and second-order factor types for $n = -1$ are presented in Figs. C.3–3 and C.3–4. Note that the phase curves are symmetrical about the break frequency.

With the standard curves of Figs. C.3–1 through C.3–4 available the construction of the magnitude and phase curves of a frequency function whose factors are known is a simple matter.

In the Bode diagram representation of a rational frequency function the magnitude curve can be approximated in a simple manner by straight-line asymptotes. Thus a preliminary study of a given system can be carried out in a rough way provided the frequency functions

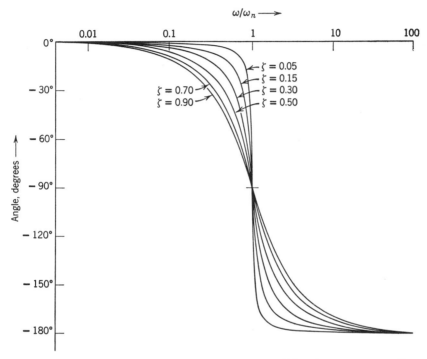

Fig. C.3–4. Phase angle curves of second-order factor $\left[\left(j\dfrac{\omega}{\omega_n}\right)^2 + 2\zeta j\dfrac{\omega}{\omega_n} + 1\right]^{-1}$.

involved are minimum-phase functions. The manner of investigation is evident from the following approximate relations. Referring to Fig. 1.7–1, if $H_f(s) = 1$ (unity feedback), the magnitude asymptotes for the closed-loop response

$$W(j\omega) = \frac{q(j\omega)}{v(j\omega)} \qquad\qquad (C.3\text{–}2)$$

can be determined from the magnitude curve of the open-loop response

$$G(j\omega) = G_c(j\omega)G_f(j\omega) \qquad\qquad (C.3\text{–}3)$$

as follows.   If

$$|G(j\omega)| \gg 1 \tag{C.3-4}$$

then

$$|W(j\omega)| \cong 1 \tag{C.3-5}$$

If

$$|G(j\omega)| \ll 1 \tag{C.3-6}$$

then

$$|W(j\omega)| \cong |G(j\omega)| \tag{C.3-7}$$

If $|G(j\omega)|$ is a monotonically decreasing function having a magnitude very much greater than unity at zero frequency, then the closed-loop response $W(j\omega)$ can be approximated by magnitude asymptotes. The frequency ω_{cm} at which

$$|G(j\omega)| = 1 \tag{C.3-8}$$

is called the magnitude crossover frequency.   From Eqs. C.3–4 through C.3–7, the low-frequency asymptote ($\omega < \omega_{cm}$) of $W(j\omega)$ is the 0 dg line and the high-frequency asymptote ($\omega > \omega_{cm}$) is the magnitude of the open-loop function $G(j\omega)$.

Thus by using the asymptotic approximations the designer can estimate rapidly the closed-loop frequency response $W(j\omega)$ from the open-loop frequency response $G(j\omega)$ when $G(j\omega)$ is a minimum-phase rational frequency function.   For non-unity feedback systems $[H_f(s) \neq 1]$ the extension of the asymptotic techniques is straightforward.

To determine the gain factor required for a specified degree of stability in applying the Bode diagram, the concepts of phase margin and gain margin are used.   Because the Nyquist stability criterion involves an investigation of the encirclements of the $-1 + j0$ point by the open-loop frequency response $G(j\omega)$ in the polar plane, the degree of stability of a stable system is measured by the nearness of the $G(j\omega)$ locus to the $-1 + j0$ point.   If the open-loop function $G(s)$ has no right-half-plane poles, the phase margin and gain margin are measures of the degree of stability of a system.

The phase margin of a unity feedback system is defined as

$$\text{Phase margin} = 180° + \angle G(j\omega_{cm}) \tag{C.3-9}$$

where ω_{cm} is the frequency at which the magnitude of $G(j\omega)$ is unity. As the phase margin decreases the $G(j\omega)$ locus comes closer to the $-1 + j0$ point.

The gain margin of a unity feedback system is defined as

$$\text{Gain margin} = -10 \log_{10} |G(j\omega_0)| \tag{C.3-10}$$

where ω_0 is the frequency at which the phase angle of $G(j\omega)$ is $-180°$. As the gain margin decreases the $G(j\omega)$ locus comes closer to the $-1 + j0$ point.

By specifying the phase margin of a system as the desired degree of stability the choice of the adjustable gain factor K associated with the open-loop function $G(j\omega)$ is fixed. Then the resulting gain margin can be used as an indication of how well the system performs. The procedure for adjusting the gain factor for a specified phase margin follows.

1. The open-loop function $G(j\omega)/K$ is plotted on the Bode diagram (K is the adjustable gain factor).

2. The frequency at which

$$\measuredangle \frac{G(j\omega)}{K} = \text{(Phase margin)} - 180° \tag{C.3–11}$$

is determined from the phase curve. This frequency will be the magnitude crossover frequency ω_{cm} after the gain factor has been adjusted.

3. The magnitude (in decilogs) of $G(j\omega)/K$ at the frequency ω_{cm} found in (2) is determined from the magnitude curve.

4. The gain factor K (in decilogs) required to satisfy the phase-margin specification is then merely the negative of the magnitude (in decilogs) found in (3), that is,

$$10 \log_{10} K = -10 \log_{10} \left| \frac{G(j\omega_{cm})}{K} \right| \tag{C.3–12}$$

The above procedure for determining the gain factor required to satisfy a specified phase margin is often used as an approximation to the determination of the gain factor for a specified M_p in the gain-phase-plane procedure that is discussed in Appendix D. Usually a phase margin of 45° is used when the magnitude crossover frequency ω_{cm} is an approximation to the resonant frequency ω_R. Care must be taken in applying the phase-margin criterion where more than one frequency satisfies this criterion. In these cases final reference should be made to Nyquist's criterion.

Cascade compensation using the phase-margin criterion for the degree of stability of a system can be studied by means of the Bode diagram. However, the objectives of compensation and methods for choosing the parameters of the cascade-compensation function are identical with those discussed in detail in connection with the gain-phase plane (Appendix D) and will not be covered here.

As an example, the use of the Bode diagram for a simple unity feedback system will be demonstrated. The compensation function here is to be a simple gain factor, that is,

$$G_c(j\omega) = K_c \qquad\qquad (C.3\text{--}13)$$

The response of the fixed elements is given by

$$G_f(j\omega) = \frac{1}{j\omega(j\omega + 1)(0.2j\omega + 1)} \qquad\qquad (C.3\text{--}14)$$

Since the open-loop function G_cG_f has a single-order pole at the origin, the velocity constant K_v is finite and equal to K_c. The phase margin of the system is specified to be 45°, and the velocity constant is to be determined.

The Bode diagram of the function $G_c(j\omega)G_f(j\omega)/K_c$ is plotted in Fig. C.3–5. From the phase curve the magnitude crossover frequency ω_{cm} will occur at

$$\angle \frac{G_c(j\omega)G_f(j\omega)}{K_c} = 45° - 180° = -135° \qquad (C.3\text{--}15)$$

or

$$\omega_{cm} = 0.74 \text{ rad sec}^{-1} \qquad\qquad (C.3\text{--}16)$$

The magnitude at this frequency is 0.6 dg. Thus from Eq. C.3–12 the adjustable gain factor K_c must be -0.6 dg to satisfy the phase-margin criterion so that the velocity constant is found to be

$$K_v = 0.87 \text{ sec}^{-1} \qquad\qquad (C.3\text{--}17)$$

C.4 FEEDBACK COMPENSATION

The use of cascade-compensation functions is described in Appendix D. This article will demonstrate the techniques for introducing auxiliary feedback loops to improve system performance.

The purpose of compensation is primarily to alter the performance of a system so that the resulting error will fall within specifications. The advantage of feedback compensation over cascade compensation is that the variation of the parameters of the fixed elements in the auxiliary feedback loop (due to non-linearity, aging, etc.) has a much smaller effect on system performance provided that the parameters of the feedback elements do not vary and provided that the gain factor of the auxiliary loop is sufficiently large. In designing feedback-compensation functions the procedure employs a combination of the gain-phase plane and the magnitude asymptotes of the Bode diagram. The design is roughed out by means of the magnitude asymptotes and

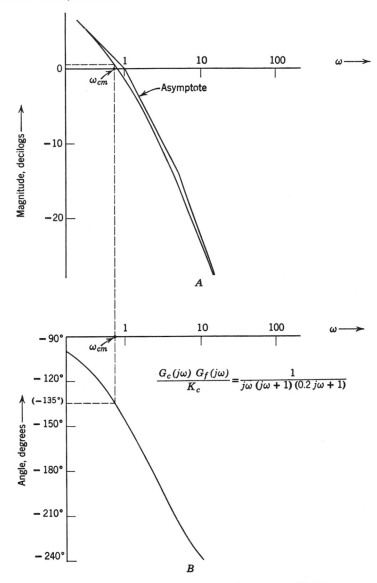

Fig. C.3–5. Bode diagram. (A) Magnitude curve. (B) Phase curve.

carried out in detail by means of the gain-phase-plane techniques. An excellent discussion of the techniques of feedback compensation is given in Reference C.3.

The basic principles of feedback compensation can be demonstrated by examination of Fig. C.4–1. Here a feedback function H_c is used to modify the characteristics of the fixed elements G_f, and a cascade function G_c is provided to aid in adjusting the performance of the major loop. In most situations the cascade compensation G_c is a simple gain factor that is used to adjust the degree of stability of the system. The burden of modifying the fixed-element transfer function G_f is placed on the feedback compensation H_c. In addition, the feedback function is usually provided with an adjustable gain factor to permit setting the degree of stability of the minor loop.

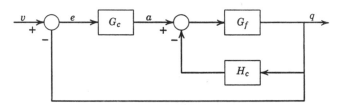

Fig. C.4–1.   General arrangement for feedback compensation.

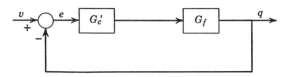

Fig. C.4–2.   Cascade equivalent of feedback compensation scheme.

The general configuration of Fig. C.4–1 can be placed in the cascade form of Fig. C.4–2. Here

$$G_c'(s) = \frac{G_c(s)}{1 + G_f(s)H_c(s)} \qquad\qquad \text{(C.4–1)}$$

Thus cascade compensation and feedback compensation are theoretically equivalent. In practice, feedback compensation is more flexible and produces a system that is less sensitive to variations of the parameters of the fixed elements.

The procedure for adjusting the feedback compensation is best understood by examining the magnitude asymptotes of the minor loop. If

$$\left|G_f(j\omega)H_c(j\omega)\right| \gg 1 \qquad\qquad \text{(C.4–2)}$$

then

$$\left|\frac{q(j\omega)}{a(j\omega)}\right| \cong \frac{1}{\left|H_c(j\omega)\right|} \qquad\qquad \text{(C.4–3)}$$

If

$$\left|G_f(j\omega)H_c(j\omega)\right| \ll 1 \qquad\qquad \text{(C.4–4)}$$

then

$$\left|\frac{q(j\omega)}{a(j\omega)}\right| \cong |G_f(j\omega)| \qquad (C.4\text{--}5)$$

In the frequency ranges where the open-minor-loop frequency-response magnitude $|G_f(j\omega)H_c(j\omega)|$ is very large, the closed-minor-loop response $|q(j\omega)/a(j\omega)|$ behaves like the reciprocal of the feedback compensation $|H_c(j\omega)|^{-1}$. When the open-minor-loop response magnitude is very small, the closed-minor-loop response behaves like the fixed elements $|G_f(j\omega)|$. Thus the frequency scale can be divided into several regions which are based on the magnitude of the open-minor-loop response. Usually the feedback compensation is so chosen that the frequency scale is divided into three ranges. These are

$$|G_f(j\omega)H_c(j\omega)| < 1 \quad \text{for } 0 < \omega < \omega_l \qquad (C.4\text{--}6)$$

$$|G_f(j\omega)H_c(j\omega)| > 1 \quad \text{for } \omega_l < \omega < \omega_u \qquad (C.4\text{--}7)$$

$$|G_f(j\omega)H_c(j\omega)| < 1 \quad \text{for } \omega_u < \omega < \infty \qquad (C.4\text{--}8)$$

where ω_l is the lower boundary and ω_u is the upper boundary. Corresponding to the three frequency ranges defined by Eqs. C.4–6 through C.4–8, the closed-minor-loop magnitude asymptotes are given by

$$\left|\frac{q(j\omega)}{a(j\omega)}\right| \cong |G_f(j\omega)| \qquad \text{for } 0 < \omega < \omega_l \qquad (C.4\text{--}9)$$

$$\left|\frac{q(j\omega)}{a(j\omega)}\right| \cong |H_c(j\omega)|^{-1} \quad \text{for } \omega_l < \omega < \omega_u \qquad (C.4\text{--}10)$$

$$\left|\frac{q(j\omega)}{a(j\omega)}\right| \cong |G_f(j\omega)| \qquad \text{for } \omega_u < \omega < \infty \qquad (C.4\text{--}11)$$

The feedback compensation is used primarily to improve the dynamic behavior of the fixed elements in the mid-frequency range without altering the desirable low-frequency behavior of the fixed elements. A high-frequency boundary will always exist since in any practical case the magnitude of $G_f(j\omega)H_c(j\omega)$ will become less than unity as frequency increases. Hence at least three regions are required.

The procedure for adjusting the feedback function H_c and the cascade gain factor $[G_c(s) = K_c]$ can thus be roughed out by means of asymptotic pictures of the various responses and then carried out in detail by means of the gain-phase plane. The purpose of the asymptotic sketches is to enable one to examine the form of the closed-minor-loop response as the feedback compensation is adjusted. The desirable properties of the closed-minor-loop response can be expressed in terms of the properties that are desirable for any open-major-loop function, namely, high gain at low frequencies, a stable shape relative to the $-1 + j0$ point, and low gain at high frequencies. Examination of the open-major-loop asymptotes of typical cascade-compensation arrangements also can serve as a guide to the shaping of the closed-minor-loop response.

Since there are usually several parameters to adjust in the feedback-compensation procedure, the process of design is one of trial and error

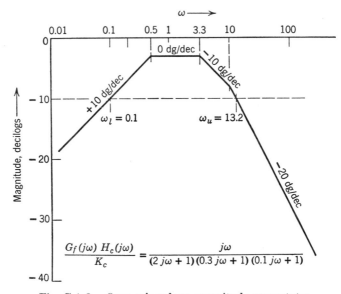

Fig. C.4–3.   Open-minor-loop magnitude asymptotes.

guided by the asymptotic sketches.   The details of the procedure are best demonstrated by an example.

In this example, the response of the fixed elements is given by

$$G_f(j\omega) = \frac{1}{j\omega(0.3j\omega + 1)(0.1j\omega + 1)} \qquad \text{(C.4–12)}$$

Feedback compensation is to be used to improve the performance of the system in conjunction with a pure gain factor cascaded with the minor loop.   The response of the feedback elements is given by

$$H_c(j\omega) = \frac{K_c(j\omega)^2}{T_c j\omega + 1} \qquad \text{(C.4–13)}$$

The cascade compensation being pure gain, its response is given by

$$G_c(j\omega) = K \tag{C.4-14}$$

The major loop will be adjusted to satisfy a 45° phase-margin criterion.
The first trial guess for the time constant T_c of the feedback elements
is

$$T_c = 2 \text{ sec} \tag{C.4-15}$$

With this value the magnitude asymptotes of $G_f(j\omega)H_c(j\omega)/K_c$ are
shown in Fig. C.4–3. The adjustment of K_c controls the degree of
stability of the closed-minor-loop response. If K_c is too large, the
closed-minor-loop response will have a quadratic factor with a very
low damping ratio, making it difficult to obtain a high-gain open-
major-loop response. Anticipating this behavior, a value of $K_c = 10$
is not unreasonable. When K_c is set in this way, the 0 dg line for the
open-minor-loop response G_fH_c is the dashed line shown in Fig. C.4–3.

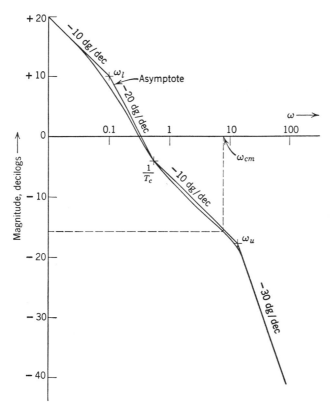

Fig. C.4–4.   Closed-minor-loop magnitude response.

This line defines the frequency boundaries

$$\omega_l = 0.1 \text{ rad sec}^{-1} \qquad (C.4\text{–}16)$$

and

$$\omega_u = 13.2 \text{ rad sec}^{-1} \qquad (C.4\text{–}17)$$

The closed-minor-loop asymptotes can now be drawn as shown in Fig. C.4–4.

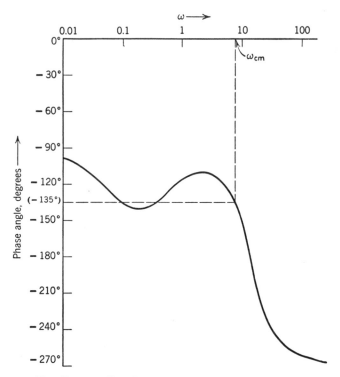

Fig. C.4–5.   Closed-minor-loop phase-angle response.

From examining the resultant curve, several points may be noted. The combination of the breaks at ω_l and $1/T_c$ appears as a cascade-lag-compensation effect which is a desirable property of the open-major-loop response.   In further trials attempts may be made to broaden the -20 dg per decade slope region bounded by these breaks and to move the region up to higher frequencies.   The break at ω_u is from a slope of -10 dg per decade to a slope of -30 dg per decade which is characteristic of a quadratic factor in the open-major-loop response.   If this factor has a low damping ratio, high-gain stabilization of the major loop may be difficult.   Thus the first trial choices of

T_c and K_c produces a set of open-major-loop asymptotes which appear reasonable but must be verified.

At this point the Nichols chart is used with a gain-phase plot of $G_f H_c$ to determine the closed-minor-loop response q/a (Appendix D). The result of the gain-phase plane construction produces the true magnitude curve of q/a shown in Fig. C.4–4. The corresponding phase curve appears in Fig. C.4–5. The shape of the true magnitude curve indicates no severe resonance effects so that a reasonable closed-loop performance may be expected. If the 45° phase-margin criterion is used to adjust the cascade compensation, the magnitude crossover frequency of the major loop is

$$\omega_{cm} = 7.7 \text{ rad sec}^{-1} \qquad (C.4–18)$$

and the gain factor of the cascade compensation is

$$K = 38 \qquad (C.4–19)$$

If the resulting system exhibits undesirable performance owing to the low-frequency location of the lag-compensation effect in the open-major-loop response, some improvement could be achieved by decreasing the feedback compensation time constant T_c and by attempting to increase the minor-loop gain factor K_c. The degree of improvement that is possible could only be ascertained by further trials.

C.5 DETERMINATION OF TRANSIENT RESPONSE FROM FREQUENCY RESPONSE

Most conventional trial-and-error design techniques use the frequency domain as the primary medium for representing system behavior, but many performance specifications are usually expressed in terms of the transient response of the system. This article is devoted to graphical methods for determining the transient response of a system from the frequency response.

Although direct inverse transformation is a straightforward method for determining the time function corresponding to a given transform, it often is a time-consuming procedure because of the necessity for factoring high-order polynomials. Furthermore, many problems start with experimentally determined frequency response data, and if inverse transformation is to be used then an analytical approximation to the experimental data is first required. The graphical design methods that are discussed in this appendix and the following one require nothing more than frequency response data before a design study can be initiated. The frequency response data can be obtained either experimentally or theoretically. Thus graphical procedures for determining the transient response of a system directly from frequency response data are extremely useful. References B.6, G.9, and T.7 present useful methods for determining the time response corresponding to a given frequency function.

If the Laplace transform $F(s)$ whose inverse is sought has no poles in the right half-plane or on the imaginary axis, then it can be shown that the time function $f(t)$ corresponding to $F(s)$ can be found from either of the following integrals:

$$f(t) = \frac{2}{\pi} \int_0^\infty d\omega \cos \omega t \; \text{Re} \, [F(j\omega)] \qquad (C.5\text{-}1)$$

$$f(t) = -\frac{2}{\pi} \int_0^\infty d\omega \sin \omega t \; \text{Im} \, [F(j\omega)] \qquad (C.5\text{-}2)$$

where $\text{Re} \, [F(j\omega)]$ is the real part and $\text{Im} \, [F(j\omega)]$ is the imaginary part of $F(j\omega)$. Using the relation

$$\mathcal{L}[t^n f(t)] = (-1)^{n/2} \frac{d^n F(j\omega)}{d\omega^n} \qquad (C.5\text{-}3)$$

for n even, from Eq. C.5–1 it is found that

$$f(t) = \frac{2}{\pi} \frac{(-1)^{n/2}}{t^n} \int_0^\infty d\omega \cos \omega t \, \frac{d^n}{d\omega^n} \, \{\text{Re} \, [F(j\omega)]\} \qquad (C.5\text{-}4)$$

In a similar manner, from Eq. C.5–2 it is found that

$$f(t) = \frac{2}{\pi} \frac{(-1)^{(n+1)/2}}{t^n} \int_0^\infty d\omega \sin \omega t \, \frac{d^n}{d\omega^n} \, \{\text{Re} \, [F(j\omega)]\} \qquad (C.5\text{-}5)$$

for n is odd.

Equations C.5–4 and C.5–5 express a time function in terms of the derivatives of the real part of the corresponding frequency function. A simple approximate method for evaluating Eq. C.5–1 has been developed by Guillemin (Reference G.9) based on these results.

1. The real-part function $\text{Re} \, [F(j\omega)]$ is plotted on a linear scale and approximated by straight lines.

2. The straight-line approximation to the real-part function is differentiated twice with respect to frequency ω so that the approximation to the second derivative of the real-part function is a set of impulses at positive and negative frequencies, i.e.,

$$\frac{d^2 \, \text{Re} \, [F(j\omega)]}{d\omega^2} \cong \sum_{k=1}^m a_k [\delta_0(\omega - \omega_k) + \delta_0(\omega + \omega_k)] \qquad (C.5\text{-}6)$$

where a_k is the magnitude of the impulse located at $\pm \omega_k$.

3. The time function corresponding to the impulse approximation given in Eq. C.5–6 is then found from

$$f(t) = -\frac{2}{\pi t^2} \sum_{k=1}^{m} a_k \cos \omega_k t \qquad (C.5–7)$$

The above procedure is restricted to functions having the following properties: a. $f(t)$ is zero for negative time; b. $|F(s)|$ behaves at least as $k/|s|$ as $|s|$ tends to infinity; c. $f(t)$ is bounded for all time. If $f(t)$ approaches a constant non-zero value as $t \to \infty$, $F(s)$ has a single-order pole at the origin. Then Eq. C.5–1 will give the quantity $[f(t) - f(\infty)]$ so that the pole of $F(s)$ at the origin can be subtracted from $F(s)$ without altering the result.

Some useful checking relations that apply to the foregoing procedure are

$$f(0) = \frac{2}{\pi} \int_0^\infty d\omega \operatorname{Re}\left[F(j\omega)\right] \qquad (C.5–8)$$

$$\sum_{k=1}^{m} a_k = 0 \qquad (C.5–9)$$

$$f(0) = \frac{1}{\pi} \sum_{k=1}^{m} a_k \omega_k{}^2 \qquad (C.5–10)$$

Since a frequency-domain design using the gain-phase plane ends with a plot of the open-loop function $q(s)/e(s)$ (Fig. 1.7–1 with $H_f(s) = 1$), charts have been included in a pocket in the rear of the book which enable one to determine

$$\operatorname{Re}\left[\frac{G(j\omega)}{1 + G(j\omega)}\right] \quad \text{and} \quad \operatorname{Im}\left[\frac{G(j\omega)}{1 + G(j\omega)}\right]$$

from the gain-phase-plane plot of $G(j\omega)$. Specifically these are Charts 1 and 2.* Thus, at the completion of a frequency-domain study, the impulse response of the system that is being studied can be determined by direct application of the real-part and imaginary-part charts to aid in the evaluation of the integrals of Eqs. C.5–1 or C.5–2.

C.6 ERROR COEFFICIENTS

In many cases the input specifications of a system consist of arbitrarily defined time functions. Determination of the error time func-

---

* To employ these charts, which are in a pocket in the rear cover of the book, graphs must be plotted to the following scales: 5 decilogs per inch; 20 degrees per inch.

tion for an arbitrary input is usually a time-consuming procedure if the Laplace or Fourier transform or the convolution integral are used directly. In this situation an expansion of the convolution integral in a Taylor series is possible which enables one to express the error time function in terms of the input and its derivatives and a set of coefficients that depend on the system only. These coefficients are called error coefficients. By terminating the series expansion after a finite number of terms, an approximate expression for the error time function is obtained. The upper bound of the remainder of the expansion can be estimated in a fairly simple way so that the accuracy of the approximation is easily ascertained. For elaboration of the expansion see References A.7, J.1, and T.7.

If the input-to-error transfer function $y_e(s)/v(s)$ is denoted by $\eta_0(s)$, then the convolution integral gives the error $y_e(t)$ in terms of the error impulse response $\eta_0(t)$ and the input time function $v(t)$, i.e.,

$$y_e(t) = \int_0^\infty dt_1 \, \eta_0(t_1) v(t - t_1) \qquad \text{(C.6–1)}$$

This equation can be repeatedly integrated by parts yielding

$$y_e(t) = \epsilon_0 v(t) + \epsilon_1 v'(t) + \cdots + \epsilon_N v^{(N)}(t) + r(t) \qquad \text{(C.6–2)}$$

where

$$\epsilon_k = -\eta_{k+1}(0) \qquad \text{(C.6–3)}$$

$$\eta_{k+1}(t) = -\int_t^\infty dt_1 \, \eta_k(t_1) \qquad \text{(C.6–4)}$$

$$r(t) = \int_0^\infty dt_1 \, \eta_{N+1}(t_1) v^{(N+1)}(t - t_1) \qquad \text{(C.6–5)}$$

In this expansion of the convolution integral ϵ_k is the kth error coefficient, $v^{(k)}(t)$ is the kth derivative of the input $v(t)$, and $r(t)$ is the remainder after N terms.

The error coefficients are functions only of the system parameters as can be seen from Eqs. C.6–3 and C.6–4 and determine the error time function $y_e(t)$ to within a bounded remainder $r(t)$ provided the input and its first N derivatives have no discontinuities in the time interval being considered. It can be shown that the error coefficients are also the coefficients of the Maclaurin series expansion of $\eta_0(s)$, i.e.,

$$\eta_0(s) = \epsilon_0 + \epsilon_1 s + \epsilon_2 s^2 + \cdots \qquad \text{(C.6–6)}$$

Thus the simplest way to determine the error coefficients of a system is to expand the error-to-input transfer function $\eta_0(s)$. If $\eta_0(s)$ is a rational function, this expansion can be carried out by dividing the numerator polynomial by the denominator polynomial. If $\eta_0(s)$ is not rational, then the error coefficients may be found from

$$\epsilon_k = \frac{1}{k!} \frac{d^k \eta_0(s)}{ds^k} \bigg|_{s=0} \tag{C.6-7}$$

The following relations involving the higher-order η functions defined by Eq. C.6–4 can be derived and show that the error coefficients are related to moments of the error impulse response $\eta_0(t)$.

$$\eta_{k+1}(t) = -\int_t^\infty dt_1 \frac{(t - t_1)^k}{k!} \eta_0(t_1) \tag{C.6-8}$$

$$\epsilon_k = \frac{(-1)^{k+1}}{k!} \int_0^\infty dt_1 \, t_1{}^k \eta_0(t_1) \tag{C.6-9}$$

$$\eta_{k+1}(s) = \frac{\eta_0(s) - \sum_{i=0}^k \epsilon_i s^i}{s^{k+1}} \tag{C.6-10}$$

Bounds on the remainder $r(t)$ can be determined by using the relation that the magnitude of an integral is smaller than or equal to the integral of the magnitude of the integrand. Thus, if

$$L \triangleq |v^{(N+1)}(t - t_1)|_{\max} \tag{C.6-11}$$

in the time interval of interest, then an upper bound on the remainder is given by

$$|r(t)| \le L \int_0^\infty dt_1 \, |\eta_{N+1}(t_1)| \tag{C.6-12}$$

If $\eta_{N+1}(t_1)$ is always positive or always negative then a simple bound on the remainder is given by

$$|r(t)| \le |v^{(N+1)}(t)|_{\max} |\epsilon_{N+1}| \tag{C.6-13}$$

C.7 THE ROOT-LOCUS METHOD

One of the drawbacks of the frequency-response techniques discussed thus far in this appendix and in Appendix D is that the transient response corresponding to a given frequency response is somewhat difficult to visualize. In addition, in some situations the frequency domain criteria used to measure the degree of stability of a system can be misleading. The root-locus method has been developed to fill this gap. The root locus of a system is a plot of the location of the closed-loop poles in the polar plane as a function of a gain factor. By observing the motion of the closed-loop poles as the gain factor is varied, a direct determination of the degree of stability of a system can be made. Thus, if a relatively small change in the gain factor causes some of the closed-loop poles to move into the right half-plane, then the system has a low degree of stability. The root locus is a useful adjunct to the other techniques that have been discussed but its major drawback is that accurate plotting of the locus is a time-consuming task. Elaboration of root-locus techniques is available in References T.3 and T.7.

Referring to Fig. 1.7–1, the poles of the closed-loop transfer function $q(s)/v(s)$ are given by the roots of

$$1 + G(s) = 0 \qquad\qquad (C.7\text{–}1)$$

where

$$G(s) \triangleq G_c(s)G_f(s)H_c(s) \qquad\qquad (C.7\text{–}2)$$

The roots of Eq. C.7–1 can be found from two conditions

$$\angle G(s) = 180° \qquad\qquad (C.7\text{–}3)$$

$$|G(s)| = 1 \qquad\qquad (C.7\text{–}4)$$

If

$$G(s) = K \frac{\displaystyle\prod_{i=1}^{N} (s - z_i)}{\displaystyle\prod_{k=1}^{M} (s - p_k)} \qquad\qquad (C.7\text{–}5)$$

where z_i is the ith zero of $G(s)$ and p_k is the kth pole of $G(s)$, then the angle condition of Eq. C.7–3 can be expressed as

$$\sum_{i=1}^{N} A_{zi} - \sum_{k=1}^{M} A_{pk} = 180° \qquad\qquad (C.7\text{–}6)$$

where $A_{zi} \triangleq$ angle of the phasor from the ith zero to s.
         $A_{pk} \triangleq$ angle of the phasor from the kth pole to s.

This equation shows how the root locus is constructed. Points in the s-plane lie on the root locus if the sum of the angles of the phasor from the open-loop zeros to the s points minus the sum of the angles of the phasors from the open-loop poles to the s points is equal to 180°. The locus of all possible roots is constructed by taking trial s points and seeing if they satisfy the angle condition. When the locus has been constructed, the magnitude condition given by Eq. C.7–4 is used to find the value of the adjustable gain factor K that corresponds to a given locus point, i.e.,

$$K = \frac{\prod\limits_{k=1}^{M} M_{pk}}{\prod\limits_{i=1}^{N} M_{zi}} \qquad \text{(C.7–7)}$$

where

$M_{pk} \triangleq$ magnitude of the phasor from the kth pole to the root-locus point.

$M_{zi} \triangleq$ magnitude of the phasor from the ith zero to the root-locus point.

The trial-and-error method for constructing the locus is the main reason why the application of the method is usually time consuming. Several theorems that are useful in speeding up the construction of the locus have been derived from the angle and magnitude conditions. These theorems are presented here.

1. The locus is symmetrical with respect to the real axis.

2. The number of branches of a root locus is equal to the number of roots of the characteristic equation (Eq. C.7–1).

3. The root locus starts ($K = 0$) at the open-loop poles and ends ($K \to \infty$) at the open-loop zeros.

4. If some branches of the root locus lie wholly on the real axis, then points on these branches always have an odd number of real open-loop poles and zeros to the right for $K > 0$.

5. If the root locus leaves a real-axis branch between two open-loop poles and enters the complex portion of the s-plane, then the point at which the locus breaks away is a point of maximum K as K is determined for the real-axis branch.

6. If the root locus leaves the complex portion of the s-plane and enters a real-axis branch between two open-loop zeros, then the point at which the locus enters is a point of minimum K as K is determined for the real-axis branch.

7. Near complex open-loop poles the direction of the locus is given by

$$180° + \Sigma\theta_z - \Sigma\theta_p$$

where

$\Sigma\theta_z \triangleq$ sum of the angles of the phasors from all the other zeros to the complex pole in question.

$\Sigma\theta_p \triangleq$ sum of the angles of the phasors from all the other poles to the complex pole in question.

Near complex open-loop zeros the direction of the locus is given by

$$-180° + \Sigma\phi_p - \Sigma\phi_z$$

where $\Sigma\phi_p$ and $\Sigma\phi_z$ are defined like $\Sigma\theta_p$ and $\Sigma\theta_z$.

8. The straight-line asymptotes of the locus for large values of s have a direction given by

$$\frac{180° \pm 360n°}{M - N} \quad (n = 0, 1, 2, \cdots) \quad \text{for } K > 0$$

where M = number of finite open-loop poles.

$\quad\quad N$ = number of finite open-loop zeros.

The intersection X_0 of the asymptotes of the locus with the real axis is the centroid of the open-loop pole-zero configuration:

$$X_0 = \frac{\displaystyle\sum_{k=1}^{M} p_k - \sum_{i=1}^{N} z_i}{M - N} \tag{C.7-8}$$

C.8 ANALOG COMPUTERS

Analogue computers greatly facilitate the analysis and design of feedback control systems. In addition to aiding the study of linear systems, analogue computers are extremely valuable in assisting the designer who is faced with a non-linear problem. They not only are useful for examining the time behavior of systems but also can be applied to the solution of optimization problems, particularly in fixed configurations. A good summary of the use of analogue computers is given in Reference L.05.

The basic elements of any analogue computer are integrators, coefficient potentiometers, summing amplifiers, multipliers, and function generators. Other special-purpose components are often used (e.g., limiters) but the foregoing list includes the more important elements. Because the detailed properties of computers differ from one manufacturer to another, this article will merely cover general principles applicable to electronic analogue computers.

The heart of a computer is the operational amplifier. This device is a high-gain d-c feedback amplifier that can be used as a summing amplifier, an integrator, or a simple inverter, or it can have any desired dynamic characteristic depending on the nature of the feedback network. A schematic diagram of a typical operational amplifier is shown in Fig. C.8–1. If it is assumed that the input impedance of the

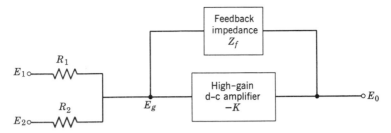

Fig. C.8–1.   Operational amplifier.

amplifier is infinite, then the equation relating the output voltage E_0 to the input voltages E_1 and E_2 is

$$\frac{1}{R_1} E_1 + \frac{1}{R_2} E_2 = -\frac{E_0}{Z_f} \left\{ 1 + \frac{1}{K} \left[\frac{Z_f}{R_1} + \frac{Z_f}{R_2} + 1 \right] \right\} \quad \text{(C.8–1)}$$

If the gain K of the d-c amplifier is very high, then the equation reduces to the approximate relation

$$\frac{1}{R_1} E_1 + \frac{1}{R_2} E_2 \cong -\frac{E_0}{Z_f} \quad \text{(C.8–2)}$$

This result shows that the functional behavior of the operational amplifier is primarily dependent on the feedback impedance Z_f. If Z_f is a resistance R_f, the device becomes a summing amplifier, i.e.,

$$E_0 \cong - \left(\frac{R_f}{R_1} E_1 + \frac{R_f}{R_2} E_2 \right) \quad \text{(C.8–3)}$$

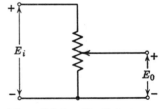

Fig. C.8–2.   Coefficient potentiometer.

If the feedback resistance R_f is equal to the input resistance R_1 and if E_2 is equal to zero, then the amplifier is a simple inverter.   It should be noted that the gain of any channel of the summing amplifier is equal to the ratio of the feedback resistance to the input resistance of that channel and is essentially independent of the gain of the d-c amplifier.

If Z_f is a capacitance, then the operational amplifier can be used as an integrator, i.e.,

$$E_0(s) \cong - \frac{1}{Cs} \left[\frac{1}{R_1} E_1 + \frac{1}{R_2} E_2 \right] \quad \text{(C.8–4)}$$

The coefficient potentiometer is shown in Fig. C.8–2.   This device produces an output voltage E_0 that is a constant function of the input voltage E_i, depending on the setting of the potentiometer, i.e.,

$$E_0 = KE_i \qquad\qquad\qquad \text{(C.8–5)}$$

where

$$0 < K < 1 \qquad\qquad\qquad \text{(C.8–6)}$$

The multiplier in an electronic analogue computer is usually a computing servomechanism. A typical multiplier is shown in Fig. C.8–3. The multiplying servo is supplied with a feedback potentiometer excited by a constant voltage source $\pm V$ as shown. If the input to the servo is x, then the output shaft rotates through an angle that is a fraction x/V of the total angle available on the feedback potentiometer. The multiplying potentiometer is excited by the second input y and rotates through the same angle as the feedback potentiometer.

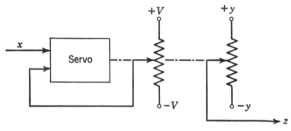

Fig. C.8–3.   Multiplier.

Therefore the voltage z which appears at the arm of the multiplying potentiometer is

$$z = xy/V \qquad\qquad\qquad \text{(C.8–7)}$$

Different functions such as division, raising to an integral power, extracting roots, etc., can be realized with the computing servomechanism by adding additional potentiometers to the output shaft and using special connections.

The function generator is a device for producing an output voltage which is an arbitrary function of the input voltage, i.e.,

$$y = f(x) \qquad\qquad\qquad \text{(C.8–8)}$$

Function generation can be accomplished in many ways, and the details of typical function generators will not be discussed here since they vary from one computer to another.

In using an analogue computer, the first step is to assemble the differential equations of the problem. Then time and amplitude scale factors are chosen. A symbolic computer diagram is drawn from the differential equations or from the block diagram of the differential equations. The computer diagram is a symbolic representation of the external connections among the various computer components that are required in order that the computer simulate the problem. This diagram is an aid in visualizing the problem and in connecting the computer components. When the time and amplitude scaling is chosen and the computer diagram is drawn, the computer is connected and the problem is then run.

To guide the choice of amplitude and time scales and the configuration of the computer diagram, the following restrictions should be noted.

1. No practical analogue computer uses a differentiator.

2. The summing amplifier and the integrators introduce a sign change.

3. The frequency scale of the computer is limited at the low end by drift and at the high end by phase shift and attenuation.

4. If computing servos are used, then the frequency scale of the computer is limited at the high end by the bandwidth of the servos.

5. The amplitude scale of the computer is limited by amplifier saturation.

TRIAL-AND-ERROR METHODS
IN THE GAIN-PHASE PLANE

D.1 INTRODUCTION

Numerous analytical and graphical techniques are available as aids for the designer using the trial-and-error design procedure (outlined in Art. C.1 of Appendix C). One of the most expeditious graphical procedures for setting the gain for a specified degree of stability and for introducing modifications of the compensation function uses the gain-phase-plane representation of frequency function. The coordinates of the gain-phase plane are angles in degrees and magnitudes in logarithmic units called decilogs.* Thus the magnitude and phase angle of a frequency function is plotted in the gain-phase plane with real frequency as a parameter.

Since the gain-phase plane presents the magnitude of a frequency function to a logarithmic scale, it is much more convenient to use than the polar plane. If two frequency functions $G_1(j\omega)$ and $G_2(j\omega)$ are cascaded in a system, the equivalent frequency function is $G_1(j\omega)G_2(j\omega)$. If the polar plane is used to obtain the magnitude of the equivalent function, one must multiply the separate magnitudes of the original functions at each frequency. If the gain-phase plane is used, however, the magnitudes of the original functions can simply be added

* A decilog (abbreviated dg) is a logarithmic unit such that the magnitude of a number N in decilogs is equal to $10 \log_{10} N$.

because they are given in logarithmic units. Replacing magnitude multiplication by log magnitude addition greatly reduces the labor involved in the graphical procedures.

In this appendix a working example is described first so that the methods that are developed in the following articles can be demonstrated with a specific problem. Next, the graphical aids that are used in the gain-phase-plane approach are presented, and then the technique for adjusting the degree of stability of a system is developed. After a specific degree of stability has been established, the designer is usually concerned with the closed-loop response of the system. Article D.6 describes how the closed-loop frequency response can be determined from the open-loop frequency response in the gain-phase plane. Techniques for using first-order lag and lead networks to improve performance are then developed, and the appendix closes with a summary of the results of applying the various gain-phase-plane procedures to the working example. For elaboration of the gain-phase-plane techniques described in this appendix, the reader is referred to References A.3, B.6, C.3, and J.1.

D.2 WORKING EXAMPLE

A working example has been chosen to illustrate the specific steps involved in the graphical procedures that are to be described. The system is the positional servomechanism shown in Fig. D.2–1. The problem is to investigate the effect of the addition of a series compensating winding to the generator of a Ward-Leonard drive on the performance of the closed-loop system in which it is used.

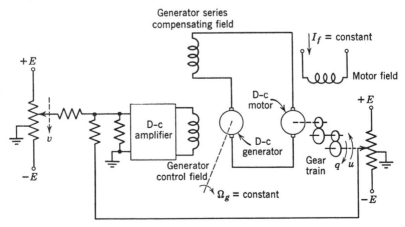

Fig. D.2–1.   Position-control system.

In the system shown in Fig. D.2–1, position is measured by rotary potentiometers, and the error or difference between input position v and output position q is amplified by means of a d-c amplifier. The output current of the amplifier drives the control field of a d-c generator which, in turn, drives a d-c motor. The d-c motor is connected to the output shaft by means of a gear train. The generator is assumed to run at constant speed Ω_g, and constant current I_f is supplied to the field of the d-c motor. In an attempt to improve the characteristics of the system, a series compensating winding is placed on the generator field structure. Preliminary analysis indicates that this compensating winding may be useful in reducing the sensitivity of the system to load-torque disturbances u provided that the sense of the compensating field flux is such as to produce positive feedback.

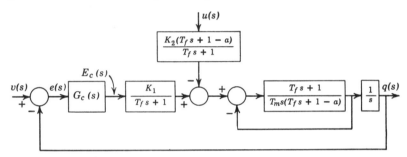

Fig. D.2–2.   Block diagram of position-control system.

A functional block diagram of the system is shown in Fig. D.2–2. In this figure field mutual inductance is neglected and

$G_c(s)$ = transfer function of d-c amplifier, compensation, and error measuring system

E_c = voltage applied to control field

$K_1 = K_0/rR_fK_b$

$K_2 = R_a/K_bK_Tr^2$

$a = N_sK_0/N_cR_a$ (compensation factor, "tuning")

$T_f = L_f/R_f$ (control field time constant)

$T_m = JR_a/K_bK_T$ (motor time constant)

K_0 = open-circuit generated voltage per unit control field current

R_f = total series resistance of control field and d-c amplifier circuit

K_b = back emf of motor per unit motor shaft velocity

r = ratio of motor shaft velocity to output shaft velocity (gear ratio)

R_a = total series resistance of generator and motor armature circuit

K_T = motor shaft torque per unit armature current

N_s = number of turns of series compensating field winding

N_c = number of turns of control field winding
L_f = control field self-inductance
J = total inertia (motor and load) referred to motor shaft

The diagram of Fig. D.2–2 was developed with the assumption that motor and generator armature circuit inductance is negligible and that the system behaves linearly at all times.

It is evident that the adjustment of the compensation factor a is critical in determining system performance. Examination of Fig. D.2–2 shows that it is theoretically possible to produce a system that exhibits zero steady-state error for a constant load torque u if perfect compensation ($a = +1$) can be achieved. Since it is quite unlikely

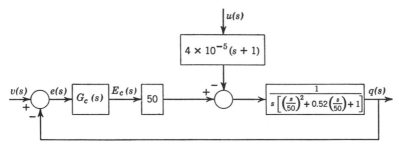

Fig. D.2–3. Numerical diagram of position-control system with series compensating field ($a = 0.99$).

that such an adjustment can be maintained in practice, we shall assume that the generator is slightly undercompensated and set $a = 0.99$. Additional numerical constants of the system are listed in Table D.2–1.

Table D.2–1.   Numerical Constants of Positional Servomechanism

$K_1 = 50$ radian per volt second
$K_2 = 0.004$ radian per inch-ounce second
$T_f = 0.01$ second
$T_m = 0.04$ second

With the given numerical values, the diagram of Fig. D.2–2 is reduced to the form shown in Fig. D.2–3. For comparison, the numerical block diagram of the system when no compensating field is used ($a = 0$) is shown in Fig. D.2–4. In both cases the velocity constant K_v (defined in Appendix C) of the system is equal to $50K_c$ where K_c is the gain factor of the compensation function. To simplify calculations, the frequency scale is normalized with respect to the natural frequency of the quadratic factor of Fig. D.2–3 ($\omega_n = 50$ rad/sec). A new frequency variable λ is chosen such that

$$\lambda = s/50 \qquad (D.2–1)$$

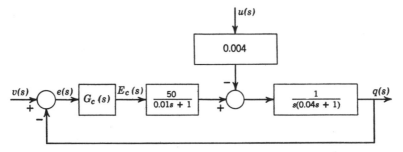

Fig. D.2–4.   Numerical diagram of position-control system without series compensating field ($a = 0$).

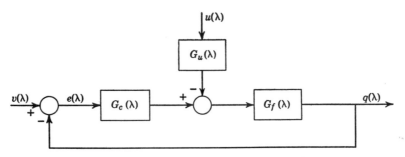

Fig. D.2–5.   General diagram of position-control system.

For generality in the ensuing discussion, Figs. D.2–3 and D.2–4 are redrawn in the form shown in Fig. D.2–5. In this figure, for the system employing the series compensating field, hereafter called system A,

$$G_c(\lambda) = G_c(s)\Big|_{s = 50\lambda} \qquad (\text{D.2–2})$$

$$G_u(\lambda) = 0.8 \times 10^{-6}(50\lambda + 1) \qquad (\text{D.2–3})$$

$$G_f(\lambda) = \frac{1}{\lambda(\lambda^2 + 0.52\lambda + 1)} \qquad (\text{D.2–4})$$

For the system that does not use the series compensating field, hereafter called system B

$$G_c(\lambda) = G_c(s)\Big|_{s = 50\lambda} \qquad (\text{D.2–5})$$

$$G_u(\lambda) = 8 \times 10^{-5}(0.5\lambda + 1) \qquad (\text{D.2–6})$$

$$G_f(\lambda) = \frac{1}{\lambda(0.5\lambda + 1)(2\lambda + 1)} \qquad (\text{D.2–7})$$

These two versions of the original system will be studied to see what advantages are gained by using the series compensating winding.

D.3 GRAPHICAL AIDS

Several graphical aids have been developed to aid the designer when working in the gain-phase plane.   Referring to Fig. 1.7–1, if discussion is limited to unity-feedback systems [$H_f = 1$], the design of a system

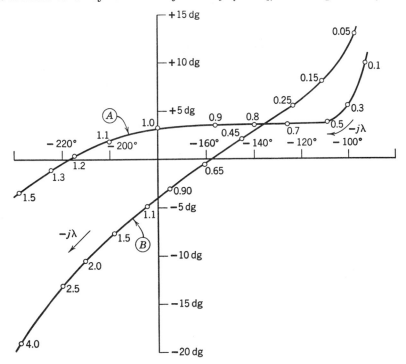

Fig. D.3–1.   Open-loop frequency responses of working example.   (A) With compensating winding.   (B) Without compensating winding.

involves the two transfer functions G_f for the fixed elements and G_c for the compensation function.   To study behavior in the frequency domain, the gain-normalized frequency response of the open-loop function $G_c G_f / K_c$ may be plotted in the gain-phase plane as a curve of magnitude versus phase angle with real frequency as a parameter. Here K_c is the adjustable gain factor of the open-loop function.   For the working example, the open-loop function $G_c G_f / K_c$ is plotted in Fig. D.3–1 for $G_c(\lambda) = K_c$.   In this figure, curve A is the response of the system with the compensating winding (system A) and curve B

is the response of the system without the compensating winding (system B).

Two charts are commonly used in the gain-phase-plane graphical procedure. The Nichols chart, shown in Fig. D.3–2, is used to go from the open-loop frequency response to the closed-loop frequency response. The region in the vicinity of the point (0 dg, $-180°$) on the Nichols chart is most useful for design purposes and has been enlarged and included separately in a pocket in the rear cover of the

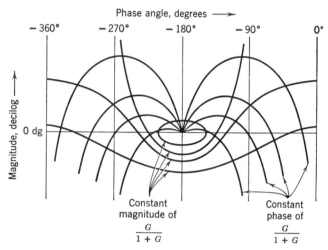

Fig. D.3–2. Nichols chart.

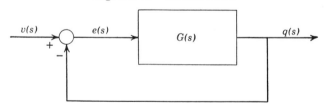

Fig. D.3–3. Unity feedback system.

book as Chart 3.* The symmetry of the Nichols chart with respect to the $-180°$ line should be noted. No symmetry exists with respect to the 0 dg line.

Figure D.3–3 shows a block diagram of a unity-feedback system where $G(s)$ corresponds to $G_c(s)G_f(s)$. The closed-loop transfer function of this system is defined by

$$W(s) \triangleq \frac{q(s)}{v(s)} \tag{D.3–1}$$

---

* To employ these charts graphs must be plotted to the following scales: 5 decilogs per inch; 20 degrees per inch.

where $q(s)$ and $v(s)$ are the Fourier transforms of $q(t)$ and $v(t)$, respectively. The open-loop transfer function of the system is

$$G(s) \triangleq \frac{q(s)}{e(s)} \qquad \text{(D.3-2)}$$

The relation between the open-loop and closed-loop transfer function is

$$W(s) = \frac{G(s)}{1 + G(s)} \qquad \text{(D.3-3)}$$

Equation D.3-3 forms a bilinear transformation from the G-plane to the W-plane. The Nichols chart (Fig. D.3-2) is merely a graphical picture of this bilinear transformation in the gain-phase plane of G. Contours of constant $|W| = M$ and constant angle of W are plotted on the gain-phase plane whose coordinates are $10 \log_{10} |G|$ and angle of G. Thus, if one plots the open-loop function G on the gain-phase plane, the magnitude and phase angle of the closed-loop function W as functions of real frequency can be determined directly from the Nichols chart by reading the points of intersection of the G curve with the constant-magnitude and constant-phase-angle contours of W at each real frequency.

A second graphical aid is the set of lead and lag function curves. These curves have been included separately in a pocket in the rear cover of the book as Chart 4.* The lead and lag function curves represent the gain-phase-plane frequency response curves of first-order compensation functions drawn with a normalized frequency scale. As shown, the curves represent the frequency response of the function

$$G_c(j\beta) = \frac{\alpha j\beta + 1}{j\beta + 1} \qquad \text{(D.3-4)}$$

This function introduces gain and phase lead if cascaded with another frequency function. If the set of curves are rotated 180°, the function represented is

$$G_c(j\beta) = \frac{j\beta + 1}{\alpha j\beta + 1} \qquad \text{(D.3-5)}$$

This function introduces attenuation and phase lag if cascaded with another frequency function.

Since the first-order compensation functions are the ones most commonly used, it is extremely convenient to have their frequency response curves available in performing a design study.

* See footnote on page 350.

D.4 DEGREE OF STABILITY

In order to specify quantitatively the degree of stability of a closed-loop system, we can examine the magnitude contours on the Nichols chart in the vicinity of the point $-1 + j0$, i.e., $10 \log_{10} |G| = 0$ dg and angle of $G = -180°$. We see that the magnitude of W becomes very large if the G curve passes near the $-1 + j0$ point. This behavior of the G curve corresponds to large peaking in the magnitude response of W and is indicative of a low degree of stability, i.e., the system will respond in a highly oscillatory manner. The maximum magnitude of W (its resonant peak) is denoted by M_p, and the value of M_p is conventionally used as a quantitative indication of the degree of stability of a system. Experience has shown for many systems that an M_p value between 1.3 and 1.5 gives satisfactory behavior.

D.5 SETTING THE GAIN FOR A SPECIFIED DEGREE OF STABILITY

After determining the range of gain factor settings allowable for stable operation of the system being studied (see Appendix B), the degree-of-stability specification M_p is used to fix a specific gain factor K_c. The frequency response G_cG_f/K_c is plotted on the gain-phase plane (usually on a transparent sheet of graph paper). The G_cG_f/K_c curve is placed over the Nichols chart with the phase angle coordinates coincident. The curve is then moved vertically until it is tangent to the specified M_p contour. To make the coordinate systems of the G_cG_f/K_c curve and the Nichols chart coincide, the adjustable gain factor K_c must be added to the G_cG_f/K_c curve. The gain factor K_c that is needed can be determined by noting the intersection of the 0 dg line of the Nichols chart with the magnitude coordinates of the G_cG_f/K_c curve. The value of K_c (in decilogs) needed to satisfy the specified degree of stability M_p is merely the negative of the magnitude (in decilogs) of G_cG_f/K_c that coincides with the 0 dg line of the Nichols chart.

Applying the foregoing procedure to the working example with $G_c = K_c$ we first determine the range of the gain factor K_c necessary for stability. From the discussion of stability given in Appendix B it follows that in this example the upper limit of the gain factor K_c for $G_c = K_c$ can be determined from the requirement that, when

$$\measuredangle G_c(\lambda)G_f(\lambda) = -180° \tag{D.5-1}$$

then

$$|G_c(\lambda)G_f(\lambda)| < 1 \tag{D.5-2}$$

From an examination of the frequency response curves of Fig. D.3–1, the allowable range of K_c for stability is found from the intersection of the curves with the $-180°$ line to be

$$0 < K_c < 0.52 \text{ volt/rad} \tag{D.5-3}$$

for system A and

$$0 < K_c < 2.5 \text{ volt/rad} \tag{D.5-4}$$

for system B.

Assume that the degree of stability is specified as

$$10 \log_{10} M_p = 1.0 \text{ dg} \quad (M_p = 1.26) \tag{D.5-5}$$

The successive steps for determining the gain factor K_c to meet the M_p specifications are shown in Fig. D.5–1 for system A. In this figure the

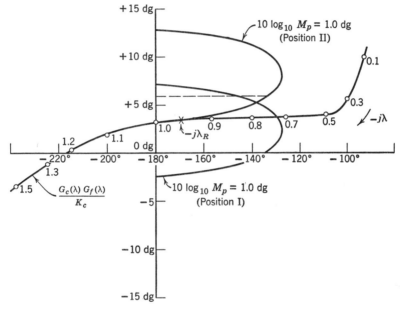

Fig. D.5–1.   Gain factor setting for specified M_p for system A.

M_p contour is shown in two positions. Position I has the 0 dg line of the M_p contour coinciding with the 0 dg line of $G_c(\lambda)G_f(\lambda)/K_c$. By moving the $G_c(\lambda)G_f(\lambda)/K_c$ curve vertically downwards (or the M_p contour vertically upwards), position II is reached. In position II the M_p contour is tangent to the $G_c(\lambda)G_f(\lambda)/K_c$ curve. The dashed line in position II is the 0 dg line associated with the M_p contour. In position II the magnitude coordinates of the M_p contour and the $G_c(\lambda)G_f(\lambda)/K_c$ curve do not agree. However, coincidence of the magnitude coordinates is achieved by multiplying $G_c(\lambda)G_f(\lambda)/K_c$ by the gain factor K_c corresponding to the intersection of the 0 dg line of the M_p contour with the magnitude coordinates of $G_c(\lambda)G_f(\lambda)/K_c$. From Fig. D.5–1 we therefore find that the gain K_c necessary to meet the M_p specification (Eq. D.5–5) for system A is given by

$$10 \log_{10} K_c = -5.9 \text{ dg} \quad (K_c = 0.257 \text{ volt/rad}) \qquad (\text{D.5–6})$$

The point of tangency (marked by a cross in Fig. D.5–1) occurs at a frequency that is called the resonant frequency of the system. From Fig. D.5–1 and Eq. D.2–1 the resonant frequency ω_R of system A is

$$\omega_R = 47.5 \text{ rad/sec} \qquad (\text{D.5–7})$$

A construction similar to the one just described yields for system B

$$10 \log_{10} K_c = -4.0 \text{ dg} \quad (K_c = 0.398 \text{ volt/rad}) \qquad (\text{D.5–8})$$

and

$$\omega_R = 17.5 \text{ rad/sec} \qquad (\text{D.5–9})$$

D.6 DETERMINATION OF CLOSED-LOOP FREQUENCY RESPONSE

When the adjustable gain factor has been determined to satisfy the degree-of-stability specification, a plot of the closed-loop frequency response is often of interest. This plot can be determined directly from the Nichols chart. The G_cG_f curve is aligned with the Nichols charts so that the specified M_p contour is tangent to the G_cG_f curve. In this position, intersection of the G_cG_f curve with the magnitude contours of the Nichols chart yields the magnitude of W (Eq. D.3–3) as a function of frequency; intersection with the phase angle contours of the Nichols chart yields the phase angle of W as a function of frequency.

If the frequency response sought is not W, the response of the system to variables other than the input v can be expressed in terms of W. Thus, for the general form of Fig. D.2–5, the response $e(\lambda)/u(\lambda)$ is of interest. This response can be readily found from

$$\frac{e(\lambda)}{u(\lambda)} = \frac{G_u(\lambda)}{G_c(\lambda)} W(\lambda) \qquad (\text{D.6–1})$$

Using the Nichols chart, the responses $W(\lambda)$ and $e(\lambda)/u(\lambda)$ have been found for systems A and B when $G_c(\lambda) = K_c$ is set for $10 \log_{10} M_p = 1.0$ dg. The magnitude responses for these circumstances are shown in Fig. D.6–1. Note that the dimensions of $e(\lambda)/u(\lambda)$ are radians per inch-ounce and that one cannot legitimately take the

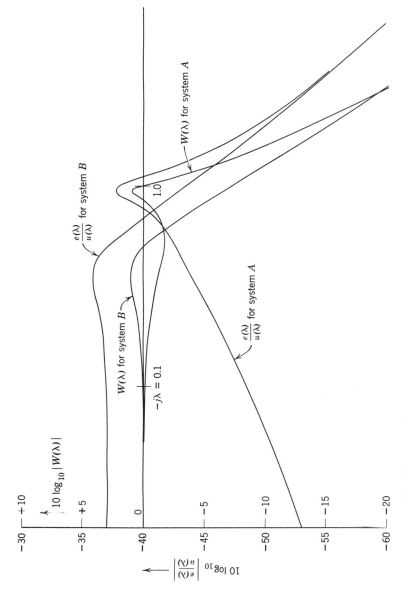

Fig. D.6–1. Magnitude response curves for working example with $G_c(\lambda) = K_c$.

logarithm of a number carrying dimensions. This difficulty is easily avoided by assuming that the response $e(\lambda)/u(\lambda)$ is divided by a non-dimensionalizing base of 1.0 radian per inch-ounce.

Comparing the curves of Fig. D.6–1, we see the effect of the series compensating winding on the closed-loop magnitude responses for the two systems. The W responses indicate that the addition of the compensating winding produces a wider system bandwidth as measured by the resonant frequency of system A relative to that of system B. However, the dip in the W response for system A which uses the compensating winding is undesirable. This dip tends to increase the settling time of the system for a step input compared with a system having the same resonant frequency but no dip. The responses $e(\lambda)/u(\lambda)$ show that system A is markedly less sensitive to the load disturbance u over most of the frequency range. If the disturbance contains frequency components greater than 37 rad/sec, however, the resonance effect in this region for system A causes its response to be poorer than the response of system B to these frequencies.

D.7 LAG-FUNCTION COMPENSATION

Lag compensation is usually used to permit an increase of gain while maintaining a specified degree of stability. The general form of the lag-compensation transfer function is:

$$G_c(j\omega) = K_c \frac{T_c j\omega + 1}{\alpha T_c j\omega + 1} \qquad (D.7–1)$$

The time constant of the function is usually chosen to correspond to a frequency that is low compared with the uncompensated resonant frequency of the system in which the function is used. In order to obtain good utilization of this compensation function, a rule of thumb is used for determining the value of the time constant T_c as a first trial. The rule is:

Choose T_c such that a phase shift of no more than $-5°$ to $-10°$ is added at the resonant frequency of the uncompensated system.

The rule of thumb places an approximate lower limit on the time constant T_c owing to the fact that too low a value of T_c reduces the effectiveness of the network in increasing the gain. Care must also be taken not to set T_c at too large a value since then the response of the system to velocity and acceleration components of the input as well as the response to disturbances deteriorates. The attenuation α is chosen by noting the desired increase in gain.

The use of the normalized lag-function curves that are included in the rear pocket of the book is as follows (see Fig. D.7–1 where the lag-function curve for $\alpha = 10$ is drawn):

1. The gain increase attainable with lag compensation is approximately 0.7α to 0.9α. Since we know the desired gain increase, the attenuation α is therefore determined.

2. The time constant T_c is chosen by allowing no more than $-5°$ to $-10°$ of phase shift to be introduced by the lag function at the uncompensated resonant frequency of the system.

3. Since $\beta = T_c\omega$, the frequency scale ratio between the normalized lag-function plots and the uncompensated open-loop curve is fixed by T_c.

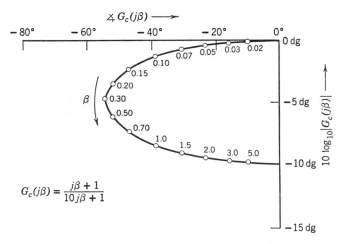

Fig. D.7–1. Lag-function curve for $\alpha = 10$ and $K_c = 1$.

4. Since we know the frequency ratio β/ω, the magnitude and phase angle added to the uncompensated curve by the compensation function at each frequency can be determined directly from the lag-function curves. A useful approximation for large values of β ($\beta > 5$) is that the phase angle of the lag function varies inversely with β as β increases. The magnitude of the function for large β is approximately α^{-1}.

5. Since a gain-phase-plane curve of G_cG_f/K_c is usually available with $G_c = K_c$, when G_c is modified to include lag compensation (Eq. D.7–1), the lag function is added to the G_f curve by offsetting the magnitude and phase angle of G_f by the magnitude and phase angle added by the lag function at each frequency.

6. When the composite curve G_cG_f/K_c is plotted with G_c given by Eq. D.7–1, the value of the adjustable gain factor K_c is determined from the M_p criterion as described in Art. D.5.

The insertion of lag compensation with $\alpha = 10$ will be demonstrated by means of system A of the working example. Expressing the compensation function in terms of the normalized frequency variable λ gives

$$G_c(\lambda) = K_c \frac{50T_c\lambda + 1}{50\alpha T_c\lambda + 1} \qquad (D.7\text{--}2)$$

where $\alpha = 10$. The uncompensated resonant frequency of system A was found to be 47.5 rad/sec (Eq. D.5–7) corresponding to $-j\lambda = 0.95$. Using the rule of thumb stated previously for lag compensation and the

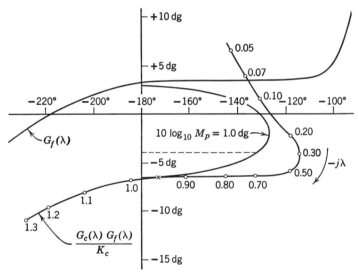

Fig. D.7–2. Open-loop frequency response curve for system A with lag compensation.

normalized lag-function curve for $\alpha = 10$ (Fig. D.7–1), a phase shift of $-5°$ occurs at $\beta = 10$. Comparing Eq. D.7–2 with the normalized lag-compensation form of Eq. D.3–5, the relation between β and λ is given by

$$j\beta = 50T_c\lambda \qquad (D.7\text{--}3)$$

From the uncompensated resonant frequency $(-j\lambda = 0.95)$ and the frequency for a phase shift of $-5°$ ($\beta = 10$), the time constant T_c is therefore

$$T_c = 0.21 \text{ sec} \qquad (D.7\text{--}4)$$

The scale ratio between β and λ is

$$\beta = -10.5j\lambda \qquad (D.7\text{--}5)$$

With the frequency ratio β/λ determined, the lag function for $\alpha = 10$ is added to the uncompensated function of system A (Fig. D.3–1), producing the composite response $G_c(\lambda)G_f(\lambda)/K_c$ shown in Fig. D.7–2. Using the specified M_p criterion ($10 \log_{10} M_p = 1.0$ dg), tangency between the composite $G_c(\lambda)G_f(\lambda)/K_c$ curve and the M_p contour is determined as shown in Fig. D.7–2. The gain factor K_c and the resonant frequency ω_R for system A with lag compensation are

$$10 \log_{10} K_c = 3.9 \text{ dg} \quad (K_c = 2.46 \text{ volt/rad}) \qquad \text{(D.7–6)}$$

$$\omega_R = 47.5 \text{ rad/sec} \qquad \text{(D.7–7)}$$

By an identical procedure the following results are obtained for system B with lag compensation ($\alpha = 10$)

$$T_c = 0.57 \text{ sec} \qquad \text{(D.7–8)}$$

$$10 \log_{10} K_c = 4.75 \text{ dg} \quad (K_c = 2.98 \text{ volt/rad}) \qquad \text{(D.7–9)}$$

$$\omega_R = 12.5 \text{ rad/sec} \qquad \text{(D.7–10)}$$

D.8 LEAD-FUNCTION COMPENSATION

Increase in the gain of a system is also obtainable by using lead compensation (Eq. D.3–4). Usually a graphical trial-and-error-maximization procedure is employed to determine the adjustment of the compensation for maximum increase in gain. Often an associated increase in the resonant frequency of the system occurs as well.

The general form of the lead-compensation transfer function is

$$G_c(j\omega) = K_c \frac{\alpha T_c j\omega + 1}{T_c j\omega + 1} \qquad \text{(D.8–1)}$$

Owing to the noise in a system and the possibility of saturation (see Chapters 7 and 8), α of the lead network is usually limited to a value of 20 or less. The choice of the time constant T_c is a matter of trial. A convenient rule of thumb to initiate the trial-and-error procedure follows.

Let

$$\Psi \triangleq \sin^{-1} \frac{1}{M_p} \qquad \text{(D.8–2)}$$

$$\phi_m \triangleq \sin^{-1} \frac{\alpha - 1}{\alpha + 1} \qquad \text{(D.8–3)}$$

$$\omega_m \triangleq \frac{1}{T_c \sqrt{\alpha}} \qquad \text{(D.8–4)}$$

Ψ is the maximum positive phase shift associated with the "nose" of the M_p contour. ϕ_m is the maximum positive phase shift of the lead function for a given α. ω_m is the frequency at which ϕ_m occurs. The initial choice of T_c can then be determined by setting ω_m equal to the solution of

$$\sphericalangle G_f(j\omega) = -180° + \Psi - \phi_m \qquad (D.8-5)$$

Note that the solution of Eq. D.8–5 can be read directly from the gain-phase plot of $G_f(j\omega)$, once Ψ and ϕ_m are known.

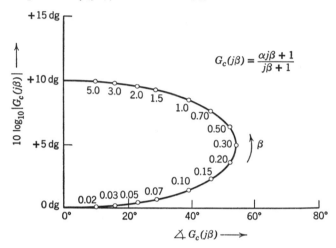

Fig. D.8–1.   Lead-function curve for $\alpha = 10$ and $K_c = 1$.

The use of the normalized lead-function curves that are included in the rear pocket of the book is as follows (see Fig. D.8–1, where the lead-function curve for $\alpha = 10$ is drawn):

1. The initial trial value of the time constant T_c is chosen by setting the frequency ω_m of maximum positive phase shift ϕ_m of the lead function equal to the solution of the "phase matching" equation (Eq. D.8–5).

2. Since $\beta = T_c\omega$, the frequency scale ratio between the normalized lead-function plots and the uncompensated open-loop curve is fixed by T_c.

3. Since we know the frequency ratio β/ω, the magnitude and phase angle added to the uncompensated curve by the compensation function at each frequency can be determined directly from the lead-function curves.

4. Since a gain-phase plane curve of G_cG_f/K_c is usually available with $G_c = K_c$, when G_c is modified to include lead compensation

(Eq. D.8–1), the lead function is added to G_f by offsetting the magnitude and phase angle of G_f by the magnitude and phase angle added by the lead function at each frequency.

5. When the composite curve $G_c G_f / K_c$ is plotted with G_c given by Eq. D.8–1, the value of the adjustable gain factor K_c is determined from the M_p criterion as described in Art. D.5.

6. Steps 2–5 are repeated with new values of T_c that are usually less than the value found from the rule of thumb for the initial choice of T_c.

7. A plot of the gain factor K_c versus time constant T_c is constructed. The peak of this curve is the maximum value of the gain factor that is attainable for the system with the specified values of α and M_p.

Because of the lightly damped quadratic factor that occurs in the fixed elements of system A (see Eq. D.2–4 and Fig. D.3–1), no improvement occurs when first-order lead compensation is used to increase the gain factor. An increase in the gain factor is possible, however, for system B. The limitations imposed on adding lead compensation to produce maximum gain increase in system B are $\alpha = 10$ and $10 \log_{10} M_p = 1.0$ dg. Thus the angles required for the solution of Eq. D.8–5 are

$$\Psi = 52.5° \tag{D.8–6}$$

$$\phi_m = 54.9° \tag{D.8–7}$$

Substituting Eqs. D.8–6 and D.8–7 into Eq. D.8–5

$$\angle G_f(j\omega) = -182.4° \tag{D.8–8}$$

By examining the open-loop frequency response of system B in Fig. D.3–1, the frequency for locating the maximum phase lead is found to be

$$\omega_m = 52.5 \text{ rad/sec} \tag{D.8–9}$$

Substituting Eq. D.8–9 into Eq. D.8–4, the time constant T_c is

$$T_c = 0.006 \text{ sec} \tag{D.8–10}$$

The frequency scale ratio between β and λ becomes

$$\beta = -0.30j\lambda \tag{D.8–11}$$

On the basis of this scale ratio the normalized lead-function curve for $\alpha = 10$ is added by the offset method to the uncompensated open-loop function of system B (Fig. D.3–1). The composite $G_c(\lambda)G_f(\lambda)/K_c$ curve is shown in Fig. D.8–2 with the M_p tangency construction added for $10 \log_{10} M_p = 1.0$ dg.   The results of the construction are

$$10 \log_{10} K_c = -0.7 \text{ dg} \quad (K_c = 0.85 \text{ volt/rad}) \qquad \text{(D.8-12)}$$

$$\omega_R = 70 \text{ rad/sec} \qquad \text{(D.8-13)}$$

Additional gain increase is possible if T_c is reduced relative to the initial trial value given by Eq. D.8-10.   By trying new values of T_c a curve of the gain factor K_c versus time constant T_c can be plotted. Figure D.8-3 shows the variation of K_c with T_c for system B, using

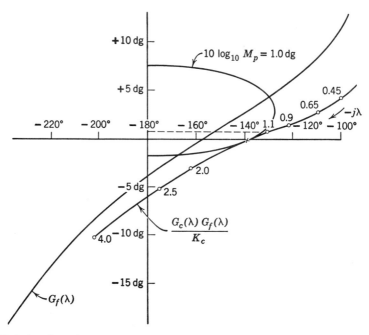

Fig. D.8-2.   Open-loop frequency response curve for system B with lead compensation.

lead compensation.   The peak of this curve gives the maximum value of the gain factor that is attainable with first-order lead compensation. For the example the maximum occurs at

$$T_c = 0.003 \text{ sec} \qquad \text{(D.8-14)}$$

$$K_c = 1.46 \text{ volt/rad} \qquad \text{(D.8-15)}$$

$$\omega_R = 45 \text{ rad/sec} \qquad \text{(D.8-16)}$$

It should be noted that the resonant frequency obtained at the point of maximum gain is less than the resonant frequency obtained with the initial trial value of T_c. In general the initial trial value of T_c produces close to the maximum resonant frequency. To obtain maximum gain, approximately one-half to one-third the initial trial value of T_c should be used.

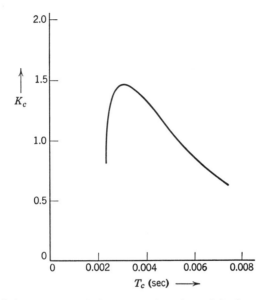

Fig. D.8–3. Gain factor variation as a function of lead-compensation time constant for system B.

D.9 SUMMARY OF WORKING EXAMPLE

To conclude the discussion of the working example a summary of design parameters is presented in Table D.9-1. The last entry in Table D.9-1 is an added design that is obtained by using a lag function with $\alpha = 10$ to further raise the gain of system B over lead compensation (item 5 in Table D.9–1). The purpose of this additional design is to provide a basis for comparison of the performance of systems A and B when the possibility of improvement through the use of first-order compensation functions has been exhausted (items 3, 4 and 5 in Table D.9–1). To make the comparison two test signals will be assumed and the error responses $e(t)$ to these signals will be presented for the systems listed as items 3 and 6 in Table D.9–1. The test signals are

$$v(t) = 2t \text{ rad}, \quad t > 0$$

$$= 0, \qquad t < 0 \tag{D.9–1}$$

$$u(t) = 3{,}500 \text{ in.-oz}, \quad t > 0$$

$$= 0, \qquad\qquad t < 0 \qquad\qquad\qquad (\text{D.9--2})$$

Table D.9–1. Design Parameters of Positional Servomechanism
$$M_p = 1.26$$

SYSTEM	K_v^*	ω_R	T_c—lag	T_c—lead
1. A—uncompensated	13	47.5	—	—
2. B—uncompensated	20	17.5	—	—
3. A—lag compensation	125	47.5	0.2	—
4. B—lag compensation	150	12.5	0.6	—
5. B—lead compensation	75	45.0	—	0.003
6. B—lead and lag compensation	500	35.0	0.2	0.003

* K_v is the system velocity constant and is equal to 50 K_c for both systems where K_c is the adjustable gain factor.

The error responses to the test signals are presented in Figs. D.9–1 and D.9–2. The steady-state and peak errors for the two systems are listed in Table D.9-2.

Table D.9–2. Errors of Positional Servomechanism Example

SYSTEM	TEST SIGNAL	STEADY-STATE ERROR (millirad)	PEAK ERROR (millirad)
3.A	v	16.0	105
3.A	u	1.12	17.4
6.B	v	4.0	32
6.B	u	28.0	310

From an examination of the results of the working example that are presented here, it is evident that a definite improvement in the

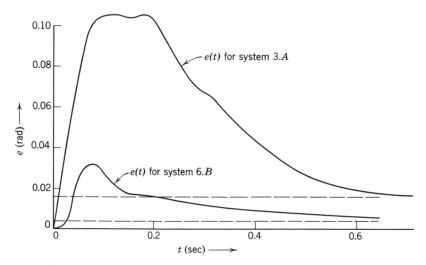

Fig. D.9–1. Error response to ramp input $v(t) = 2t$ rad, $t > 0$
$= 0$ rad, $t < 0$.

response to a load disturbance is possible if a series compensating winding is used (system A). However, this improvement is obtained at the cost of deteriorated response to a ramp input. If the adjustment of the compensating winding is varied so that a larger steady-state error for a load disturbance is produced, it may be possible to obtain an improved ramp response. A complete study of the system should include the effects of adjustment of the compensating winding but space does not permit further examination of this problem in this appendix.

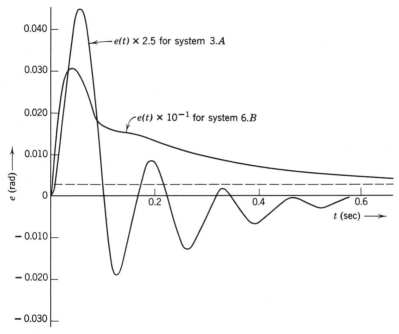

Fig. D.9–2. Error response to step disturbance $u(t) = 3,500$ in.-oz, $t > 0$
$= 0 \qquad , t < 0.$

The example emphasizes two important considerations. When lag compensation is used, the steady-state errors that result are poor indications of performance since the peak errors often are orders of magnitude greater than the steady-state errors. In addition, the presence of a lightly damped quadratic factor in the fixed elements of a system places a severe limitation on the ultimate performance that can be achieved with these simple methods of compensation.

In conclusion it can be said that lag compensation must be used with care since it is difficult to visualize the frequency-domain equivalent of excessive peaking of transient responses of a system when the time constant of the lag compensation is set at too large a value.

APPENDIX **E**

TABLE OF INTEGRALS*

E.1 EVALUATION OF A DEFINITE INTEGRAL

In engineering investigations, integrations frequently occur with the form

$$I_n = \frac{1}{2\pi j} \int_{-j\infty}^{j\infty} ds \, \frac{c(s)c(-s)}{d(s)d(-s)} \qquad \text{(E.1--1)}$$

where

$$c(s) = \sum_{k=0}^{n-1} c_k s^k$$

$$d(s) = \sum_{k=0}^{n} d_k s^k \qquad \text{(E.1--2)}$$

and

$d(s)$ has zeros in the left half-plane only

Although in most applications $c(s)$ has zeros in the left half-plane only, this is not necessary for the following derivation. Indeed, as will be seen in the derivation of the values of the integrals, it is not necessary

---

*The material contained in this appendix is taken from *Report* 70 of the Massachusetts Institute of Technology, Dynamic Analysis and Control Laboratory, entitled "Nonlinear Servomechanisms with Random Inputs" by R. C. Booton, Jr., M. V. Mathews, and W. W. Seifert (August 20, 1953), and is reproduced with permission of the authors.

to know the values of the coefficients c_k. The integrals can be evaluated in terms of the coefficients of the even polynomial of degree $2n - 2$ in the numerator of the integrand. However, it is more convenient to present the table in terms of the coefficients c_k and d_k.

The values of these integrals can be expressed as rational functions of the coefficients c_k and d_k, and tables of the integrals for n from 1 to 7 have already been published (see Reference J.1). Both to obtain a check of the previously calculated tables and to extend their range, an independent derivation of the values of the integrals was undertaken at the Dynamic Analysis and Control Laboratory,* using a method suggested by Dr. A. C. Hall. The tables presented here include values of n from 1 to 10. Comparison of the tables reveals two errors in the seventh-order integral of the James, Nichols, and Phillips table (Reference J.1).

The following paragraphs show that the evaluation of the integral depends upon the solution of a system of linear algebraic equations. The general form of these equations is derived. Solution of these equations for values of n from 1 to 10, which is the essential part of the calculation, yields the table of integrals.

For s imaginary $(s = j\omega)$, $\overline{c(s)} = c(\bar{s}) = c(-s)$, where the bar denotes the complex conjugate. Similarly, $\overline{d(s)} = d(-s)$. The integrand may then be written in the form

$$\frac{c(s)c(-s)}{d(s)d(-s)} = \frac{c(s)\overline{c(s)}}{d(s)\overline{d(s)}} \tag{E.1-3}$$

This can always be separated into the sum of two fractions†

$$\frac{c(s)c(-s)}{d(s)d(-s)} = \frac{a(s)}{d(s)} + \frac{b(s)}{d(-s)} \tag{E.1-4}$$

where $a(s) = \displaystyle\sum_{i=0}^{n-1} a_i s^i$ and $b(s) = \displaystyle\sum_{i=0}^{n-1} b_i s^i$ are polynomials of degree $n - 1$. Because $c(s)c(-s)$ is an even function of s, it can be seen that $b(s) = a(-s)$.

---

* The details of the calculation were carried out by Misses B. L. White, V. D. Lee, and J. M. Murphy.

† The calculation of these fractions is an algebraic problem and will be considered later. As will be seen, only one coefficient a_{n-1} is needed to evaluate I_n.

The integral then appears in the form

$$I_n = \frac{1}{2\pi j} \int_{-j\infty}^{j\infty} ds \left[\frac{a(s)}{d(s)} + \frac{a(-s)}{d(-s)} \right]$$

$$= \frac{1}{2\pi j} \int_{-j\infty}^{j\infty} ds \frac{a(s)}{d(s)} + \frac{1}{2\pi j} \int_{-j\infty}^{j\infty} ds \frac{a(-s)}{d(-s)} \qquad \text{(E.1–5)}$$

$$= \frac{1}{\pi j} \int_{-j\infty}^{j\infty} ds \frac{a(s)}{d(s)}$$

The last equality results from the fact that a change of variable $(s = -s')$ shows

$$\int_{-j\infty}^{j\infty} ds \frac{a(s)}{d(s)} = -\int_{j\infty}^{-j\infty} ds' \frac{a(-s')}{d(-s')} \qquad \text{(E.1–6)}$$

The value of I_n is thus twice the inverse Laplace transform of $a(s)/d(s)$ evaluated at $t = 0$. Because at $t = 0$ the inverse Laplace transform is one-half of the limit of the inverse transform as $t \to 0$, the value of the integral I_n is given by the initial-value theorem as

$$I_n = 2\mathcal{L}^{-1} \left[\frac{a(s)}{d(s)} \right]_{t=0}$$

$$= \lim_{t \to 0} \mathcal{L}^{-1} \left[\frac{a(s)}{d(s)} \right] \qquad \text{(E.1–7)}$$

$$= \lim_{s \to \infty} \frac{sa(s)}{d(s)}$$

$$= \frac{a_{n-1}}{d_n}$$

Therefore, the evaluation of the integral requires the calculation of only the one coefficient a_{n-1}.

It might be remarked that the properties of the Laplace transformation are not needed to evaluate the integral I_n because I_n can be evaluated in terms of the residues of the integrand. It can be shown that I_n is equal to the sum of the residues of $a(s)/d(s)$ and that the sum of the residues of $a(s)/d(s)$ is a_{n-1}/d_n.

Reference to Eq. E.1-4 shows that $a(s)$ must satisfy the equation

$$a(s)d(-s) + a(-s)d(s) = c(s)c(-s) \qquad \text{(E.1–8)}$$

Substitution of the expressions for $a(s)$ and $d(s)$ results in

$$a(s)d(-s) = \left(\sum_{i=0}^{n-1} a_i s^i \right) \left[\sum_{k=0}^{n} d_k(-s)^k \right]$$

$$= \sum_{i=0}^{n-1} \sum_{k=0}^{n} (-1)^k a_i d_k s^{i+k} \qquad \text{(E.1–9)}$$

Collection of terms with equal powers of s yields

$$a(s)d(-s) = \sum_{m=0}^{2n-1} E_m s^m \qquad \text{(E.1–10)}$$

where

$$E_m = \sum_{i=0}^{m} (-1)^{m-i} a_i d_{m-i} \qquad \text{for } 0 \leq m \leq n-1$$

$$= \sum_{i=m-n}^{n-1} (-1)^{m-i} a_i d_{m-i} \qquad \text{for } n \leq m \leq 2n-1 \qquad \text{(E.1–11)}$$

Similarly,

$$a(-s)d(s) = \sum_{m=0}^{2n-1} (-1)^m E_m s^m \qquad \text{(E.1–12)}$$

The right side of Eq. 1–8 may be written as

$$c(s)c(-s) = \left(\sum_{i=0}^{n-1} c_i s^i \right) \left[\sum_{k=0}^{n-1} c_k(-s)^k \right]$$

$$= \sum_{i,k=0}^{n-1} (-1)^k c_i c_k s^{i+k} \qquad \text{(E.1–13)}$$

Collection of terms yields

$$c(s)c(-s) = \sum_{m=0}^{2n-2} 2C_m s^m \qquad \text{(E.1–14)}$$

where*

$$2C_m = \sum_{k=0}^{m} (-1)^k c_k c_{m-k} \qquad \text{for } 0 \leq m \leq n-1$$

$$= \sum_{k=m-n+1}^{n-1} (-1)^k c_k c_{m-k} \qquad \text{for } n \leq m \leq 2n-2 \qquad \text{(E.1–15)}$$

* The factor 2 is introduced merely for convenience later.

Substitution of Eqs. E.1–10, E.1–12, and E.1–14 into Eq. E.1–8 results in

$$\sum_{m=0}^{2n-1} \frac{1 + (-1)^m}{2} E_m s^m = \sum_{m=0}^{2n-2} C_m s^m \qquad \text{(E.1–16)}$$

Equating coefficients of the even* powers of s yields the n algebraic equations

$$E_m = C_m, \quad (m = 0, 2, 4, \cdots, 2n - 2) \qquad \text{(E.1–17)}$$

Substitution of Eq. E.1–11 into Eq. E.1–17 results in the n equations

$$\sum_{i=0}^{m} (-1)^i a_i d_{m-i} = C_m \quad \text{for } 0 \leqq m \leqq n - 1$$

$$\qquad\qquad\qquad\qquad\qquad\qquad\qquad\qquad \text{(E.1–18)}$$

$$\sum_{i=m-n}^{n-1} (-1)^i a_i d_{m-i} = C_m \quad \text{for } n \leqq m \leqq 2n - 1$$

in the n quantities

$$(-1)^i a_i \quad (i = 0, 1, \cdots, n - 1)$$

In matrix form Eq. E.1–18 is

$$D \times A = C \qquad \text{(E.1–19)}$$

where

$$C = \begin{bmatrix} C_0 \\ C_2 \\ \cdot \\ \cdot \\ \cdot \\ C_{2n-2} \end{bmatrix} \qquad \text{(E.1–20)}$$

and

$$A = \begin{bmatrix} a_0 \\ -a_1 \\ \cdot \\ \cdot \\ \cdot \\ (-1)^{n-1} a_{n-1} \end{bmatrix} \qquad \text{(E.1–21)}$$

* All the odd coefficients vanish.

For n odd, D is of the form

$$D = \begin{bmatrix} d_0 & 0 & 0 & \cdots & 0 \\ d_2 & d_1 & d_0 & \cdots & 0 \\ \cdot & & & & \cdot \\ \cdot & & & & \\ \cdot & & & & \cdot \\ d_{n-1} & d_{n-2} & d_{n-3} & \cdots & d_0 \\ 0 & d_n & d_{n-1} & \cdots & d_2 \\ \cdot & & & & \cdot \\ \cdot & & & & \\ \cdot & & & & \cdot \\ 0 & 0 & 0 & \cdots & d_{n-1} \end{bmatrix} \qquad \text{(E.1–22)}$$

For n even, D is of the form

$$D = \begin{bmatrix} d_0 & 0 & 0 & \cdots & 0 \\ d_2 & d_1 & d_0 & \cdots & 0 \\ \cdot & & & & \cdot \\ \cdot & & & & \\ \cdot & & & & \cdot \\ d_n & d_{n-1} & d_{n-2} & \cdots & d_1 \\ 0 & 0 & d_n & \cdots & d_3 \\ \cdot & & & & \cdot \\ \cdot & & & & \\ \cdot & & & & \cdot \\ 0 & 0 & 0 & \cdots & d_{n-1} \end{bmatrix} \qquad \text{(E.1–23)}$$

Solution of Eq. E.1–18 for a_{n-1} and use of Eq. E.1–7 yield the value of I_n.

E.2 TABULATED VALUES OF THE INTEGRAL FORM

Table E.2–1 gives the value of I_n for values of n from 1 to 10 where

$$I_n = \frac{1}{2\pi j} \int_{-j\infty}^{j\infty} ds \, \frac{c(s)c(-s)}{d(s)d(-s)} \qquad \text{(E.2–1)}$$

and

$$c(s) = c_{n-1}s^{n-1} + \cdots + c_0 \qquad \text{(E.2–2)}$$

$$d(s) = d_n s^n + \cdots + d_0 \qquad \text{(E.2–3)}$$

Table E.2-1

$$I_1 = \frac{c_0^2}{2d_0 d_1}$$

$$I_2 = \frac{c_1^2 d_0 + c_0^2 d_2}{2d_0 d_1 d_2}$$

$$I_3 = \frac{c_2^2 d_0 d_1 + (c_1^2 - 2c_0 c_2)d_0 d_3 + c_0^2 d_2 d_3}{2d_0 d_3(-d_0 d_3 + d_1 d_2)}$$

$$I_4 = \frac{c_3^2(-d_0^2 d_3 + d_0 d_1 d_2) + (c_2^2 - 2c_1 c_3)d_0 d_1 d_4 + (c_1^2 - 2c_0 c_2)d_0 d_3 d_4 + c_0^2(-d_1 d_4^2 + d_2 d_3 d_4)}{2d_0 d_4(-d_0 d_3^2 - d_1^2 d_4 + d_1 d_2 d_3)}$$

$$I_5 = \frac{1}{2\Delta_5}\left[c_4^2 m_0 + (c_3^2 - 2c_2 c_4)m_1 + (c_2^2 - 2c_1 c_3 + 2c_0 c_4)m_2 + (c_1^2 - 2c_0 c_2)m_3 + c_0^2 m_4\right]$$

where

$$m_0 = \frac{1}{d_5}(d_3 m_1 - d_1 m_2)$$

$$m_1 = -d_0 d_3 + d_1 d_2$$

$$m_2 = -d_0 d_5 + d_1 d_4$$

$$m_3 = \frac{1}{d_0}(d_2 m_2 - d_4 m_1)$$

$$m_4 = \frac{1}{d_0}(d_2 m_3 - d_4 m_2)$$

$$\Delta_5 = d_0(d_1 m_4 - d_3 m_3 + d_5 m_2)$$

$$I_6 = \frac{1}{2\Delta_6}\left[c_5^2 m_0 + (c_4^2 - 2c_3 c_5)m_1 + (c_3^2 - 2c_2 c_4 + 2c_1 c_5)m_2 + (c_2^2 - 2c_1 c_3 + 2c_0 c_4)m_3 \right.$$
$$\left. + (c_1^2 - 2c_0 c_2)m_4 + c_0^2 m_5\right]$$

where

$$m_0 = \frac{1}{d_6}(d_4 m_1 - d_2 m_2 + d_0 m_3)$$

$$m_1 = -d_0 d_1 d_5 + d_0 d_3^2 + d_1^2 d_4 - d_1 d_2 d_3$$

$$m_2 = d_0 d_3 d_5 + d_1^2 d_6 - d_1 d_2 d_5$$

$$m_3 = d_0 d_5^2 + d_1 d_3 d_6 - d_1 d_4 d_5$$

$$m_4 = \frac{1}{d_0}(d_2 m_3 - d_4 m_2 + d_6 m_1)$$

$$m_5 = \frac{1}{d_0}(d_2 m_4 - d_4 m_3 + d_6 m_2)$$

$$\Delta_6 = d_0(d_1 m_5 - d_3 m_4 + d_5 m_3)$$

Table E.2-1 (continued)

$$I_7 = \frac{1}{2\Delta_7}\left[c_6^2 m_0 + (c_5^2 - 2c_4 c_6)m_1 + (c_4^2 - 2c_3 c_5 + 2c_2 c_6)m_2 + (c_3^2 - 2c_2 c_4 + 2c_1 c_5 - 2c_0 c_6)m_3 \right.$$
$$\left. + (c_2^2 - 2c_1 c_3 + 2c_0 c_4)m_4 + (c_1^2 - 2c_0 c_2)m_5 + c_0^2 m_6 \right]$$

where

$$m_0 = \frac{1}{d_7}(d_5 m_1 - d_3 m_2 + d_1 m_3)$$

$$m_1 = -(d_1 d_4 - d_0 d_5)^2 + (d_0 d_3 - d_1 d_2)(d_0 d_7 - d_1 d_6 + d_2 d_5 - d_3 d_4)$$

$$m_2 = (d_0 d_7 - d_1 d_6)(-d_0 d_5 + d_1 d_4) + (d_0 d_3 - d_1 d_2)(d_2 d_7 - d_3 d_6)$$

$$m_3 = -(d_0 d_7 - d_1 d_6)^2 + (d_0 d_3 - d_1 d_2)(d_4 d_7 - d_5 d_6)$$

$$m_4 = \frac{1}{d_0}(d_2 m_3 - d_4 m_2 + d_6 m_1)$$

$$m_5 = \frac{1}{d_0}(d_2 m_4 - d_4 m_3 + d_6 m_2)$$

$$m_6 = \frac{1}{d_0}(d_2 m_5 - d_4 m_4 + d_6 m_3)$$

$$\Delta_7 = d_0(d_1 m_6 - d_3 m_5 + d_5 m_4 - d_7 m_3)$$

$$I_8 = \frac{1}{2\Delta_8}\left[c_7^2 m_0 + (c_6^2 - 2c_5 c_7)m_1 + (c_5^2 - 2c_4 c_6 + 2c_3 c_7)m_2 + (c_4^2 - 2c_3 c_5 + 2c_2 c_6 - 2c_1 c_7)m_3 \right.$$
$$\left. + (c_3^2 - 2c_2 c_4 + 2c_1 c_5 - 2c_0 c_6)m_4 + (c_2^2 - 2c_1 c_3 + 2c_0 c_4)m_5 + (c_1^2 - 2c_0 c_2)m_6 + c_0^2 m_7 \right]$$

where

$$m_0 = \frac{1}{d_8}(d_6 m_1 - d_4 m_2 + d_2 m_3 - d_0 m_4)$$

$$m_1 = (d_0 d_7 + d_2 d_5)(-d_0 d_1 d_7 + d_0 d_3 d_5 + 2d_1^2 d_6) + (d_3 d_7 - d_5^2)(d_0^2 d_5 + d_1 d_2^2)$$

$$+ d_1 d_3 d_8 (d_0 d_3 - d_1 d_2) - d_1^2 d_8 (d_0 d_5 - d_1 d_4)$$

$$+ (-d_2 d_7 + d_3 d_6 - d_4 d_5)(d_0 d_3^2 + d_1^2 d_4) - d_1 d_6 (d_1^2 d_6 + 3d_0 d_3 d_5)$$

$$- d_1 d_2 d_3 (d_3 d_6 - d_4 d_5) + 2d_0 d_1 d_4^2 d_5$$

$$m_2 = (d_0 d_3 - d_1 d_2)(d_0 d_7^2 - d_1 d_5 d_8 - d_1 d_6 d_7 + d_2 d_5 d_7) + (d_3 d_8 - d_4 d_7)(-d_0 d_1 d_5 + d_0 d_3^2 - d_1 d_2 d_3 + d_1^2 d_4)$$

$$- d_0 d_5 d_7 (d_0 d_5 - d_1 d_4) + d_1^2 d_8 (d_0 d_7 - d_1 d_6)$$

$$m_3 = -d_1 (d_1 d_8 - d_2 d_7)^2 + (-d_5 d_8 + d_6 d_7)(d_0 d_1 d_5 - d_0 d_3^2 + d_1 d_2 d_3 - d_1^2 d_4)$$

$$+ d_0 d_7^2 (-d_0 d_5 + d_1 d_4 + d_2 d_3) - 2d_0 d_1 d_3 d_7 d_8$$

$$m_4 = (-d_5 d_8 + d_6 d_7)(2d_0 d_1 d_7 - d_0 d_3 d_5 + d_1 d_2 d_5 - d_1^2 d_6) + (-d_3 d_8 + d_4 d_7)(d_0 d_3 d_7 - d_1 d_2 d_7 + d_1^2 d_8) - d_0^2 d_7^3$$

Table E.2-1 (continued)

$$m_5 = \frac{1}{d_0}(d_2 m_4 - d_4 m_3 + d_6 m_2 - d_8 m_1)$$

$$m_6 = \frac{1}{d_0}(d_2 m_5 - d_4 m_4 + d_6 m_3 - d_8 m_2)$$

$$m_7 = \frac{1}{d_0}(d_2 m_6 - d_4 m_5 + d_6 m_4 - d_8 m_3)$$

$$\Delta_8 = d_0(d_1 m_7 - d_3 m_6 + d_5 m_5 - d_7 m_4)$$

$$I_9 = \frac{1}{2\Delta_9}\left[c_8^2 m_0 + (c_7^2 - 2c_6 c_8)m_1 + (c_6^2 - 2c_5 c_7 + 2c_4 c_8)m_2 + (c_5^2 - 2c_4 c_6 + 2c_3 c_7 - 2c_2 c_8)m_3 \right.$$

$$+ (c_4^2 - 2c_3 c_5 + 2c_2 c_6 - 2c_1 c_7 + 2c_0 c_8)m_4 + (c_3^2 - 2c_2 c_4 + 2c_1 c_5 - 2c_0 c_6)m_5$$

$$\left. + (c_2^2 - 2c_1 c_3 + 2c_0 c_4)m_6 + (c_1^2 - 2c_0 c_2)m_7 + c_0^2 m_8 \right]$$

where

$$m_0 = \frac{1}{d_9}(d_7 m_1 - d_5 m_2 + d_3 m_3 - d_1 m_4)$$

$$m_1 = a_1(a_1 a_{10} - a_2 a_9 + a_3 a_6 + a_3 a_8 + 2a_4 a_6 - a_5^2 - a_5 a_7 - a_7^2) + a_2(-a_2 a_6 - a_3 a_7 + a_4 a_5 + 2a_4 a_7) - a_4^3$$

$$m_2 = a_1(a_3 a_9 + a_4 a_9 - a_5 a_8 + a_6 a_7 - a_7 a_8) + a_2(-a_2 a_9 + a_4 a_8 + a_7^2) - a_4^2 a_7$$

$$m_3 = a_1(a_3 a_{10} + a_4 a_{10} + a_7 a_9 - a_8^2) + a_2(-a_2 a_{10} + a_7 a_8) - a_4^2 a_7$$

$$m_4 = a_1(a_5 a_{10} + 2a_7 a_{10} - a_8 a_9) + a_2(a_7 a_9 - a_4 a_{10}) - a_7^3$$

$$m_5 = \frac{1}{d_0}(d_2 m_4 - d_4 m_3 + d_6 m_2 - d_8 m_1)$$

$$m_6 = \frac{1}{d_0}(d_2 m_5 - d_4 m_4 + d_6 m_3 - d_8 m_2)$$

$$m_7 = \frac{1}{d_0}(d_2 m_6 - d_4 m_5 + d_6 m_4 - d_8 m_3)$$

$$m_8 = \frac{1}{d_0}(d_2 m_7 - d_4 m_6 + d_6 m_5 - d_8 m_4)$$

$$\Delta_9 = d_0(d_1 m_8 - d_3 m_7 + d_5 m_6 - d_7 m_5 + d_9 m_4)$$

where

$$a_1 = d_1 d_2 - d_0 d_3$$

$$a_2 = d_1 d_4 - d_0 d_5$$

$$a_3 = d_3 d_4 - d_2 d_5$$

$$a_4 = d_1 d_6 - d_0 d_7$$

$$a_5 = d_3 d_6 - d_2 d_7$$

$$a_6 = d_5 d_6 - d_4 d_7$$

$$a_7 = d_1 d_8 - d_0 d_9$$

$$a_8 = d_3 d_8 - d_2 d_9$$

$$a_9 = d_5 d_8 - d_4 d_9$$

$$a_{10} = d_7 d_8 - d_6 d_9$$

Table E.2-1 (continued)

$$I_{10} = \frac{1}{2\Delta_{10}} \left[c_9^2 m_0 + (c_8^2 - 2c_7 c_9)m_1 + (c_7^2 - 2c_6 c_8 + 2c_5 c_9)m_2 + (c_6^2 - 2c_5 c_7 + 2c_4 c_8 - 2c_3 c_9)m_3 \right.$$

$$+ (c_5^2 - 2c_4 c_6 + 2c_3 c_7 - 2c_2 c_8 + 2c_1 c_9)m_4 + (c_4^2 - 2c_3 c_5 + 2c_2 c_6 - 2c_1 c_7 + 2c_0 c_8)m_5$$

$$\left. + (c_3^2 - 2c_2 c_4 + 2c_1 c_5 - 2c_0 c_6)m_6 + (c_2^2 - 2c_1 c_3 + 2c_0 c_4)m_7 + (c_1^2 - 2c_0 c_2)m_8 + c_0^2 m_9 \right]$$

where

$$m_0 = \frac{1}{d_{10}}(d_8 m_1 - d_6 m_2 + d_4 m_3 - d_2 m_4 + d_0 m_5)$$

$$m_1 = a_1 \left[d_1(-a_2 b_5 + a_4 b_4 - a_5 a_{10} - a_6 b_2 - 2a_7 a_{10} + a_8 a_9 + a_9 b_1) \right.$$

$$+ d_3(a_1 b_5 + a_3 a_{10} + a_4 a_{10} - a_4 b_3 + a_5 b_2 + a_7 a_9 - a_8^2 - a_8 b_1 - b_1^2)$$

$$+ d_5(-a_1 b_4 + a_2 b_3 - a_3 a_9 - a_3 b_2 - a_4 a_9 + a_5 a_8 - a_6 a_7 + a_7 a_8 + a_7 b_1)$$

$$+ d_7(a_1 a_{10} - a_2 a_9 + a_3 a_6 + a_3 a_8 + a_3 b_1 + 2a_4 a_6 + a_4 b_1 - a_5^2 - a_5 a_7 - a_7^2)$$

$$+ a_2 \left[d_1(a_4 a_{10} + a_6 b_1 - a_7 a_9 + b_1^2) + d_3(-a_2 a_{10} - a_5 b_1 + a_7 a_8 + a_7 b_1) \right.$$

$$\left. + d_5(a_2 a_9 + a_3 b_1 - a_4 a_8 - a_4 b_1 - a_7^2) + d_7(-a_2 a_6 - a_2 b_1 - a_3 a_7 + a_4 a_5 + 2a_4 a_7) \right]$$

$$\left. + a_4 \left[a_7(-d_3 a_7 + d_5 a_4 - 2d_1 b_1) + a_4(d_3 b_1 - d_7 a_4) \right] + d_1 a_7^3 \right]$$

$$m_2 = a_1 \left[d_1(-a_5 b_4 - a_7 b_4 + a_8 b_3 - a_{10} b_1 + b_1 b_3) + d_3(a_3 b_4 + a_4 b_4 - a_8 b_2 + a_9 b_1 - b_1 b_2) \right.$$

$$+ d_5(- a_3 b_3 - a_4 b_3 + a_5 b_2 - a_6 b_1 + a_7 b_2)$$

$$+ d_9(a_1a_{10} - a_2a_9 + a_3a_6 + a_3a_8 + a_3b_1 + 2a_4a_6 + a_4b_1 - a_5^2 - a_5a_7 - a_7^2)\Big]$$

$$+ a_2\Big[d_1(a_4b_4 - a_7b_3) + d_3(-a_2b_4 + a_7b_2 + b_1^2) + d_5(a_2b_3 - a_4b_2 - a_7b_1)$$

$$+ d_9(-a_2a_6 - a_2b_1 - a_3a_7 + a_4a_5 + 2a_4a_7)\Big]$$

$$+ a_4\Big[b_1(-d_3a_7 + d_5a_4 - d_1b_1) - d_9a_4^2\Big] + d_1a_7b_1$$

$$m_3 = a_1\Big[d_1(-a_5b_5 - a_7b_5 - b_1b_4 + b_2b_3) + d_3(a_3b_5 + a_4b_5 + b_1b_3 - b_2^2)$$

$$+ d_7(-a_3b_3 - a_4b_3 + a_5b_2 - a_6b_1 + a_7b_2)$$

$$+ d_9(a_1b_4 - a_2b_3 + a_3b_2 + a_3a_9 + a_4a_9 - a_5a_8 + a_6a_7 - a_7a_8 - a_7b_1)\Big]$$

$$+ a_2\Big[d_1(a_4b_5 - b_1b_3) + d_3(-a_2b_5 + b_1b_2) + d_7(a_2b_3 - a_4b_2 - a_7b_1)$$

$$+ a_4\Big[a_4(d_7b_1 - d_9a_7) - b_1^2d_3\Big] + a_7b_1^2d_1$$

$$+ d_9(-a_2a_9 - a_3b_1 + a_4a_8 + a_4b_1 + a_7^2)\Big]$$

$$m_4 = a_1\Big[d_1(-a_8b_5 - 2b_1b_5 + b_2b_4) + d_5(a_3b_5 + a_4b_5 + b_1b_3 - b_2^2)$$

$$+ d_7(-a_3b_4 - a_4b_4 + a_8b_2 - a_9b_1 + b_1b_2)$$

$$+ d_9(a_1b_5 + a_3a_{10} + a_4a_{10} - a_4b_3 + a_5b_2 + a_7a_9 - a_8^2 - a_8b_1 - b_1^2)\Big]$$

$$+ a_2\Big[d_1(a_7b_5 - b_1b_4) + d_5(b_1b_2 - a_2b_5) + d_7(a_2b_4 - a_7b_2 - b_1^2)$$

$$+ a_4\Big[d_9(-a_7^2 + a_4b_1) + b_1(d_7a_7 - d_5b_1)\Big] + d_1b_1^3$$

$$+ d_9(-a_2a_{10} - a_5b_1 + a_7a_8 + a_7b_1)\Big]$$

Table E.2–1 (continued)

$$m_5 = a_1\left[d_3(-a_8b_5 - 2b_1b_5 + b_2b_4) + d_5(a_5b_5 + a_7b_5 + b_1b_4 - b_2b_3)\right.$$
$$+ d_7(-a_5b_4 - a_7b_4 + a_8b_3 - a_{10}b_1 + b_1b_3)$$
$$\left.+ d_9(a_2b_5 - a_4b_4 + a_5a_{10} + a_6b_2 + 2a_7a_{10} - a_8a_9 - a_9b_1)\right]$$
$$+ a_2\left[d_3(a_7b_5 - b_1b_4) + d_5(b_1b_3 - a_4b_5) + d_7(a_4b_4 - a_7b_3)\right.$$
$$\left.+ d_9(-a_4a_{10} - a_6b_1 + a_7a_9 - b_1^2)\right] + a_7\left[d_9(2a_4b_1 - a_7^2) + b_1(d_7a_7 - d_5b_1)\right]$$
$$+ b_1^2(d_3b_1 - d_7a_4)$$

$$m_6 = \frac{1}{d_0}(d_2m_5 - d_4m_4 + d_6m_3 - d_8m_2 + d_{10}m_1)$$

$$m_7 = \frac{1}{d_0}(d_2m_6 - d_4m_5 + d_6m_4 - d_8m_3 + d_{10}m_2)$$

$$m_8 = \frac{1}{d_0}(d_2m_7 - d_4m_6 + d_6m_5 - d_8m_4 + d_{10}m_3)$$

$$m_9 = \frac{1}{d_0}(d_2m_8 - d_4m_7 + d_6m_6 - d_8m_5 + d_{10}m_4)$$

$$\Delta_{10} = d_0(d_1m_9 - d_3m_8 + d_5m_7 - d_7m_6 + d_9m_5)$$

where

$a_1 = d_1 d_2 - d_0 d_3$

$a_2 = d_1 d_4 - d_0 d_5$

$a_3 = d_3 d_4 - d_2 d_5$

$a_4 = d_1 d_6 - d_0 d_7$

$a_5 = d_3 d_6 - d_2 d_7$

$a_6 = d_5 d_6 - d_4 d_7$

$a_7 = d_1 d_8 - d_0 d_9$

$a_8 = d_3 d_8 - d_2 d_9$

$a_9 = d_5 d_8 - d_4 d_9$

$a_{10} = d_7 d_8 - d_6 d_9$

$b_1 = d_1 d_{10}$

$b_2 = d_3 d_{10}$

$b_3 = d_5 d_{10}$

$b_4 = d_7 d_{10}$

$b_5 = d_9 d_{10}$

GAIN-PHASE RELATIONS
FOR MINIMUM-PHASE
TRANSFER FUNCTIONS

F.1 GAIN-PHASE RELATIONS

In this article we derive the relations that exist between the gain and the phase for minimum-phase transfer functions. The existence of such relations was asserted in Art. 6.2 in our discussion of the meaning of the phrase "minimum phase." After the basic relationships of phase-to-gain and gain-to-phase are set forth, a second article discusses a procedure for finding an approximation to the phase characteristic that corresponds to a given gain characteristic.

The relationship of the phase to the gain of a minimum-phase transfer function is found from the interdependence of the imaginary and real parts of any complex function of frequency which has no poles in the right half-plane. This follows from the fact that the logarithm of a complex number is equal to the logarithm of the magnitude plus j times the phase angle. Thus the real part of the logarithm of a transfer function is the logarithm of the magnitude or gain, and the imaginary part is the phase angle. This relationship is expressed as

$$\ln G(s) = \ln |G(s)| + j\underline{/G(s)} \qquad \text{(F.1–1)}$$

If a transfer function characterizes a stable, minimum-phase system, and therefore possesses no poles or zeros in the right half-plane, then it follows that the logarithm of the transfer function will have no poles in the right half-plane. As a consequence, the imaginary part of the logarithm of a stable, minimum-phase transfer function will be definitely linked to the real part; that is, the phase of the transfer function will be definitely related to the gain.

Because of the importance of establishing the relationship of the phase to the gain of a minimum-phase network, we now consider in some detail how the imaginary part is found from the real part of a complex function of real frequency. In the time domain there exists a function of time corresponding to any Fourier transform $F(s)$. Let the time function corresponding to $F(s)$ be $f(t)$. In general, this time function can be resolved into an odd part $f_1(t)$ and an even part $f_2(t)$, that is,

$$f(t) = f_1(t) + f_2(t) \tag{F.1--2}$$

In the frequency domain the corresponding relationship is

$$F(s) = F_1(s) + F_2(s) \tag{F.1--3}$$

where

$$F_1(s) = \int_{-\infty}^{\infty} dt\, e^{-st} f_1(t) \tag{F.1--4}$$

and

$$F_2(s) = \int_{-\infty}^{\infty} dt\, e^{-st} f_2(t) \tag{F.1--5}$$

The transform $F_1(s)$ is an odd function of the real frequency ω and is a pure imaginary. This follows from the oddness of $f_1(t)$ and can be seen by replacing the exponential in Eq. F.1--4 by its rectangular components. Similarly $F_2(s)$ is an even function of the real frequency ω and is purely real.

Now let us consider functions $F(s)$ that have no poles in the right half-plane. As discussed in Appendix A, such functions correspond to time functions that are identically zero for negative time. That is,

$$f(t) = 0 \quad \text{for } t < 0 \tag{F.1--6}$$

For this to be so, the odd component of the time function must cancel the even component for negative time. It therefore follows that

$$f_1(t) = -f_2(t) \quad \text{for } t < 0$$

$$= f_2(t) \qquad \text{for } t \geq 0 \tag{F.1--7}$$

We may therefore express the transform of the odd part of the time function in terms of the even part by using the relationship in Eq. F.1–4. The result is

$$F_1(s_1) = - \int_{-\infty}^{0} dt_1\, e^{-s_1 t_1} f_2(t_1) + \int_{0}^{\infty} dt\, e^{-s_1 t} f_2(t) \qquad \text{(F.1–8)}$$

The frequency variable s_1 is used in this equation to avoid confusion with another frequency variable to be used later on. In the first term of the right side let us replace t_1 by $-t$. We then have for the frequency function $F_1(s_1)$

$$F_1(s_1) = \int_{0}^{\infty} dt\, e^{-s_1 t} f_2(t) - \int_{0}^{\infty} dt\, e^{+s_1 t} f_2(t) \qquad \text{(F.1–9)}$$

In this equation we introduce a convergence factor e^{-at} and write

$$F_1(s_1) = \lim_{a \to 0} \left[\int_{0}^{\infty} dt\, e^{-s_1 t} e^{-at} f_2(t) - \int_{0}^{\infty} dt\, e^{+s_1 t} e^{-at} f_2(t) \right] \qquad \text{(F.1–10)}$$

But $f_2(t)$ can be regarded as the inverse transform of $F_2(s)$; i.e.,

$$f_2(t) = \frac{1}{2\pi j} \int_{-j\infty}^{j\infty} ds\, e^{st} F_2(s) \qquad \text{(F.1–11)}$$

Substituting this value of $f_2(t)$ into Eq. F.1–10 yields

$$F_1(s_1) = \lim_{a \to 0} \frac{1}{2\pi j} \left[\int_{-j\infty}^{j\infty} ds\, F_2(s) \int_{0}^{\infty} dt\, e^{(s-s_1-a)t} \right.$$
$$\left. - \int_{-j\infty}^{j\infty} ds\, F_2(s) \int_{0}^{\infty} dt\, e^{(s+s_1-a)t} \right] \qquad \text{(F.1–12)}$$

As a consequence of the convergence factor the integrals with respect to time t converge to the value zero in the upper limit provided both s and s_1 are purely imaginary. Integrating with respect to time in Eq. F.1–12 therefore yields

$$F_1(s_1) = \lim_{a \to 0} \left[-\frac{1}{2\pi j} \right] \left[\int_{-j\infty}^{j\infty} ds\, F_2(s) \left(\frac{1}{s - s_1 - a} \right) \right.$$
$$\left. - \int_{-j\infty}^{j\infty} ds\, F_2(s) \left(\frac{1}{s + s_1 - a} \right) \right] \qquad \text{(F.1–13)}$$

which in the limit for $a = 0$ becomes

$$F_1(s_1) = -\frac{1}{2\pi j} \int_{-j\infty}^{j\infty} ds\, F_2(s) \left(\frac{1}{s - s_1} \right) + \frac{1}{2\pi j} \int_{-j\infty}^{j\infty} ds\, F_2(s) \left(\frac{1}{s + s_1} \right) \qquad \text{(F.1–14)}$$

Since s has been restricted to imaginary values throughout the integration and therefore $F_2(s)$ is an even function, it follows that the second term of Eq. F.1–14 is identically equal to the first term (including the negative sign). This can be seen by making the change of variable $s = -s_2$. Consequently, the second term in Eq. F.1–14 can be replaced by the first term with the result that

$$F_1(s_1) = -\frac{1}{\pi j} \int_{-j\infty}^{j\infty} ds \, \frac{F_2(s)}{s - s_1} \qquad \text{(F.1–15)}$$

But both s_1 and s are pure imaginaries. We therefore let $s_1 = j\nu$ and $s = j\omega$ with the result that

$$\frac{F_1(j\nu)}{j} = \frac{1}{\pi} \int_{-\infty}^{\infty} d\omega \, \frac{F_2(j\omega)}{\omega - \nu} \qquad \text{(F.1–16)}$$

This is a very basic expression for the imaginary part of a complex function of real frequency in terms of the real part.

In passing, it should be noted that a derivation similar to the above can be carried out for the purpose of expressing the real part of a complex function of real frequency as a function of the imaginary part. The result of such a derivation is found to be

$$F_2(j\nu) = -\frac{1}{\pi} \int_{-\infty}^{\infty} d\omega \, \frac{\left[\frac{1}{j} F_1(j\omega)\right]}{\omega - \nu} \qquad \text{(F.1–17)}$$

This expression is identical in form with Eq. F.1–16 except for the negative sign.

The basic relationship between the imaginary and real parts of a complex function of real frequency as expressed in Eq. F.1–16 can be put into many different forms. One common form is obtained by integrating the right member of Eq. F.1–16 by parts. This results in

$$\frac{F_1(j\nu)}{j} = \frac{1}{\pi} \int_0^{\infty} d\omega \, F_2'(j\omega) \ln \left|\frac{\nu + \omega}{\nu - \omega}\right| \qquad \text{(F.1–18)}$$

provided

$$\lim_{\omega \to \infty} \frac{F_2(j\omega)}{\omega} = 0$$

Here $F_2'(j\omega)$ stands for the first derivative of $F_2(j\omega)$ with respect to ω. As discussed by Bode (Reference B.4) this relationship, when expressed in terms of a logarithmic frequency scale, shows that the imaginary part is a weighted function of the slope of the real part. For transfer functions this means that the phase is a weighted function of the slope of the gain-versus-log-frequency characteristic.

Another alternate form for the relation between the imaginary and real parts results from integrating the right member of Eq. F.1–18 by parts. This represents a double integration by parts of the right member of Eq. F.1–16 and is given by

$$\frac{F_1(j\nu)}{j} = \frac{1}{\pi} \int_0^\infty d\omega \left\{ 2\nu - \nu \ln \left| \nu^2 - \omega^2 \right| \right.$$

$$\left. - \omega \ln \left| \frac{\nu + \omega}{\nu - \omega} \right| \right\} F_2''(j\omega) \quad \text{(F.1–19)}$$

provided

$$\lim_{\omega \to \infty} \frac{F_2(j\omega)}{\omega} = 0$$

and

$$\lim_{\omega \to \infty} \omega F_2'(j\omega) < \infty.$$

Here $F_2''(j\omega)$ represents the second derivative of $F_2(j\omega)$ with respect to ω.

The foregoing relationships of imaginary to real parts are seldom integrated analytically to find the relationship between phase and gain. In practice it is customary to use approximations to simplify the necessary integrations. The next article discusses a technique that employs one such approximation.

F.2 APPROXIMATING THE PHASE CORRESPONDING TO A GIVEN GAIN CHARACTERISTIC

The relationship between the imaginary and real parts given by Eq. F.1–19 can be used rather effectively in a procedure for approximating the phase characteristic corresponding to a given gain characteristic. This procedure is based on the idea of approximating the gain-versus-frequency characteristic by straight-line segments so that the second derivative $F_2''(j\omega)$ is a set of impulses. For gain functions which begin at zero frequency and end at infinite frequency with zero slope a particularly effective way of expressing the second derivative is in terms of groups of two impulses. Each group comprises a positive impulse at the origin and a negative impulse at a frequency ω_n. Thus the second derivative of the gain characteristic can be expressed as

$$F_2''(j\omega) \cong \sum_n a_n[\delta(\omega) - \delta(\omega - \omega_n)] \quad \text{(F.2–1)}$$

Since we are going to integrate over positive frequencies, only positive ω_n's need to be considered. We now substitute the approximate expression for the second derivative of the gain given by this equation into Eq. F.1–19. Carrying out the integration yields

$$\frac{F_1(j\nu)}{j} \cong \frac{1}{\pi} \sum_n a_n \left(2\nu - \nu \ln |\nu^2| - 0 - 2\nu + \nu \ln |\nu^2 - \omega_n{}^2| \right.$$

$$\left. + \omega_n \ln \left| \frac{\nu + \omega_n}{\nu - \omega_n} \right| \right) \times (1 \text{ unit of } \omega) \quad \text{(F.2–2)}$$

This result is easily reduced to

$$\frac{F_1(j\nu)}{j} \cong \frac{1}{\pi} \sum_n a_n \omega_n \phi \left(\frac{\nu}{\omega_n} \right) \quad \text{(F.2–3)}$$

where

$$\phi \left(\frac{\nu}{\omega_n} \right) \triangleq \left(\frac{\nu}{\omega_n} + 1 \right) \ln \left| \frac{\nu}{\omega_n} + 1 \right| + \left(\frac{\nu}{\omega_n} - 1 \right) \ln \left| \frac{\nu}{\omega_n} - 1 \right|$$

$$- 2 \left(\frac{\nu}{\omega_n} \right) \ln \left| \frac{\nu}{\omega_n} \right| \quad \text{(F.2–4)}$$

Figure F.2–1 is a plot of the ϕ function for positive ν. Only positive ν values need to be considered since ϕ is an odd function of ν. By

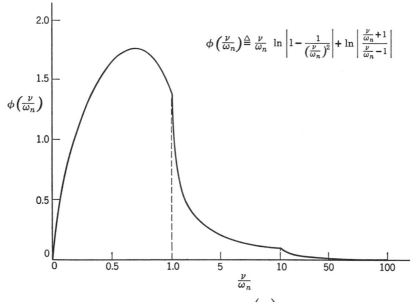

$$\phi \left(\frac{\nu}{\omega_n} \right) \triangleq \frac{\nu}{\omega_n} \ln \left| 1 - \frac{1}{(\frac{\nu}{\omega_n})^2} \right| + \ln \left| \frac{\frac{\nu}{\omega_n} + 1}{\frac{\nu}{\omega_n} - 1} \right|$$

Fig. F.2–1. Plot of $\phi \left(\dfrac{\nu}{\omega_n} \right)$.

means of this function an approximation to the phase at a specified frequency is readily found from Eq. F.2–3 as a sum of numbers. These numbers are determined by a broken-line approximation to the gain-versus-frequency characteristic.

We now illustrate the degree of approximation involved in Eq. F.2–3 for the specific example of a lead network that has the transfer function

$$G(s) = \frac{10s + 1}{s + 1} \tag{F.2–5}$$

The exact gain and phase characteristics for this transfer function are shown in Fig. F.2–2 as the solid-line curves. On the basis of the

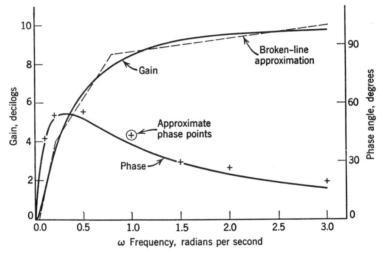

Fig. F.2-2.   Approximate and true phase for $\dfrac{10s + 1}{s + 1}$.

dashed broken-line approximation to the gain characteristic, the approximate phase points indicated by the crosses were computed. The degree of agreement could be improved by using a larger number of line segments in approximating the gain characteristic. Only four corners were used in Eq. F.2–3 in order to compute the phase points shown in Fig. F.2–2. In general, there is one term in Eq. F.2–3 for each corner in the broken-line approximation.

In Eq. F.2–3 it must be carefully noted that the broken-line approximation used to obtain the a_n and ω_n must be an approximation to the gain-versus-*arithmetic*-frequency characteristic. So far we have not obtained an expression similar to Eq. F.2–3 in closed form when the

gain is plotted against the logarithm of the frequency. It should also be noted that the procedure of Eq. F.2–3 cannot be employed when the gain characteristic has slopes different from zero at zero and at high frequency. This restriction usually is no great handicap, however. The phase characteristic of a factor in a transfer function whose gain characteristic does not have the property of zero initial and final slopes usually can be computed easily as a separate operation. Adding this phase characteristic to that of the other factors as computed by Eq. F.2–3 gives the over-all phase characteristic.

In closing this appendix we wish to point out that a practical application of the foregoing procedure for computing the phase corresponding to a given gain is in the determination of whether an experimentally determined transfer function is minimum phase. The fixed elements for many control systems can be described only in terms of experimental data. From Chapter 6 we know that important limitations on performance may exist if the fixed elements are non-minimum phase. By comparing the actual measured phase with the phase computed on the basis of assumed minimum-phase behavior for the fixed elements it is easy to determine if these elements are non-minimum phase to any substantial degree.

PROBLEMS

2.1 The system shown in the following figure is subjected to a step input

$$v(t) = N_i \delta_{-1}(t)$$

The ideal output $i(t)$ is equal to the input.

(a) Find the integral-square error

$$I_e = \int_{-\infty}^{\infty} dt \, y_e^2(t)$$

in terms of N_i, K_a, and T. Determine the value of K_a that minimizes I_e and the minimum value of I_e.

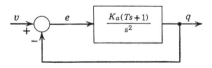

Prob. 2–1.

(b) The system is now subject to a constraint on the integral-square output velocity

$$I_v = \int_{-\infty}^{\infty} dt \, [\dot{q}(t)]^2$$

If T is held fixed and K_a is allowed to vary, what is the lowest value that can be specified for I_v?

2.2 For the feedback control system shown in Fig. Prob. 2.2

$$v(t) = N_i \delta_{-1}(t)$$

$$u(t) = 0$$

and the ideal output $i(t)$ is equal to the input $v(t)$.

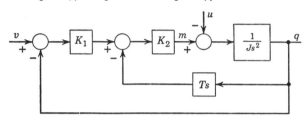

Prob. 2–2.

(a) If T and J are held fixed, determine K_1 and K_2 such that the integral-square error

$$I_e = \int_{-\infty}^{\infty} dt\, y_e{}^2(t)$$

is minimized subject to the constraint that the integral-square value I_m of $m(t)$

$$I_m = \int_{-\infty}^{\infty} dt\, m^2(t)$$

shall not exceed M, a specified constant. What is the minimum value of I_e?

(b) If $v(t) = 0$ and the parameters are set as in (a), what is the maximum size of an impulse of the disturbance $u(t)$ that can be applied to the system such that

$$I_m \leq M$$

2.3 A position-control system uses a split-field d-c motor to drive its load. The motor armature current is supplied by a well-regulated constant-current

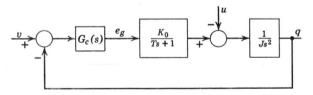

Prob. 2–3.

supply, and the split control field is driven by a push-pull power amplifier. A block diagram of the control system is shown in the figure. The given data are

$$K_0 = 0.03 \text{ newton meter per volt}$$

$$T = 0.01 \text{ second}$$

$$J = 10^{-3} \text{ kilogram meter}^2$$

(a) If the compensation is

$$G_c(s) = K_c(T_c s + 1)$$

find by conventional methods K_c and T_c such that K_c is a maximum for $10 \log_{10} M_p = 1.5$ dg.

(b) The input to the system is a ramp

$$v(t) = \Omega_i \delta_{-2}(t)$$

and the desired output is equal to the input. Find the values of K_c and T_c that minimize the integral-square error

$$I_e = \int_{-\infty}^{\infty} dt\, y_e^2(t)$$

What is the minimum value of I_e?

(c) The system is now constrained such that

$$\int_{-\infty}^{\infty} dt\, e_g^2(t) \leq 20 \text{ volt}^2 \text{ second}$$

when $\Omega_i = 20$ radian per second. Find the values of K_c and T_c that minimize the integral-square error I_e subject to the above constraint and the conditions stated in (b). What is the minimum value of I_e?

2.4 The control system discussed in Appendix D can be placed in the standard form of Fig. 2.1–2, p. 42. For this problem the given data are

$$G_f(s) = \frac{1}{s(0.01s + 1)(0.04s + 1)}$$

$$H_f(s) = 1$$

$$v(t) = N_i \delta_{-1}(t)$$

$$i(t) = v(t)$$

(a) If

$$G_c(s) = K_v$$

find the value of K_v that minimizes the integral-square error

$$I_e = \int_{-\infty}^{\infty} dt\, y_e^2(t)$$

What is the minimum value of I_e?

(b) Now the compensation is changed to

$$G_c(s) = K_v \frac{10 T_c s + 1}{T_c s + 1}$$

Find the values of K_v and T_c that minimize I_e, and find the minimum value of I_e.

2.5 An amplidyne and d-c motor combination is used to drive a pure inertia load in a position-control system. The block diagram of the system is shown in the figure. In this figure

$v =$ input position, radian
$q =$ output position, radian

e_i = input voltage to the power amplifier which drives the control field of the amplidyne, volt

e_a = induced armature voltage of the amplidyne, volt

e_b = back emf of the d-c motor, volt

m = d-c motor air-gap torque, foot pound

u = load torque, foot-pound

θ_m = d-c motor shaft position, radian

$G_c(s)$ = compensation network and amplification

K_0 = 2.0 volts per volt

K_m = 0.921 foot-pound per ampere (motor torque constant)

K_e = 1.25 volt-seconds per radian (motor back emf constant)

T_q = 0.11 second (amplidyne quadrature-axis time constant)

T_a = 0.08 second (total armature-circuit time constant)

R_a = 5 ohms (total armature-circuit resistance)

J_m = 0.023 foot-pound second^2 per radian (motor inertia)

J_2 = 46.6 foot-pound seconds^2 per radian (load inertia)

r = 45 (gear ratio)

The input to the control system is a step function

$$v(t) = N_i \delta_{-1}(t)$$

and the ideal output is equal to the input.

(a) If

$$G_c(s) = K_c$$

find the value of K_c that minimizes the integral-square error

$$I_e = \int_{-\infty}^{\infty} dt \, y_e^2(t)$$

What is the minimum value of I_e?

(b) The compensation is changed to

$$G_c(s) = K_c(T_c s + 1)$$

Find the values of K_c and T_c that minimize I_e, and find the minimum value of I_e.

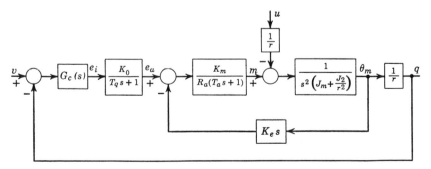

Prob. 2–5.

(c) The system is now constrained so that the integral-square value I_v of the output velocity $\dot{q}(t)$ is held below a specified upper limit L, i.e.,

$$\int_{-\infty}^{\infty} dt \, [\dot{q}(t)]^2 \leq L$$

The integral-square error I_e is to be minimized subject to the above constraint. Finding the trading curve for the problem under these conditions. The trading curve will be a plot of the minimum value of the integral-square error versus the upper limit placed on the integral-square value of the output velocity. The curve can be normalized with respect to the magnitude of the step input if all integral-square quantities are divided by N_i^2.

2.6 A control system has the standard form shown in Fig. 2.1–2, p. 42. The given data are

$$G_f(s) = \cfrac{1}{s(Ts+1)\left[\left(\dfrac{s}{\omega_n}\right)^2 + 2\zeta\dfrac{s}{\omega_n} + 1\right]}$$

$$H_f(s) = 1$$

$$v(t) = N_i \delta_{-1}(t)$$

$$i(t) = v(t)$$

$$T \ll \frac{1}{\omega_n} \text{ and may be taken to be zero}$$

$$\omega_n = 50 \text{ radians per second}$$

$$\zeta = 0.5$$

(a) If

$$G_c(s) = K_v$$

find the value of K_v that minimizes the integral-square error

$$I_e = \int_{-\infty}^{\infty} dt \, y_e^2(t)$$

What is the minimum value of I_e?

(b) The compensation is changed to

$$G_c(s) = K_v \frac{10T_c s + 1}{T_c s + 1}$$

Find the values of K_v and T_c that minimize I_e, and find the minimum value of I_e.

(c) The compensation is changed to

$$G_c(s) = K_v(T_c s + 1)$$

and the integral-square error I_e is to be minimized subject to the constraint that the integral-square value I_a of the output acceleration $\ddot{q}(t)$ shall be held below a specified upper limit A, i.e.,

$$\int_{-\infty}^{\infty} dt \, [\ddot{q}(t)]^2 \leq A$$

Plot the trading curve for the problem, normalizing with respect to the amplitude of the input step by dividing all integral-square quantities by N_i^2. The trading curve is thus a plot of the minimum value of the normalized integral-square error $[I_e/N_i{}^2]_{min}$ versus the normalized upper limit $A/N_i{}^2$ placed on the normalized integral-square value $I_a/N_i{}^2$ of the output acceleration $\ddot{q}(t)$.

3.1 A stochastic variable consists of rectangular pulses of duration T and amplitude A which occur at event points uniformly spaced in time with a

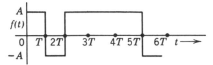

Prob. 3–1.

period T. The probability of a positive pulse is two-thirds and a negative pulse one-third at any event point. Determine the autocorrelation function for this variable. The figure shows a sample of $f(t)$.

3.2 A stationary stochastic process consists of a sequence of constant-amplitude segments. The amplitude suddenly changes at event points that are Poisson distributed in time with an average frequency ν. The amplitudes

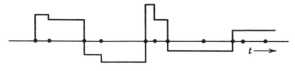

Prob. 3–2.

have a normal distribution with zero mean and standard deviation σ. The amplitude after an event point is independent of the amplitude preceding the event point. A sketch of the process is shown in the accompanying figure. Find the autocorrelation function $\varphi(\tau)$ of the process.

3.3 A stochastic process consists of a sequence of randomly distributed event points. At each event point, an impulse of $\pm A$ volt-sec occurs. The sign of the impulse is purely random and equally likely to be positive as negative. The events are independent. Prove, by starting with a finite pulse, that the autocorrelation function of the process is an impulse at $\tau = 0$.

3.4 A certain pulse-duration modulation system generates a train of rectangular pulses all having the amplitude $+E$ volts. Any particular pulse

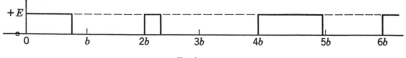

Prob. 3–4.

can have a time duration x such that $0 < x < b$, where b is the maximum possible pulse duration time. The probability distribution function of pulse-duration times is flat, i.e., it is just as likely for a pulse to have a particular duration as it is for it to have any other duration. Pulses are initiated every $2b$ seconds. The duration of a pulse is independent of the duration of any other pulse. A sketch of the process is shown in Fig. Prob. 3.4. Find the autocorrelation function of the process.

3.5 A stochastic process generates a train of oblong pulses as shown in the figure for Prob. 3.5. Each pulse has a width of 1.0 millisecond, and the pulse

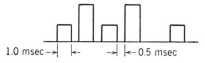

1.0 msec →| |←-   →| |←- 0.5 msec

Prob. 3-5.

separation is 0.5 millisecond. A given pulse can have amplitudes of 0, 1, and 2 volts with the probabilities one-third, one-sixth, and one-half, respectively. The amplitude of any one pulse is independent of the amplitude of any other pulse. Plot the autocorrelation function of the process.

3.6 A stochastic process is generated as follows:

1. A ball is drawn from an urn, containing three white balls and three black balls, once a second, starting at time $t = 0$.
2. If the ball is white, it is returned to the urn. If the ball is black, it is not returned to the urn.
3. A concurrent signal is $+1$ volt if a white ball is drawn and -1 volt if a black ball is drawn.
Show that the above process is non-stationary by determining the probability of drawing a white ball from the urn at $t = 0, 1, 2,$ and 3 seconds.

3.7 A stationary time series consists of a train of impulses of current with random sign ($+$ or $-$ equally likely). Each impulse carries a charge of $\pm 10^{-12}$ coulomb. The impulses are Poisson distributed in time and occur at

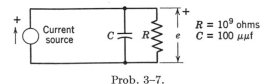

Prob. 3-7.

an average rate of 1,000 per second. The current impulses are filtered by an RC network as shown in Fig. Prob. 3.7. Find the average value of $e(t)$, the autocorrelation function of $e(t)$, and the standard deviation of the first amplitude probability distribution function of $e(t)$.

3.8 A stochastic signal $v(t)$ is formed of positive and negative rectangular pulses of amplitude β and length L. The pulses start at event points which

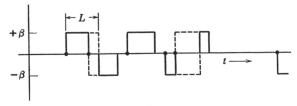

Prob. 3-8.

are Poisson distributed with average frequency ν. They are alternately positive and negative. A sample of this signal is shown in Fig. Prob. 3.8. Find the average value of $v(t)$, the mean-square value of $v(t)$, and the auto-correlation function $\varphi_{vv}(\tau)$.

4.1 The autocorrelation function of

$$\dot{v} = \frac{dv}{dt}$$

is

$$\varphi_{\dot{v}\dot{v}}(\tau) = Ae^{-b|\tau|}\cos \omega\tau$$

Find the power spectrum of v, $\Phi_{vv}(s)$.

4.2 Determine whether

$$\varphi_{vv}(\tau) = \frac{1}{a^4 + \tau^4}$$

is the autocorrelation function of a stationary stochastic process.

4.3 In Fig. Prob. 4.3, the functions $v_1(t)$ and $q(t)$ are stationary stochastic

$$\xrightarrow{v_1}\boxed{G_1(s)}\xrightarrow{v_2}\boxed{G_2(s)}\xrightarrow{v_3}\boxed{G_3(s)}\xrightarrow{q}$$

Prob. 4–3.

processes. Derive an expression for the cross-power spectrum, $\Phi_{v_2v_3}(s)$ in terms of the system functions and the cross-power spectrum $\Phi_{v_1q}(s)$.

4.4 Measurements are taken on the system shown in Fig. Prob. 4.4. $\varphi_{vv}(\tau)$ and $\varphi_{vq}(\tau)$ are determined. It is known that $v(t)$ is a stationary

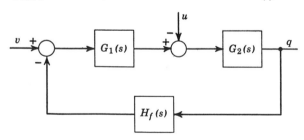

Prob. 4–4.

stochastic input and that $u(t)$ is a stationary stochastic disturbance that is uncorrelated with $v(t)$. Can the system function $W(s) = q(s)/v(s)$ in the absence of the disturbance be determined from the given data? Prove your answer.

4.5 Using the terminology given in the diagram for Fig. Prob. 4.5

$$G_f(s) = \frac{1}{s} \qquad v(t) = v_d(t) + v_n(t) \qquad \Phi_{dd}(s) = \frac{\gamma_d}{-\pi s^2} \qquad \gamma_d = 10 \text{ in.}^2 \text{ sec}^{-1}$$

$$H_f(s) = 1 \qquad i(t) = v_d(t) \qquad \Phi_{nn}(s) = \frac{\gamma_n}{\pi} \qquad \gamma_n = 2.5 \text{ in.}^2 \text{ sec}$$

$$G_c(s) = K_v \qquad\qquad\qquad \Phi_{dn}(s) = 0$$

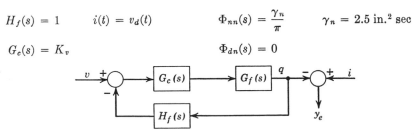

Prob. 4–5.

Find the value of K_v for the minimum rms error and the value of the rms error when K_v is set for this minimum.

4.6 For the system shown in Fig. Prob. 4.6 the following data are given:

$$\Phi_{dd}(s) = \frac{B^2}{\pi s^4} \qquad\qquad i(t) = v_d(t)$$

$$\Phi_{nn}(s) = \frac{A^2}{\pi} \qquad\qquad v(t) = v_d(t) + v_n(t)$$

$$\Phi_{dn}(s) = 0 \qquad\qquad A^2 = 1 \text{ volt}^2 \text{ sec}$$

$$B^2 = 64 \text{ volt}^2 \text{ sec}^{-3}$$

(a) Find K_a and τ to minimize the mean-square error $\overline{y_e{}^2}$ to the given stochastic input. What is the value of the minimum mean-square error?

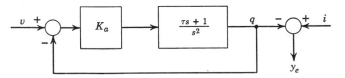

Prob. 4–6.

(b) Find K_a and τ to minimize the mean-square error to the stochastic input subject to the constraint that the value of the integral-square error I_y to a unit step input be equal to or less than the value I_{ym}. Let I_{ym} have the value 0.05 volt² sec; repeat for $I_{ym} = 0.20$ volt² sec. The stochastic and transient signals are applied, and the errors evaluated, independently of each other.

4.7 For a system of the form as shown in Fig. Prob. 4.7, the following data are given:

$$G_f(s) = \frac{(\tau s + 1)}{s \left[\left(\dfrac{s}{\omega_n} \right)^2 + 2\zeta \left(\dfrac{s}{\omega_n} \right) + 1 \right]} \qquad \Phi_{\dot{d}\dot{d}}(s) = \frac{\sigma_d{}^2 \beta}{\pi(\beta^2 - s^2)}$$

$$G_c(s) = K_v \qquad\qquad\qquad\qquad \Phi_{nn}(s) = \frac{\gamma_n}{\pi}$$

$$H_f(s) = 1 \qquad\qquad\qquad \Phi_{dn}(s) = 0$$

$$v(t) = v_d(t) + v_n(t) \qquad\qquad i(t) = v_d(t)$$

where $\omega_n = 50$ rad sec^{-1} $\qquad\qquad \beta = 0.5$ sec^{-1}

$\qquad \zeta = 0.5$ $\qquad\qquad\qquad\qquad \sigma_d = 3$ rad sec^{-1}

$\qquad \tau = 0.005$ sec $\qquad\qquad\qquad \gamma_n = 0.1$ rad^2 sec

Find the value of K_v that minimizes the mean-square error $\overline{y_e{}^2}$ and the minimum value of $\overline{y_e{}^2}$. Assume now that $G_c(s) = K_v(\tau_c s + 1)$, and calculate

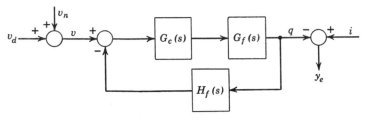

Prob. 4–7.

the values of τ_c and K_v that minimize the mean-square error $\overline{y_e{}^2}$. Find also this new value of $\overline{y_e{}^2}$. Has this different form of compensation resulted in a lower value of mean-square error?

4.8 A system has the configuration shown in Fig. Prob. 4.8. The transfer functions and signals are described by

$$\Phi_{dd}(s) = -\frac{\sigma}{\pi s^2} \qquad\qquad G_c(s) = K_c \qquad\qquad \sigma = 100 \text{ sec}^{-1}$$

$$\qquad\qquad\qquad\qquad\qquad\qquad\qquad\qquad\qquad \alpha = 4 \text{ sec}$$

$$\Phi_{nn}(s) = \frac{\alpha}{\pi} \qquad\qquad G_f(s) = \frac{K_m}{s^2} \qquad\qquad \beta = 0.01 \text{ sec}$$

$$\Phi_{uu}(s) = \frac{\beta}{\pi} \qquad\qquad H_c(s) = K_t s \qquad\qquad K_m = 10 \text{ volt}^{-1} \text{ sec}^{-2}$$

There is no correlation among v_d, v_n, and u. The ideal output $i(t) = v_d(t)$.

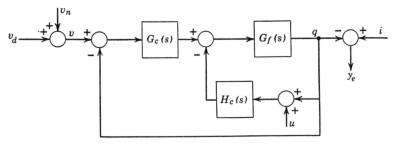

Prob. 4–8.

Find K_c and K_t to minimize the mean-square error $\overline{y_e{}^2}$ and the minimum value of the mean-square error.

4.9   A feedback system of standard form is characterized by the data

$$G_c(s) = K(\tau_c s + 1)$$

$$G_f(s) = \frac{20}{s^2(0.01s + 1)}$$

$$H_f(s) = 1$$

The input $v(t)$ is a stochastic signal consisting of a series of normally distributed velocities with changes in velocity occurring at Poisson-distributed event points.   The power-density spectrum of dv/dt is given by

$$\Phi_{\dot{v}\dot{v}}(s) = \frac{\sigma^2 \nu}{\pi(\nu^2 - s^2)} \qquad \sigma = 20 \text{ rad sec}^{-1}$$

$$\nu = 10 \text{ sec}^{-1}$$

(a) Find K and τ_c to minimize the mean-square error $\overline{y_e{}^2}$ where the ideal output is $i(t) = v(t)$.

(b) If the mean-square value of the input to the fixed elements $m(t)$ is to be limited to 20 volt², find the values of K and τ_c that minimize the mean-square error.   What is the value of the minimum mean-square error?

(c) Noise is present at the input.   The power-density spectrum of the noise is given by

$$\Phi_{nn}(s) = \frac{\gamma}{\pi} \qquad \text{where } \gamma = 5 \text{ rad}^2\text{-sec}$$

With no constraint on $m(t)$, find K and τ_c to minimize the mean-square error. What is the minimum value of the mean-square error?

4.10   The system function $W(s)$ shown in Fig. Prob. 4.10a represents a feedback control system for measuring the first derivative $\dfrac{dv_d(t)}{dt}$ of the input data $v_d(t)$ in the presence of noise $v_n(t)$.   Thus $G_i(s)$ is simply s.   The input signals to the system have the following power-density spectra

$$\Phi_{\dot{d}\dot{d}}(s) = \frac{\sigma_\Omega^2 \nu}{\pi(\nu^2 - s^2)}$$

$$\Phi_{nn}(s) = \frac{\eta}{\pi}$$

$$\Phi_{dn}(s) = 0$$

where
$$\sigma_\Omega = 300 \text{ ft sec}^{-1}$$

$$\nu = 0.0625 \text{ sec}^{-1}$$

$$\eta = 9 \text{ ft}^2 \text{ sec}$$

Consider that the system function $W(s)$ is realized as in Fig. Prob. 4.10b.

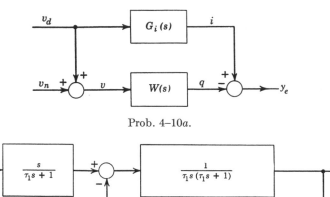

Prob. 4–10a.

Prob. 4–10b.

(a) For this fixed configuration, determine the value of τ_1 that minimizes the mean-square error $\overline{y_e{}^2}$.

(b) What is the value of the minimum mean-square error?

(c) Determine the fraction of this total mean-square error caused by the data. By the noise. State units where appropriate.

4.11 The input to the system shown in Fig. Prob. 4.11 consists of a ramp plus noise where

$$\Phi_{nn}(s) = \frac{A^2}{\pi} \qquad\qquad v_d(t) = \begin{cases} Nt & \text{for } t \geq 0 \\ 0 & \text{for } t < 0 \end{cases}$$

$$i(t) = v_d(t) \text{ (signal only)} \qquad i(t) = 0 \text{ for noise acting alone}$$

(a) Find K and τ in terms of A, N, and I_{em} to minimize the integral-square error to the ramp input $v_d(t)$ subject to the constraint that the mean-square error at the output (when the noise is acting alone) be equal to or less than I_{em}. This system is a typical damper-stabilized position servo operating off radar range as its input.

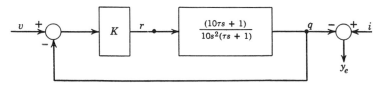

Prob. 4–11.

(b) Plot the integral-square error from (a) as a function of I_{em}. This is the "trading curve" for the constraint.

(c) With $\Phi_{dd}(s) = \dfrac{-1}{\pi s^2}$ $\Phi_{nn}(s) = \dfrac{10}{\pi(-s^2 + 10,000)}$

$$v(t) = v_d(t) + v_n(t) \qquad i(t) = v_d(t)$$

find K and τ to minimize $\overline{y_e^2(t)}$ subject to the constraint $\overline{r^2(t)} \leq 100$.

5.1   For the system shown in Fig. Prob. 5.1, derive the integral equation

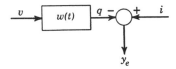

Prob. 5–1.

whose solution gives the optimum system weighting function $w(t)$ that minimizes the integral

$$J = \int_{-\infty}^{\infty} dt\; a(t) y_e^2(t)$$

where $a(t)$ is an arbitrary specified function of time and $v(t)$ and $i(t)$ are transient signals.

5.2   A control system has the standard form shown in Fig. 1.4–3, p. 19. The given data are

$$G_f(s) = \frac{1}{s} \qquad\qquad \Phi_{dn}(s) = 0$$

$$H_f(s) = 1 \qquad\qquad i(t) = v_d(t);\; u(t) = 0$$

$$\Phi_{dd}(s) = \frac{A}{-\pi s^2} \qquad\qquad A = 10 \text{ in.}^2 \text{ per sec}$$

$$\Phi_{nn}(s) = \frac{B}{\pi} \qquad\qquad B = 2.5 \text{ in.}^2 \text{ sec}$$

Find the compensation $G_c(s)$ that minimizes the mean-square error $\overline{y_e^2(t)}$, and find the minimum value of the mean-square error.

5.3   A control system has the standard form shown in Fig. 1.4–3, p. 19. The given data are

$$G_f(s) = \frac{30}{s^2(0.01s + 1)}$$

$$H_f(s) = 1$$

$$i(t) = v_d(t);\; u(t) = 0$$

The power spectrum of the derivative of the data signal $v_d(t)$ is

$$\Phi_{\dot{d}\dot{d}}(s) = \frac{\sigma^2 \nu}{\pi(\nu^2 - s^2)}$$

The power spectrum of the noise component $v_n(t)$ of the input is

$$\Phi_{nn}(s) = \frac{\gamma}{\pi}$$

The data and noise are uncorrelated.

$$\sigma = 20 \text{ rad per sec}$$
$$\nu = 0.1 \text{ sec}^{-1}$$
$$\gamma = 0.5 \text{ rad}^2 \text{ sec}$$

Find the compensation $G_c(s)$ that minimizes the mean-square error $\overline{y_e{}^2(t)}$, and find the minimum value of $\overline{y_e{}^2(t)}$.

5.4 A control system has the standard form shown in Fig. 1.4–3, p. 19. The given data are

$$G_f(s) = 1 \qquad\qquad\qquad i(t) = \frac{d}{dt}[v_d(t)]$$

$$H_f(s) = 1 \qquad\qquad\qquad u(t) = 0$$

$$\Phi_{dd}(s) = \frac{\sigma^2 \nu}{\pi(\nu^2 - s^2)(-s^2)} \qquad\qquad \gamma = 1.00 \text{ mil}^2 \text{ sec}$$

$$\Phi_{nn}(s) = \frac{\gamma}{\pi} \qquad\qquad\qquad \sigma = 50.6 \text{ mil sec}^{-1}$$

$$.\,\Phi_{dn}(s) = 0 \qquad\qquad\qquad \nu = 0.1 \text{ sec}^{-1}$$

Find the compensation $W_m(s)$ that minimizes the mean-square error $\overline{y_e{}^2(t)}$. What is the minimum value of $\overline{y_e{}^2(t)}$?

6.1 A feedback control system of the standard configuration (Fig. 1.7–1), p. 34, has fixed elements G_f whose impulse response is shown in the graph for Fig. Prob. 6.1.

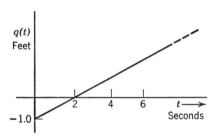

Prob. 6–1.

The input $v(t)$ to the system is a ramp $\Omega t \delta_{-1}(t)$. The desired output $i(t)$ is the derivative of the input, i.e., it is $\Omega \delta_{-1}(t)$. Find the functions $g_c(t)$ and $h_f(t)$ or transforms thereof that make the integral-square error between the actual output and the desired output a minimum. What is this minimum value of integral-square error for $\Omega = 5 \text{ ft sec}^{-1}$? Draw a schematic diagram of the physical equipment that you would use to realize this compensation.

6.2 A control system of standard form (Fig. 1.4–3) is described by

$$G_f(s) = \frac{-(T/2)s + 1}{(T/2)s + 1}, \qquad H_f(s) = 1, \qquad \Phi_{nn}(s) = \frac{\gamma}{\pi}$$

$$\Phi_{dd}(s) = \frac{\sigma^2 \nu}{\pi(\nu^2 - s^2)}, \qquad \Phi_{dn}(s) = 0, \qquad i(t) = v_d(t)$$

Determine $G_{cm}(s)$. Plot the rms error when using this compensation as a function of T for $0 < T < 3$ sec when $\sigma = 10$ rad, $\nu = 0.1$ sec^{-1}, $\gamma = 1$ rad^2 sec.

7.1 A control system has the general form shown in Fig. 2.1–2, p. 42. The system is subjected to a stochastic input and an occasional transient input. The transient and stochastic inputs do not occur simultaneously. It is desired to minimize the mean-square stochastic error between the ideal stochastic output and the actual stochastic output subject to the condition that the integral-square transient error between the ideal transient output and the actual transient output is limited to a specified upper limit M. Derive the integral equation whose solution gives the optimum system weighting function $w(t)$ that satisfies the foregoing conditions.

7.2 A control system has the standard form shown in Fig. 2.1–2, p. 42. The given data are

$$G_f(s) = \frac{K_f}{s^2} \qquad\qquad i(t) = v(t)$$

$$H_f(s) = 1 \qquad\qquad K_f = 100 \text{ in. per volt sec}^2$$

$$v(t) = \Omega_i \delta_{-2}(t) \qquad\qquad \Omega_i = 5 \text{ in. per sec}$$

Find the compensation $G_c(s)$ that minimizes the integral-square value I_f of the input $m(t)$ to the fixed elements

$$I_f = \int_{-\infty}^{\infty} dt \, m^2(t)$$

subject to the constraint that the integral-square error

$$I_e = \int_{-\infty}^{\infty} dt \, y_e^2(t)$$

shall not exceed a specified upper limit M where $M = 0.025$ in.^{2} sec.

7.3 A control system has the configuration shown in Fig. 1.4–3, p. 19. The given data are

$$G_f(s) = 1 \qquad\qquad v_n(t) = 0; \; u(t) = 0$$

$$H_f(s) = 1 \qquad\qquad i(t) = v_d(t)$$

$$\Phi_{dd}(s) = -\frac{\sigma^2}{\pi s^2}$$

(a) Find the compensation $G_c(s)$ that minimizes the mean-square error $\overline{y_e^2(t)}$ subject to the constraint that for a step input

$$v(t) = N_i \delta_{-1}(t)$$

the integral-square output velocity

$$I_v = \int_{-\infty}^{\infty} dt\, [\dot{q}(t)]^2$$

does not exceed a specified upper limit M, i.e.,

$$I_v \leq M$$

Note that the step input and the stochastic input do not occur simultaneously.

(b) Find the expression for the trading curve of the problem

$$\overline{[y_e^2(t)]}_{\min} \text{ versus } M$$

7.4 A control system has the configuration shown in Fig. 1.4–3, p. 19. The given data are

$$G_f(s) = 1 \qquad\qquad \Phi_{nn}(s) = \frac{\gamma}{\pi}$$

$$H_f(s) = 1 \qquad\qquad i(t) = v_d(t)$$

$$\Phi_{dd}(s) = -\frac{\sigma^2}{\pi s^2}$$

(a) Find the compensation $G_c(s)$ that minimizes the mean-square error $\overline{y_e^2(t)}$ subject to the constraint that the mean-square output velocity $\overline{[\dot{q}^2(t)]}$ is held below a specified upper limit L.

(b) Find the expression for the trading curve of the problem

$$\overline{[y_e^2(t)]}_{\min} \text{ versus } \overline{[\dot{q}^2(t)]}_{\max}$$

7.5 The control system shown in Fig. Prob. 7.5 is to integrate its input $v(t)$. The given data are

$$G_f(s) = \frac{1}{s + \omega_0} \qquad\qquad \omega_0 = 10 \text{ rad per sec}$$

$$\Phi_{vv}(s) = \frac{\sigma^2 \nu}{\pi(\nu^2 - s^2)} \qquad\qquad \sigma = 2 \text{ volt per sec}$$

$$i(t) = \int_{-\infty}^{t} dx\, v(x) \qquad\qquad \nu = 0.5 \text{ sec}^{-1}$$

Find the compensation $G_c(s)$ that minimizes the mean-square error $\overline{y_e^2(t)}$ subject to the constraint that the mean-square value of the rate of change dq/dt of

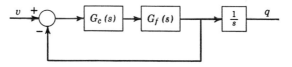

Prob. 7–5.

the output $q(t)$ is held below a specified upper limit $M = 2.5$ volt^2 per sec^2. Also find the minimum value of $\overline{y_e^2(t)}$.

7.6 A feedback control system has the configuration shown in Fig. 1.4–3, p. 19. The feedback elements are fixed, and the fixed elements have a unity transfer function $G_f(s) = 1$. The mean-square error $\overline{y_e{}^2(t)}$ for a stochastic input and a corresponding ideal output is to be minimized by adjustment of the compensation $G_c(s)$. In adjusting $G_c(s)$ the integral-square value I_e of the actuating signal $e(t)$, i.e.,

$$I_e = \int_{-\infty}^{\infty} dt\, e^2(t)$$

for a transient input is to be held below a specified upper limit M. The transient input is applied independently of the stochastic input.

(a) Assuming transformable correlation, translation, and system functions, derive an expression for $G_c(s)$ in terms of the necessary power spectra and other transforms.

(b) In a specific case the given data are for the stochastic signal input

$$i(t) = v(t)$$

$$\Phi_{vv}(s) = -\frac{A}{\pi s^2}$$

$$A = 8 \text{ in.}^2 \text{ per sec}$$

For the transient input signal

$$v(t) = N_i \delta_{-1}(t)$$

$$N_i = 2 \text{ in.}$$

The feedback-element transfer function is

$$H_f(s) = T_f s + 1$$

$$T_f = 0.5 \text{ sec}$$

Find $G_c(s)$ for minimum $\overline{y_e{}^2(t)}$ when $M = 0.5$ in.^{2} sec. What is the minimum value of $\overline{y_e{}^2(t)}$?

7.7 A Ward-Leonard drive is used as the output member of a position-control system. The load is pure inertia and is driven by a shunt d-c motor whose armature is driven by an identical d-c generator. The field current for the d-c generator is supplied by a push-pull power amplifier. The schematic diagram for the output member is shown in Fig. Prob. 7.7a.

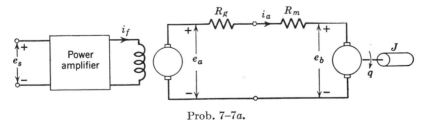

Prob. 7–7a.

The constants of the system are:

Power amplifier gain = 0.6 milliampere per volt

Generator open-circuit voltage per unit field currenᵥ = 1.0 volt per ma

Motor torque constant = 100 in.-ounce per ampere

Motor armature resistance = generator armature resistance = 2.0 ohms

Total inertia = 800 ounce-in.²

The control system is shown in Fig. Prob. 7.7b.   In this figure

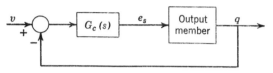

Prob. 7-7b.

v = input position e_s = power amplifier input voltage

q = output position $G_c(s)$ = compensation network

The power spectrum of the input velocity $\dot{v}(t)$ is given as

$$\Phi_{\dot{v}\dot{v}}(s) = \frac{\sigma^2 \nu}{\pi(\nu^2 - s^2)}$$

where σ = 50 rad per sec
     ν = 0.2 sec^{-1}

The ideal output is equal to the input.

Find the compensation $G_c(s)$ that minimizes the mean-square error $\overline{y_e{}^2(t)}$ with the constraint that the rms value of the armature current i_a is to be held below 5 amperes.   What is the minimum value of $\overline{y_e{}^2(t)}$?

8.1   A system of free form is subjected to a step input.   The desired output is the input delayed by T sec.   The mathematical statement of the problem is

$$v(t) = N\delta_{-1}(t) \qquad\qquad W_b(s) = \frac{1}{1 + (s/\omega_b)}$$

$$i(t) = v(t - T) \qquad\qquad \Phi_{bvv}(s) = \frac{A^2}{2\pi}$$

$$W_f(s) = 1$$

$$I_y \leq I_{ym}$$

$$I_y = \int_0^\infty dt\, y_e{}^2(t)$$

(a) Determine the optimum system weighting function $w(t)$ which has minimum bandwidth as defined by the bandwidth test (Fig. 8.4–1) and which satisfies the constraint on the integral-square error.

(b) Sketch the step response of the optimum system.   What is the error to the step input as a function of time?

(c) For $T = 1$ unit of time, plot the curve of integral-square error I_{ym} versus bandwidth.

8.2 A system is desired to function as a pure differentiator, i.e., the desired output is the first time derivative of the input. Because of the possible presence of wide-band noise at the input to the system, we wish the system to have a cutoff rate of at least 20 dg per decade at the high frequencies. The normal input to the system is stochastic in nature, and hence it is necessary to keep the mean-square error to the input signal below a fixed level $\sigma_{em}{}^2$. The mathematical statement of the problem is

$$i(t) = \frac{dv(t)}{dt} \qquad\qquad W_f(s) = s$$

$$\overline{y_e}^2 \le \sigma_{em}{}^2 \qquad\qquad W_b(s) = \frac{s}{\left(\dfrac{1}{\omega_b} s + 1\right)^3}$$

$$\Phi_{vv}(s) = \frac{\gamma}{\pi s^4} \qquad\qquad \Phi_{bvv}(s) = \frac{\eta}{\pi}$$

(a) Determine the optimum system function $W(s)$ which possesses minimum bandwidth as defined by the test and which results in a mean-square error that satisfies the constraint placed on it.

(b) Determine the mean-square error as a function of bandwidth.

(c) How might this system be realized by a feedback configuration when the input is a voltage and the output is to be a shaft position proportional to the derivative of the input?

GLOSSARY

The general symbols used to represent signals and system elements are given in Figs. 1.4–3, p. 19 and 1.7–2, p. 35, and are listed below. In general, lower-case letters are used for time functions and transforms. Exceptions are the capitalization of system functions, transfer functions, and power-density spectra.

e	actuating signal
$g_c(t)$	weighting function of compensating elements
$g_f(t)$	weighting function of fixed elements
$g_i(t)$	weighting function of ideal system
$g_s(t)$	weighting function relating the saturating signal to the input to the fixed elements (Fig. 7.1–1)
$h_f(t)$	weighting function of feedback elements
i	ideal output or desired output
m	input to the fixed elements
q	output
q_s	saturation signal
u	disturbance
v	input or command
v_d	data or signal component of the input
v_n	noise component of the input
$w(t)$	weighting function of the control system
$w_c(t)$	weighting function of equivalent cascade compensation
$w_y(t)$	weighting function relating error y_e to the input
y_e	error

The following integral definitions and notations are used in the discussions of integral-square error:

$$I_y \triangleq \int_{-\infty}^{\infty} dt \, y_e{}^2(t) \qquad \text{integral-square error}$$

$$I_y = I_{yy}(0) \tag{2.4-8}$$

where

$$I_{yy}(\tau) \triangleq \int_{-\infty}^{\infty} dt \, y_e(t) y_e(t + \tau) \tag{2.4-7}$$

is the autotranslation function of the error y_e

$$I_{12}(\tau) \triangleq \int_{-\infty}^{\infty} dt \, x_1(t) x_2(t + \tau) \tag{2.4-2}$$

$$I_{vq}(\tau) \triangleq \int_{-\infty}^{\infty} dt \, v(t) \, q(t + \tau)$$

For stochastic signals the mean-square error is used with the notations

$$\overline{y_e{}^2(t)} \triangleq \lim_{T \to \infty} \frac{1}{2T} \int_{-T}^{T} dt \, y_e{}^2(t) \qquad \text{mean-square error}$$

$$\overline{y_e{}^2(t)} = \varphi_{yy}(0) \tag{4.4-1}$$

where

$$\varphi_{yy}(\tau) \triangleq \lim_{T \to \infty} \frac{1}{2T} \int_{-T}^{T} dt \, y_e(t) y_e(t + \tau)$$

is the autocorrelation function of the error $y_e(t)$

$$\varphi_{12}(\tau) \triangleq \lim_{T \to \infty} \frac{1}{2T} \int_{-T}^{T} dt \, x_1(t) x_2(t + \tau)$$

$$\varphi_{vq}(\tau) \triangleq \lim_{T \to \infty} \frac{1}{2T} \int_{-T}^{T} dt \, v(t) q(t + \tau) \tag{4.1-8}$$

The Fourier and Laplace transform pairs as used throughout this book are defined by:

Fourier transform pair
$$\begin{cases} F(s) \triangleq \int_{-\infty}^{\infty} dt \, e^{-st} f(t) & \text{(A.1-1)} \\[2mm] f(t) \triangleq \frac{1}{2\pi j} \int_{-j\infty}^{j\infty} ds \, e^{st} F(s) & \text{(A.1-2)} \end{cases}$$

Laplace transform pair
$$\begin{cases} F(s) \triangleq \int_{0}^{\infty} dt \, e^{-st} f(t) & \text{(A.2-4)} \\[2mm] f(t) \triangleq \frac{1}{2\pi j} \int_{c-j\infty}^{c+j\infty} ds \, e^{st} F(s) & \text{(A.2-5)} \end{cases}$$

The power-density spectrum of a signal is defined as $1/2\pi$ times the Fourier transform of the correlation function of the signal. Thus

$$\Phi_{vv}(s) \triangleq \frac{1}{2\pi}\left[\int_{-\infty}^{\infty} d\tau\ e^{-s\tau}\varphi_{vv}(\tau)\right]$$

Other symbols used frequently are:

$$s = \text{complex frequency variable}$$

$$\lambda = \text{normalized complex frequency variable}$$

$$\omega = \text{real frequency variable}$$

$$\rho = \text{Lagrangian multiplier}$$

$$N = \text{amplitude}$$

$$p = \text{probability density function}$$

$$P = \text{probability function}$$

The general form of the Wiener-Hopf equation is given by

$$\int_{-\infty}^{\infty} dt_1\ \psi(t_1)\Delta(\tau - t_1) - \Gamma(\tau) = 0 \quad \text{for } \tau \geq 0 \qquad (5.4\text{--}1)$$

The transforms of $\Delta(t)$ and $\Gamma(t)$ are $\Delta(s)$ and $\Gamma(s)$, respectively. The notation Δ^-, Δ^+, and $[\quad]_+$ is explained in Art. 5.4.

BIBLIOGRAPHY

A.3   Ahrendt, W. R., and J. F. Taplin, *Automatic Feedback Control*, McGraw-Hill Book Co., New York, 1951.

A.5   AIEE Committee Report, "Proposed Symbols and Terms for Feedback Control Systems," *Elec. Eng.*, **70**, 905–909 (1951).

A.6   AIEE Committee Report, "Bibliography on Feedback Control," *Applications and Industry*, No. 10, 430–462 (1954).

A.7   Arthurs, E., and L. H. Martin, "A Closed Expansion of the Convolution Integral," *J. Appl. Phys.*, **26**, 58–60 (1955).

B.4   Bode, H. W., *Network Analysis and Feedback Amplifier Design*, D. Van Nostrand Co., New York, 1945.

B.5   Bode, H. W., and C. E. Shannon, "A Simplified Derivation of Linear Least Square Smoothing and Prediction Theory," *Proc. I.R.E.*, **38**, 417–424 (1950).

B.6   Brown, G. S., and D. P. Campbell, *Principles of Servomechanisms*, John Wiley and Sons, New York, 1948.

B.7   Bruns, R. A., and R. M. Saunders, *Analysis of Feedback Control Systems*, McGraw-Hill Book Co., New York, 1955.

C.1   Campbell, G. A., and R. M. Foster, *Fourier Integrals for Practical Applications*, D. Van Nostrand Co., New York, 1948.

C.2   Campbell, N., "The Study of Discontinuous Phenomena," *Proc. Cambridge Phil. Soci.*, **15**, 117–136 (1909).

C.3   Chestnut, H., and R. W. Mayer, *Servomechanisms and Regulating System Design*, John Wiley and Sons, New York, Vol. 1, 1951.

C.5   Copson, E. T., *Theory of Functions of a Complex Variable*, Oxford Univ. Press, London, 1935.

C.55 Cossar, J., and A. Erdelyi, *Dictionary of Laplace Transforms*, Admiralty Computing Service, London, 1944–46.

C.7 Cramer, H., *Mathematical Methods of Statistics*, Princeton Univ. Press, Princeton, 1946.

E.7 Erdelyi, A., *Tables of Integral Transforms*, McGraw-Hill Book Co., New York, Vol. 1, 1954.

F.7 Franklin, P., *Methods of Advanced Calculus*, McGraw-Hill Book Co., New York, 1944.

G.1 Gadd, C. J., "Babylonian Law," *Encyclopedia Britannica*, 14th Ed., **2**, 863 (1929).

G.2 Gardner, M. F., and J. L. Barnes, *Transients in Linear Systems*, John Wiley and Sons, New York, Vol. 1, 1942.

G.8 Guillemin, E. A., *The Mathematics of Circuit Analysis*, John Wiley and Sons, New York, 1949.

G.9 Guillemin, E. A., "Computational Techniques Which Simplify the Correlation between Steady-State and Transient Response of Filters and Other Networks," *Proc. Natl. Electronics Conf.*, **9**, 513–532 (1954).

H.1 Hall, A. C., *Analysis and Synthesis of Linear Servomechanisms*, Technology Press, Cambridge, 1943.

H.2 Hazen, H. L., "Theory of Servomechanisms," *J. Franklin Inst.*, **218**, 543–580 (1934).

H.25 Hildebrand, F. B., *Advanced Calculus for Engineers*, Prentice-Hall, New York, 1950.

H.3 Hildebrand, F. B., *Methods of Applied Mathematics*, Prentice-Hall, New York, 1952.

H.9 Hurwitz, A., "Ueber die Bedingungen, unter welchen eine Gleichung nur Wurzeln mit negativen reellen Theilen besitzt," *Math. Ann.*, **46**, 273–284, (1895).

J.1 James, H. M., N. B. Nichols, and R. S. Phillips, *Theory of Servomechanisms*, McGraw-Hill Book Co., New York, 1947.

K.5 Knopp, K., *Theory of Functions*, Dover Publications, New York, Parts I and II, 1945.

L.05 Laning, J. H., and R. H. Battin, *Random Processes in Automatic Control*, McGraw-Hill Book Co., New York, 1956.

L.1 Lee, Y. W., "Application of Statistical Methods to Communication Problems," *Mass. Inst. Technol. Research Lab. Electronics Tech. Rept.*, **181**, (1950).

L.2 Lee, Y. W., "Synthesis of Electric Networks by means of the Fourier Transforms of Laguerre's Functions," *J. Math. and Phys.*, **11**, 2, 83–113 (1932).

M.1 MacColl, LeR. A., *Fundamental Theory of Servomechanisms*, D. Van Nostrand Co., New York, 1945.

M.2 Maxwell, J. C., "On Governors," *Proc., Roy. Soc. (London)*, **16**, 270–283 (1868).

M.25 McCormick, R. A., "Structure of Atmospheric Turbulence," *J. Meteorol.*, **10**, 434–449, (1953).

M.3 Minorsky, N., "Directional Stability of Automatically Steered Bodies," *J. A. Soc. Naval Engs.*, **34**, 280 (1922).

N.1 Newton, G. C., Jr., "Compensation of Feedback Control Systems Subject to Saturation," *J. Franklin Inst.*, **254**, 281–286, 391–413 (1952).

N.2   Newton, G. C., Jr., "Design of Control Systems for Minimum Bandwidth," *Trans. AIEE*, **74**, pt. II, 161–168 (1955).

N.9   Nyquist, H., "Regeneration Theory," Bell System Tech. J., **11**, 126–147 (1932).

R.3   Rice, S. O., "Mathematical Analysis of Random Noise," *Bell System Tech. J.*, **23**, 282–332 (1944), and **24**, 46–156 (1945).

R.5   Routh, E. J., *Stability of a Given State of Motion*, Adams Prize Essay, MacMillan, London, 1877.

S.3   Singer, I. A., "Data on Wind Gust Frequencies at Oak Ridge, Tenn." quoted by Dr. R. M. Emberson to Associated Universities, Inc., in memorandum dated March 19, 1956 (private communication).

S.5   Sneddon, I. N., *Fourier Transforms*, McGraw-Hill Book Co., New York, 1951.

S.6   Solodovnikov, V. V., *Vvedeniye v Statisticheskuyu Dinamiku Sistem Automaticheskovo Upravleniya* (Translation: *Introduction to the Statistical Dynamics of Automatic Control Systems*), State Publishing House for Theoretical Technical Literature, Moscow, 1952.

T.3   Thaler, G. J., and R. G. Brown, *Servomechanisms Analysis*, McGraw-Hill Book Co., New York, 1953.

T.4   Titchmarsh, E. C., *Introduction to the Theory of Fourier Integrals*, Oxford, Clarendon Press, 1937.

T.7   Truxal, J. G., *Automatic Feedback Control System Synthesis*, McGraw-Hill Book Co., New York, 1955.

T.8   Tsien, H. S., *Engineering Cybernetics*, McGraw-Hill Book Co., New York, 1954.

U.7   Usher, A. P., *A History of Mechanical Inventions*, Harvard Univ. Press, Cambridge, revised edition, 1954.

W.05   Wax, N., Editor, *Selected Papers on Noise and Stochastic Processes*, Dover Publications, New York, 1954.

W.1   Westcott, J. H., "The Introduction of Constraints into Feedback System Designs," *Transactions of the I.R.E.*, CT-1, Institute of Radio Engineers, New York, 39–49 (1954).

W.2   Wiener, N., *Cybernetics*, John Wiley and Sons, New York, 1948.

W.3   Wiener, N., *Extrapolation, Interpolation, and Smoothing of Stationary Time Series*, Technology Press, Cambridge, 1949.

W.4   Wolf, A., *A History of Science, Technology and Philosophy in the XVIth and XVIIth Centuries*, The MacMillan Co., New York, 1950.

W.5   Wolf, A., *A History of Science, Technology and Philosophy in the XVIIIth Century*, The MacMillan Co., New York, 1939.

Z.1   Zadeh, L. A., and J. R. Ragazzini, "An Extension of Wiener's Theory of Prediction," *J. Appl. Phys.*, **21**, 645–655 (1950).

INDEX